NAMING ORGANIC COMPOUNDS

A PROGRAMED INTRODUCTION TO ORGANIC CHEMISTRY

JAMES E. BANKS, Ph.D.

ASSOCIATE PROFESSOR OF CHEMISTRY
UNITED STATES AIR FORCE ACADEMY

W. B. SAUNDERS COMPANY • PHILADELPHIA AND LONDON •

W. B. Saunders Company: West Washington Square
Philadelphia, Pa.   19105

12 Dyott Street
London, WC1A 1DB

833 Oxford Street
Toronto 18, Ontario

Naming Organic Compounds   ISBN 0-7216-1535–X

Print No.:   9   8   7

PREFACE

This self-instructional program is designed to help you understand the rules used by chemists to name and represent structurally the compounds dealt with in organic chemistry. My goal in writing this program is to help you to learn to derive the names of organic compounds from their formulas and to write their structural formulas from the names. At the same time you will begin to learn that certain structures and words identify compounds that are related to each other and therefore have similar chemical reactivity. Where space permits, some odd or unusual compounds are described for their interest or entertainment value.

You should be able to work through this program without difficulty if you are familiar with the use of atomic symbols and their combination to show the formulas of inorganic compounds such as NaCl, $Mg(NO_3)_2$, and H_2SO_4. It will be useful if you know something about covalent bonds. Very little descriptive chemistry is included in the program, and no prior knowledge of organic chemistry is assumed.

Success in the study of organic chemistry demands an understanding of the rules that govern organic nomenclature. If you read the program diligently and practice using the principles of nomenclature with compounds you encounter in your daily work, you will gain the satisfaction of an increasing knowledge and familiarity with the language of organic chemistry.

James E. Banks
Lt. Colonel, USAF

United States Air Force Academy

INSTRUCTIONS FOR
USING THE PROGRAM

This is a programed book. Its somewhat unconventional format is designed to help you use the book as an aid for self-instruction. At the bottom of page 1, where a question is presented, select the answer which you think is correct. Then turn to the following page to confirm your choice or find out why it was wrong. Continue working through the book in this manner.

In some sections, several problems are presented on a single page. The answer to each problem is printed immediately below the question. On these pages, you will find it helpful to use the cardboard mask provided in the book. As you read the review pages, cover the printed answers with the mask to prevent seeing them before you have solved the problems for yourself.

Throughout the program, new or difficult words are followed at their first appearance by guides to pronunciation. Here are the sound values for these pronouncing guides:

āle	ēve	īce	ōld	ūse
senăte	ĕvent		ŏbey	ūnite
ăm	ĕnd	ĭll	ŏdd	ŭp
câre			ôrb	ûrn
ärm	makĕr		fōōd	
sofȧ			fŏŏt	

Good luck!

CONTENTS

4

5

1

Classification of Organic Compounds

The function of a chemical name is similar to the function of a personal name. It provides the chemist with a word or set of words that is unique to the substance. The name of a compound conveys at least its empirical formula and also, if possible, its main structural features.

1.1 HYDROCARBONS

Compounds that contain only carbon and hydrogen are known as *hydrocarbons*. They are the basic substances of organic chemistry. There are literally millions of hydrocarbons and their derivatives. Although most organic compounds contain elements besides carbon and hydrogen, these derivatives are all related to the hydrocarbons.

Sometimes a given molecular formula may represent more than one compound. Such compounds are called *isomers* (ī′ sŏ mĕrz). Although they share the same molecular formula, isomers are distinctly different compounds. They have specific chemical and physical properties which distinguish them from one another. For example, there are 35 isomers with the molecular formula C_9H_{20}. One chemist who is also a mathematician calculates that there could be 4,111,846,763 isomers with the formula $C_{30}H_{62}$.

As we will see in the next few pages, isomers sometimes differ in the way the atoms are bound to one another. By assigning a unique name to each compound, the chemist can avoid having to specify the properties of the particular compound he has in mind.

In the formulas below, which pair represents two hydrocarbon isomers? (Check your answer on the following page.)

A ‖‖‖

C_2H_6O C_2H_5OH

B ‖‖‖

C_4H_{10} C_4H_8

C ‖‖‖

C_5H_{12} C_5H_{12}

A ||||||||||||||||||||||||||||||||||||||||||||||||||||||||||||||||||||||||||||||||||||||||||||||||||||||||||||||||||||||||||||||||||||||||||||||||||||||||||||

You are wrong. Your answer is that C_2H_6O and C_2H_5OH represent two hydrocarbons that are isomers. They are indeed isomers, because they do have the same molecular formula. However, they do not fulfill the other condition: they are not hydrocarbons. Hydrocarbons are organic compounds which contain *only* carbon and hydrogen. Go back and choose another answer.

B ||||||||||||||||||||||||||||||||||||||||||||||||||||||||||||||||||||||||||||||||||||||||||||||||||||||||||||||||||||||||||||||||||||||||||||||||||||||||||||

You are incorrect. Your answer is that C_4H_{10} and C_4H_8 represent two hydrocarbons that are isomers. Since each formula contains only carbon and hydrogen, they are both hydrocarbons. They are not isomers, however, because isomers are compounds which have the same molecular formula. For instance, C_2H_6O and C_2H_5OH are isomers. Go back and select another pair of formulas.

C ||||||||||||||||||||||||||||||||||||||||||||||||||||||||||||||||||||||||||||||||||||||||||||||||||||||||||||||||||||||||||||||||||||||||||||||||||||||||||||

You are correct. Since they contain only hydrogen and carbon, and since they have identical molecular formulas, C_5H_{12} and C_5H_{12} represent two hydrocarbons that are isomers. Go on to page 3.

Molecular formulas obviously do not provide enough information to distinguish between isomers. Structural formulas do provide this information. They indicate the order in which the atoms are bound to one another. A dash is used to represent a covalent bond or shared pair of electrons. For example, here is a structural formula for one isomer with the formula C_3H_8:

$$H-\underset{\underset{H}{|}}{\overset{\overset{H}{|}}{C}}-\underset{\underset{H}{|}}{\overset{\overset{H}{|}}{C}}-\underset{\underset{H}{|}}{\overset{\overset{H}{|}}{C}}-H$$

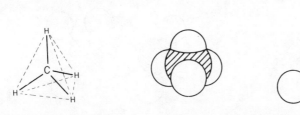

The drawing beside the formula shows one kind of model of the same molecule.

You may find it difficult to see that the model and the formula represent the same molecule. The trouble is caused by the fact that the structural formula attempts to show a three-dimensional object on a two-dimensional piece of paper. There are bound to be some distortions. Even the simplest hydrocarbon, methane, CH_4, cannot be accurately shown because the four covalent bonds on the carbon atom form a tetrahedral shape rather than lying in a plane. Below are three different models, all of which represent CH_4.

You can make a model of a tetrahedron by following the directions given in Figure 1, on page 5. The vertices of the tetrahedron coincide with the bonds on a carbon atom. For convenience, chemists usually write structural formulas with the bonds at right angles. The structural formula for methane is written $H-\underset{\underset{H}{|}}{\overset{\overset{H}{|}}{C}}-H$. Consider this structural formula:

$$H-\underset{\underset{H}{|}}{\overset{\overset{H}{|}}{C}}-\underset{\underset{H}{|}}{\overset{\overset{H}{|}}{C}}-\underset{\underset{H}{|}}{\overset{\overset{H}{|}}{C}}-H$$

Are all the the atoms in the same plane? That is, does it represent a "flat" molecule?

A ‖‖‖

Yes

B ‖‖‖

No

A ||||||||||||||||||||||||||||||||||||||||||||||||||||||||||||||||||||||||||||||||||||||||||||||||||||||||||||||||||||||||||

You are not correct. Always bear in mind that real molecules are three-dimensional. Moreover, the four covalent bonds that can be formed by a carbon atom are directed toward the vertices of a tetrahedron, as shown:

In order to write formulas on paper, bonds are usually drawn as if they were at right angles to each other. Remember that the important feature of structural formulas is that they show the *order* in which atoms are bound to one another. Continue and read answer *B* below.

B ||||||||||||||||||||||||||||||||||||||||||||||||||||||||||||||||||||||||||||||||||||||||||||||||||||||||||||||||||||||||||

You are correct. Writing its formula on a flat piece of paper does not make a molecule flat. If you compare carefully the structural formula and the model for C_3H_8

$$\begin{array}{ccc} H & H & H \\ | & | & | \\ H-C-C-C-H \\ | & | & | \\ H & H & H \end{array}$$

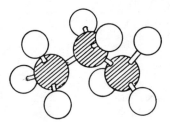

you will see that carbon and hydrogen atoms are bound in the same order in both. That is all a structural formula can show; it cannot depict spatial relationships accurately. Go on to page 7.

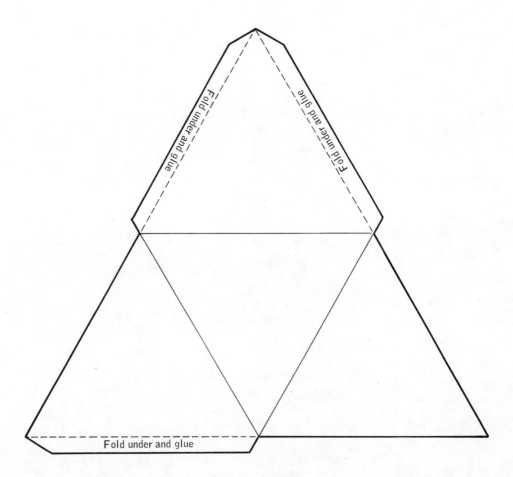

Figure 1. Model of a tetrahedron. If the center of the tetrahedron is taken to represent the nucleus of a carbon atom, the vertices will show the orientation of the four covalent bonds of the atom.

To assemble the model, cut out along solid lines around the edges. Fold the other solid lines over a ruler. Glue faces together with the aid of the three glue flaps.

The compound with the molecular formula CH_3Cl, represented by this model

may have its structural formula written in many ways. Here are a few of them:

$$\begin{array}{cccccc}
\text{Cl} & \text{H} & \text{H} & \text{H} & \text{H} & \text{Cl} \\
| & | & | & | & | & | \\
\text{H}-\text{C}-\text{H} & \text{Cl}-\text{C}-\text{H} & \text{H}-\text{C}-\text{Cl} & \text{H}-\text{C}-\text{H} & \text{Cl}-\text{C}-\text{H} & \text{H}-\text{C}-\text{H} \\
| & | & | & | & | & | \\
\text{H} & \text{H} & \text{H} & \text{Cl} & \text{H} & \text{H}
\end{array}$$

Structural formulas cannot give information about the orientation of the molecules in space. Any structural formula that shows three hydrogen atoms and one chlorine atom bound to a carbon atom is a satisfactory formula for this compound.

Which of these pairs of structural formulas represents the same molecule?

A ||||||||||||||||||||||||||||||||||||||||||||||||||||||||||||||||||||||||||||||||||||||||||||||||||||||||||||||||

$$\begin{array}{ccc}
\text{H} & \text{H} & \text{H} \\
| & | & | \\
\text{H}-\text{C}-\text{C}-\text{C}-\text{H} \\
| & | & | \\
\text{H} & \text{H} & \text{Cl}
\end{array}
\qquad
\begin{array}{ccc}
\text{H} & \text{Cl} & \text{H} \\
| & | & | \\
\text{H}-\text{C}-\text{C}-\text{C}-\text{H} \\
| & | & | \\
\text{H} & \text{H} & \text{H}
\end{array}$$

B ||||||||||||||||||||||||||||||||||||||||||||||||||||||||||||||||||||||||||||||||||||||||||||||||||||||||||||||||

$$\begin{array}{cc}
\text{H} & \text{H} \\
| & | \\
\text{H}-\text{C}-\text{C}-\text{H} \\
| & | \\
\text{H} & \text{Cl}
\end{array}
\qquad
\begin{array}{cc}
\text{H} & \text{H} \\
| & | \\
\text{H}-\text{C}-\text{C}-\text{Cl} \\
| & | \\
\text{H} & \text{H}
\end{array}$$

C ||||||||||||||||||||||||||||||||||||||||||||||||||||||||||||||||||||||||||||||||||||||||||||||||||||||||||||||||

$$\begin{array}{ccc}
\text{H} & \text{H} & \text{Cl} \\
| & | & | \\
\text{H}-\text{C}-\text{C}-\text{C}-\text{H} \\
| & | & | \\
\text{H} & \text{H} & \text{H}
\end{array}
\qquad
\begin{array}{ccc}
\text{H} & \text{H} & \text{Br} \\
| & | & | \\
\text{H}-\text{C}-\text{C}-\text{C}-\text{H} \\
| & | & | \\
\text{H} & \text{H} & \text{H}
\end{array}$$

A ||||||||||||||||||||||||||||||||||||||||||||||||||||||||||||||||||||||||||||||||||||||||||||||||||||||||||||||||||||||||||||||||||||||||

You are wrong. The structural formulas

$$
\begin{array}{ccccccc}
 & H & H & H & & & \\
 & | & | & | & & & \\
H- & C- & C- & C & -H & & \\
 & | & | & | & & & \\
 & H & H & Cl & & &
\end{array}
\qquad
\begin{array}{ccccc}
 & H & Cl & H & \\
 & | & | & | & \\
H- & C- & C- & C & -H \\
 & | & | & | & \\
 & H & H & H &
\end{array}
$$

do not represent the same molecule. If you look at them closely, you can see that there is a chain of three carbon atoms in each formula. It could be written as —C—C—C—. In the first formula the chlorine atom is bound to one of the end carbon atoms. The chlorine atom in the second formula is bound to the carbon in the middle of the chain. Since not all the atoms are bound in exactly the same order, the formulas represent two different substances, or molecules. You should recognize, however, that they are isomers. Turn back and choose another answer.

B ||||||||||||||||||||||||||||||||||||||||||||||||||||||||||||||||||||||||||||||||||||||||||||||||||||||||||||||||||||||||||||||||||||||||

Correct. These two formulas represent exactly the same molecule. Since all the covalent bonds formed by the carbon atom are chemically identical, it makes no difference how they are oriented when the structural formula is written. Continue to page 9.

C ||||||||||||||||||||||||||||||||||||||||||||||||||||||||||||||||||||||||||||||||||||||||||||||||||||||||||||||||||||||||||||||||||||||||

You are incorrect. Look at the formulas carefully again. You will find that they do not even represent isomers. The molecular formula of one is C_2H_5Cl and the other is C_2H_5Br. Choose another answer.

Atoms joined by a single pair of electrons in a covalent bond can rotate about the axis of the bond (i.e., the line joining the two atoms). Although this property has some importance in the reactivity of some compounds, it does not affect structural formulas. You already know that the formula does not show the spatial orientation of the molecule or of the atoms within the molecule. For example, these drawings show the same molecule, C_5H_{12}

Molecules do not change their structure as they move about in space or change their shape. Although it is customary to write structural formulas as straight as possible, bends and crooks in them have no more meaning than bends and crooks in the molecule itself. These three structural formulas all represent the same molecule:

```
                                                                    H
                                                                    |
                                                                H—C—H
                                                                    |
                              H H          H                        H
                               \|          |                        |
                                C————————C—H                   H—C—C—H
                                |          |                    |   |
     H H H H H                  H          |                    H   H
     | | | | |                  |          |                    |
  H—C—C—C—C—C—H          H—C—C—H   H—C—H              H—C—C—H
     | | | | |                  | |          |                 |   |
     H H H H H                  H H          H                    H H
```

The atoms in all three are connected to one another in the same order.

Choose the pair of structural formulas that represents two different compounds rather than the same molecule in different orientations.

A ||||||||||||||||||||||||||||||||||||||||||||||||||||||||||||||||||||||||||||||||||||||||||||||||||||||||||||||||||||||||||||||||||||||||||||||

```
                                                  H
                                                  |
                                              H—C—H
                                                  |
                                              H—C—H
                                                  |
        H H H H                                 H
        | | | |                                 |
     H—C—C—C—C—H                          H—C—C—H
        | | | |                               |   |
        H H H H                               H   H
```

B |||||||||||||||||||||||||||||||||||||||||||||||||||||||||||||||||||||||||||||||||||||||||||||||||||||||||||||||||||||||||||||||||||||||

```
       H H H                                   H
       | | |                                   |
    H—C—C—C—H                             H—C—H
       |   |                                   |
       H   H                               H   H
       |                                   |   |
    H—C—H                          H—C—C—C—H
       |                               |   |   |
       H                               H   H   H
```

C |||||||||||||||||||||||||||||||||||||||||||||||||||||||||||||||||||||||||||||||||||||||||||||||||||||||||||||||||||||||||||||||||||||||||||

```
       H H H                                 H H H
       | | |                                 | | |
    H—C—C—C—H                           H—C—C—C—H
       | |                                   |   |
       H H                                   H   H
           |                                     |
        H—C—H                              H—C—H
           |                                     |
           H                                     H
```

A ||||||||||||||||||||||||||||||||||||||||||||||||||||||||||||||||||||||||||||||||||||||||||||||||||||||||||||||||||||||||||||||||||||

You are incorrect. The two structural formulas you chose do represent the same compound. The only difference between them is that the chain of carbon atoms in the second is bent near one end Remember that molecules can change their shapes without changes in structure. Since the structural formula specifies structure but not shape, it can be written in different orientations without a change in structure. Turn back and choose another answer.

B ||||||||||||||||||||||||||||||||||||||||||||||||||||||||||||||||||||||||||||||||||||||||||||||||||||||||||||||||||||||||||||||||||||

Wrong. These two structural formulas are identical. The only difference between them is that the second has been rotated 180° around the axis of the chain of carbon atoms. This is just a difference in orientation, not a difference in structure. Remember, structural formulas do not give information on spatial orientation. They represent structure only. Turn back and choose another answer.

C ||||||||||||||||||||||||||||||||||||||||||||||||||||||||||||||||||||||||||||||||||||||||||||||||||||||||||||||||||||||||||||||||||||

You are right. These two structural formulas represent different compounds. In the first, four carbon atoms are attached to one another in a continuous chain. In the second, the continuous chain has only three carbon atoms with the fourth attached to the middle carbon atom in the chain. This is a structural difference, not just a difference in orientation. Note also that the dashes which indicate covalent bonds may be shown with whatever length is needed to fit all the atomic symbols. Go on to page 11.

Summary

1. Structural formulas are used to show the order in which the atoms of an organic compound are bound to each other.

2. Structural formulas do not show the actual shape of organic molecules because formulas are two-dimensional representations of three-dimensional objects.

3. Molecules are in constant motion. Structural formulas, therefore, do not give information about the spatial orientation of the molecules they represent.

4. Rotation of atoms around the axis of the covalent bond which joins them allows molecules to assume different shapes without changing their structure. Structural formulas, too, may take different shapes without reflecting different structures.

Careful attention to these points will enable you to compare structural formulas and recognize true structural differences as opposed to different ways of writting the same formula.

On the next page are several pairs of formulas. Decide whether they represent the same or different molecules. The correct answers are just below the formulas. Use the special mask to cover the printed answers until you have decided on your own response.

Do the pairs of structural formulas given below represent the same or different molecules?

1.

```
    H  H  H                    H  H  H
    |  |  |                    |  |  |
 H—C—C—C—Cl              H—C—C—C—H
    |  |  |                    |  |  |
    H  H  H                    H  H  Cl
```

Same. All four covalent bonds on a carbon atom are equivalent.

2.

```
    H  H  H  H                 H  H  H  H
    |  |  |  |                 |  |  |  |
 H—C—C—C—C—Cl           H—C—C—C—C—H
    |  |  |  |                 |  |  |  |
    H  H  H  H                 H  Cl H  H
```

Different. The chlorine atoms are bound to different carbon atoms in the chain. (Note: the two are isomers.)

3.

```
    H  H  H                    H  H  H  H
    |  |  |                    |  |  |  |
 H—C—C—C—H               H—C—C—C—C—H
    |  |  |                    |  |  |  |
    H  H  |                    H  H  H  H
         H—C—H
            |
            H
```

Same. Bends and crooks do not indicate different structures.

4.

```
     H  H  H                   H  H  H
     |  |  |                   |  |  |
 Cl—C—C—C—H              H—C—C—C—Cl
     |  |  |                   |  |  |
     H  H  H                   H  H  H
```

Same. Molecules are in constant motion through space. These two formulas can be superimposed if one is rotated 180° on a vertical line through the middle carbon atom.

5.

```
    H  H  H  H                 H  H  H
    |  |  |  |                 |  |  |
 H—C—C—C—C—H             H—C—C—C—H
    |  |  |  |                 |  |  |
    H  H  H  H                 H  |  H
                                 H—C—H
                                    |
                                    H
```

Different. The first formula shows a continuous chain of four carbon atoms while the second has a continuous chain of only three with the fourth carbon atom attached to the middle one.

Review any question that you missed to be sure you understand the correct answer. Then go on to page 13.

In the early days of organic chemistry, compounds were given names related to their natural source. For instance, acetic acid derives its name from the Latin word for vinegar, *acetum*. As soon as compounds began to be synthesized from materials other than natural products, the problem of naming them became acute. Chemists soon recognized that some sort of system was needed. One system was adopted at an international congress of chemists held in Geneva in 1892. Although it has been modified and extended since then, it is still in use under the name "Geneva system." Today, rules for naming organic compounds are established by the International Union of Pure and Applied Chemistry (IUPAC). These rules are followed throughout the world. In this program the IUPAC rules will be emphasized. In certain instances where the custom of American chemists differs from these rules, the usage of *Chemical Abstracts* will be followed. Many of the non-systematic names that are accepted by the IUPAC rules and used by *Chemical Abstracts* will be mentioned.

The first step in classifying organic compounds is to separate them into two main divisions, open-chain or aliphatic (ăl' ĭ făt" ĭk) compounds and cyclic (sī klĭk) compounds. The word aliphatic is derived from the Greek word for fat; fatty acids are aliphatic compounds (See section 3.4). The division is shown by this diagram

Notice that there is a closed ring, or cycle, of carbon atoms joined to one another in the cyclic compound, whereas the aliphatic compound has none.

Which of these structural formulas represents an aliphatic hydrocarbon?

A ||||||||||||||||||||||||||||||||||||||||||||||||||||||||||||||||||||||||||||||||||||||||||||||||

B ||||||||||||||||||||||||||||||||||||||||||||||||||||||||||||||||||||||||||||||||||||||||||||||||||

C ||||||||||||||||||||||||||||||||||||||||||||||||||||||||||||||||||||||||||||||||||||||||||||||||

A⎪⎪⎪

You are not correct. The compound represented by the structural formula

$$
\begin{array}{c}
\quad\ \text{H}\quad\ \text{O}\quad\ \text{H} \\
\quad\ | \quad\ \| \quad\ | \\
\text{H}-\text{C}-\text{C}-\text{C}-\text{H} \\
\quad\ | \quad\quad\quad | \\
\quad\ \text{H}\quad\quad\quad \text{H}
\end{array}
$$

is indeed aliphatic since it does not contain any ring structures. It is not a hydrocarbon, however, since hydrocarbons contain only hydrogen and carbon. This compound contains oxygen. Turn back and choose another answer.

B⎪⎪

You are correct. The formula

$$
\begin{array}{c}
\quad\ \text{H}\quad\ \text{H} \\
\quad\ | \quad\ | \\
\text{H}-\text{C}-\text{C}-\text{H} \\
\quad\ | \quad\ | \\
\quad\ \text{H}\quad\ \text{H}
\end{array}
$$

contains only hydrogen and carbon. There are no ring structures. Therefore, it represents an aliphatic hydrocarbon. Go on to page 15.

C⎪⎪⎪

Incorrect. The formula

$$
\begin{array}{c}
\quad\quad\ \text{H}\quad\ \text{H} \\
\quad \text{H}\ \ \ |\quad\ | \\
\quad \backslash\ \ \text{C}-\text{C}-\text{H} \\
\text{H}\quad / \\
\ \backslash\ \text{C} \\
\ /\ \ \backslash \\
\text{H}\quad\ \text{C}-\text{C}-\text{H} \\
\quad \ /\ |\quad\ | \\
\quad \text{H}\ \ \text{H}\quad\ \text{H}
\end{array}
$$

represents a hydrocarbon since it contains only carbon and hydrogen. However, it contains a ring of five carbon atoms. Therefore it is a cyclic compound, not aliphatic. Aliphatic compounds do not contain ring structures. Turn back and select another answer.

Cyclic compounds can be further divided into homocyclic (hō′ mō sī klǐk) and heterocyclic (hĕt′ ĕr ŏ sī′ klǐk) compounds. Homocyclic compounds have rings consisting of carbon atoms only, whereas the heterocyclic compounds have rings containing two or more elements. Our diagram can now be extended as shown here:

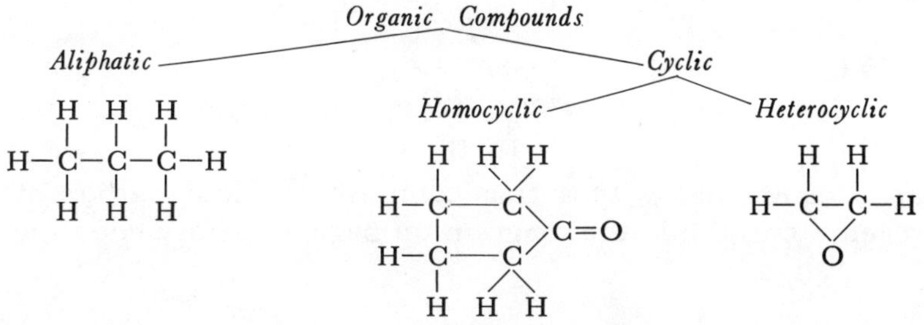

Organic Compounds

Aliphatic ——————————————————————— *Cyclic*

Homocyclic ——— ——— *Heterocyclic*

Notice that the homocyclic compounds have only carbon atoms in their ring structure, although the compounds may contain other elements besides carbon and hydrogen. (We will see later that homocyclic compounds can further be divided into two classes.)

As you know, the formulas that have been used so far are called structural formulas since they show the way the atoms are joined together as well as the composition of the compound.

Making use of the diagram above, how would you classify the compound represented by this structural formula?

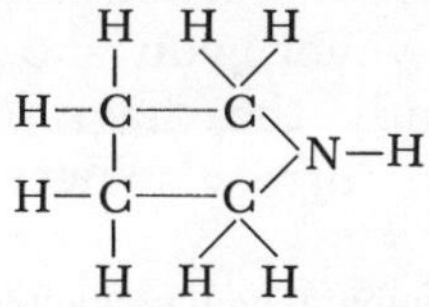

A |||||||||||||||||||||||||||||||||||||||||||||||||||||||||||||||||||||||||||||||||||||||||||||||||||||||||||||||||||||||||||||||||

aliphatic

B |||||||||||||||||||||||||||||||||||||||||||||||||||||||||||||||||||||||||||||||||||||||||||||||||||||||

cyclic

C |||||||||||||||||||||||||||||||||||||||||||||||||||||||||||||||||||||||||||||||||||||||||||||||||||||||||||||||||||

homocyclic

D ||||||||||||||||||||||||||||||||||||||||||||||||||||||||||||||||||||||||||||||||||||||||||||||||||||||||||||||||||||||||||||||

heterocyclic

A ||||||||||||||||||||||||||||||||||||||||||||||||||||||||||||||||||||||||||||||||||||||||||||||||||||||

You are incorrect. You should recall that aliphatic compounds contain no ring structures. The formula

$$\begin{array}{c} H \quad H \quad H \\ | \quad \quad \diagdown \diagup \\ H-C——C \\ | \quad \quad \diagdown \\ \quad \quad \quad N-H \\ | \quad \quad \diagup \\ H-C——C \\ | \quad \quad | \\ H \quad H \quad H \end{array}$$

represents a compound with a ring composed of four carbon atoms and one nitrogen atom. Study the diagram on page 15 before choosing another answer.

B ||||||||||||||||||||||||||||||||||||||||||||||||||||||||||||||||||||||||||||||||||||||||||||||||||||

You are partly correct. The compound represented by the formula

$$\begin{array}{c} H \quad H \quad H \\ | \quad \quad \diagdown \diagup \\ H-C——C \\ | \quad \quad \diagdown \\ \quad \quad \quad N-H \\ | \quad \quad \diagup \\ H-C——C \\ | \quad \quad \diagup \diagdown \\ H \quad H \quad H \end{array}$$

contains a ring composed of four carbon atoms and one nitrogen atom. It is a cyclic compound. However, you should have learned to classify cyclic compounds further. Study the diagram carefully when your turn back to page 15 to choose the correct answer.

C ||||||||||||||||||||||||||||||||||||||||||||||||||||||||||||||||||||||||||||||||||||||||||||||||||||

Wrong. The compound represented by the formula

$$\begin{array}{c} H \quad H \quad H \\ | \quad \quad \diagdown \diagup \\ H-C——C \\ | \quad \quad \diagdown \\ \quad \quad \quad N-H \\ | \quad \quad \diagup \\ H-C——C \\ | \quad \quad | \diagdown H \\ H \quad H \end{array}$$

is not homocyclic. Homocyclic compounds contain rings of carbon atoms only. The ring in this compound is composed of four carbon atoms and one nitrogen atom. It cannot be called homocyclic, can it? The diagram on page 15 will help you to select the right answer.

D ||||||||||||||||||||||||||||||||||||||||||||||||||||||||||||||||||||||||||||||||||||||||||||||||||||

You are correct. The formula

$$\begin{array}{c} H \quad H \quad H \\ | \quad \quad \diagdown \diagup \\ H-C——C \\ | \quad \quad \diagdown \\ \quad \quad \quad N-H \\ | \quad \quad \diagup \\ H-C——C \\ | \quad \quad \diagup \diagdown \\ H \quad H \quad H \end{array}$$

represents a heterocylic compound. It has a ring consisting of four carbon atoms and one nitrogen atom. Continue on to page 17.

1.2 ALKANES

There are several families, or groups, of aliphatic hydrocarbons. The simplest is called the *alkane* (ăl′ kāne) family. Alkanes are saturated aliphatic hydrocarbons. The word *saturated* indicates that they have no double or triple covalent bonds between carbon atoms. An alkane containing three carbon atoms can be represented by the structural formula

$$\begin{array}{ccccc} & H & H & H & \\ & | & | & | & \\ H- & C- & C- & C- & H \\ & | & | & | & \\ & H & H & H & \end{array}$$

Detailed structural formulas of this sort use a great deal of space and are often not necessary. For this reason chemists often write condensed structural formulas in which all atoms attached to a given carbon atom are written after the "C" and on the same line. For example, the formula for the alkane shown above can be condensed to $CH_3CH_2CH_3$.

If other elements are present in the compound, they can be indicated in the same way. When two different kinds of atoms are attached to one carbon atom, hydrogen is usually written first. These three examples should make the point clear.

Structural formula	*Condensed formula*
$\begin{array}{cccc} & H & H & H \\ & | & | & | \\ Cl- & C- & C- & C-H \\ & | & | & | \\ & H & H & H \end{array}$	$CH_2ClCH_2CH_3$
$\begin{array}{ccc} & H & H \\ & | & | \\ Cl- & C- & C-F \\ & | & | \\ & Cl & F \end{array}$	$CHCl_2CHF_2$
$\begin{array}{ccc} & Cl & H \\ & | & | \\ Cl- & C- & C-H \\ & | & | \\ & Cl & H \end{array}$	CCl_3CH_3

On the reverse side of this page are three questions concerning condensed structural formulas. The answer to each is given just below the question. Cover the printed answers until you have worked out your own. Check each one and then go to the next.

1. Are these two structural formulas for the same compound?

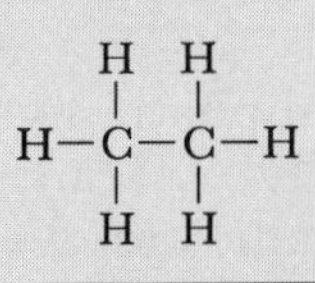

$$H-\underset{\underset{H}{|}}{\overset{\overset{H}{|}}{C}}-\underset{\underset{H}{|}}{\overset{\overset{H}{|}}{C}}-H \qquad\qquad CH_3CH_3$$

Yes, both represent a compound with the molecular formula C_2H_6.

2. The structural formula for a compound is

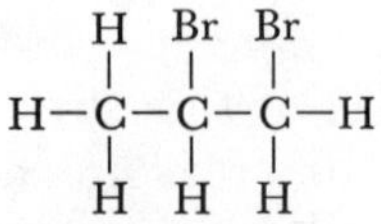

$$H-\underset{\underset{H}{|}}{\overset{\overset{H}{|}}{C}}-\underset{\underset{H}{|}}{\overset{\overset{Br}{|}}{C}}-\underset{\underset{H}{|}}{\overset{\overset{Br}{|}}{C}}-H$$

Is this the correct condensed structural formula?

$$CH_3CHBr_2CH_2$$

No. All atoms attached to a given carbon atom are written after that carbon atom. The correct answer is: $CH_3CHBrCH_2Br$.

3. The condensed structural formula of a compound is

$$CH_3CCl_2CHClCH_2Cl$$

Write its structural formula.

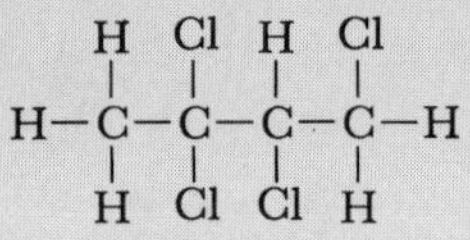

$$H-\underset{\underset{H}{|}}{\overset{\overset{H}{|}}{C}}-\underset{\underset{Cl}{|}}{\overset{\overset{Cl}{|}}{C}}-\underset{\underset{Cl}{|}}{\overset{\overset{H}{|}}{C}}-\underset{\underset{H}{|}}{\overset{\overset{Cl}{|}}{C}}-H$$

Go on to page 19.

The names of the alkanes are based on the number of carbon atoms they contain and on the way in which the carbons are attached to one another. Here are the structural formulas of two alkanes. Each contains four carbon atoms and ten hydrogen atoms, yet they are not the same compound. Since they both have the molecular formula C_4H_{10}, they must be isomers. Since they differ in the way the atoms are attached to one another, they are *structural isomers*.

$$
\begin{array}{cccc}
\text{H} & \text{H} & \text{H} & \text{H} \\
| & | & | & | \\
\text{H}-\text{C}-\text{C}-\text{C}-\text{C}-\text{H} \\
| & | & | & | \\
\text{H} & \text{H} & \text{H} & \text{H}
\end{array}
\qquad
\begin{array}{ccc}
\text{H} & \text{H} & \text{H} \\
| & | & | \\
\text{H}-\text{C}-\text{C}-\text{C}-\text{H} \\
| & | & | \\
\text{H} & | & \text{H} \\
& \text{H}-\text{C}-\text{H} \\
& | \\
& \text{H}
\end{array}
$$

You can see that the four carbon atoms in the compound on the left are attached in a continuous chain of four atoms. The carbons on the right are in the form of a "T". Skeleton formulas are often used to make such differences more apparent. A *skeleton formula* shows all of the atoms in a compound except hydrogen. It is assumed that all of the remaining valences of each carbon are filled by hydrogen. To use skeleton formulas you must know that a carbon atom is capable of forming four covalent bonds and that a hydrogen atom forms only one. The skeleton formulas of the two alkanes shown above are

$$
\text{C}-\text{C}-\text{C}-\text{C}
\qquad
\begin{array}{c}
\text{C}-\text{C}-\text{C} \\
| \\
\text{C}
\end{array}
$$

It is much easier to recognize the difference, isn't it?

Remember that a single covalent bond between two atoms does not restrict the rotation of the atoms. Structural formulas can be written around corners and jogs without changing their structure. Likewise, formulas can be reversed from left to right and top to bottom without affecting the structural representation.

The next page gives some skeletons for you to compare. Answer each question, expose the correct answer, and go on to the next.

Indicate by yes or no whether each of these skeletons represents the same compound.

1.

```
                                      C
                                      |
    C—C—C—C                      C—C—C
```

Yes. both have a continuous chain of four carbon atoms.

2.

```
         Cl
         |
    C—C—C—C                      C—C—C—C
                                      |
                                      Cl
```

Yes. They can be superimposed by a 180° rotation left to right and top to bottom.

3.

```
       C                             C
       |                             |
    C—C—C—C                      C—C—C—C
       |                             |
       C                             C
```

No. The longest continuous chain on the left is four atoms. The longest on the right is five atoms.

4.

```
    C—C—C  C—C                   C—C—C—C—C
        |  |                             |
        C—C                             C
                                        |
                                        C
```

Yes. There are seven carbon atoms in each continuous chain.

5.

```
                                      O
                                      ‖
    C—C—O—C—C                    C—C—C—C
```

No. Oxygen is between two carbon atoms on the left, but joined to only one carbon on the right.

6.

```
         Cl                          Cl
         |                           |
    Cl—C—C—C—C                   C—C—C—C—Cl
         |                           |
         Cl                          Cl
```

No. Chlorine atoms are attached to adjacent carbon atoms on the left, but not on the right.

7.

```
    C—C  C—C                      C—C—C—C
      |  |                          |   |
      C—C                           C—C
```

No. Compound on left is aliphatic; compound on right is homocyclic.

8.

```
    C                                   C
     \                                  |
      C—C—C                        C—C—C—C
     /
    C
```

Yes. Each has a chain of four carbons, with a fifth carbon attached to the carbon next to the end of the chain.

Review any questions you missed to be sure you understand your mistakes. Then go on to page 21.

Remember, an alkane is a saturated aliphatic hydrocarbon. It contains only carbon and hydrogen atoms and there are no double or triple covalent bonds.

The alkanes in which all of the carbon atoms are in a continuous chain are known as *normal alkanes*. You should be able to recognize normal alkanes readily at this point. Alkanes that do not have all of the carbon atoms in a continuous chain are called branched alkanes. You can see that, of the two alkanes containing four carbon atoms, one is a normal alkane and the other is a branched alkane.

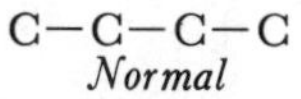

$$
\begin{array}{cc}
& \text{C} \\
& | \\
\text{C}-\text{C}-\text{C}-\text{C} & \text{C}-\text{C}-\text{C} \\
\textit{Normal} & \textit{Branched}
\end{array}
$$

Which of these skeletons does *not* represent a normal alkane?

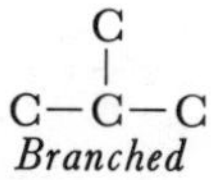

A ||||||||||||||||||||||||||||||||||||||||||||||||||||||||||||||||||||||||||||||||||||||||||||||||||||||||||||||||||

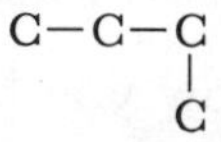

$$
\begin{array}{c}
\text{C}-\text{C}-\text{C} \\
| \\
\text{C}
\end{array}
$$

B ||||||||||||||||||||||||||||||||||||||||||||||||||||||||||||||||||||||||||||||||||||||||||||||||||||||||||||||||||

$$
\begin{array}{c}
\text{C} \\
| \\
\text{C}-\text{C}-\text{C} \\
| \\
\text{C}
\end{array}
$$

C ||||||||||||||||||||||||||||||||||||||||||||||||||||||||||||||||||||||||||||||||||||||||||||||||||||||||||||||||||

$$
\begin{array}{c}
\text{C}-\text{C}-\text{C}-\text{C} \quad \text{C} \\
\quad\quad\quad | \quad\quad | \\
\quad\quad\quad \text{C}-\text{C}
\end{array}
$$

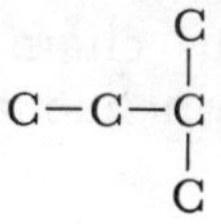

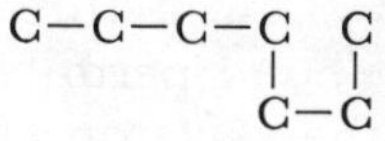

A ||||||||||||||||||||||||||||||||||||||||||||||||||||||||||||||||||||||||||||||||||||||||||||||||||||||||||||||||||||

Incorrect. The skeleton formula C—C—Ċ *does* represent a normal
$$\underset{\underset{C}{|}}{\text{C—C—C}}$$
alkane. You should recall that carbon atoms joined by a single covalent
bond can rotate freely around the axis of the bond. The structural formula
can be written with any sort of bend or crook. The formula above might
just as well be

$$\text{C—C—C—C} \quad or \quad \underset{\underset{C}{|}}{\overset{\overset{C}{|}\ \overset{C}{|}}{\text{C—C}}} \quad or \quad \overset{\overset{C}{|}}{\text{C—C}}$$

They all represent the same compound. Turn back and choose another
answer.

B ||||||||||||||||||||||||||||||||||||||||||||||||||||||||||||||||||||||||||||||||||||||||||||||||||||||||||||||||||||

You are right. No matter how you rearrange it, the skeleton formula

$$\underset{\underset{C}{|}}{\overset{\overset{C}{|}}{\text{C—C—C}}}$$

cannot be written as a continuous chain without breaking some carbon-
carbon bonds. It represents a branched alkane. Continue on to page 23.

C ||||||||||||||||||||||||||||||||||||||||||||||||||||||||||||||||||||||||||||||||||||||||||||||||||||||||||||||||||||||||

You are incorrect. Remember that any formula written on paper is
a two-dimensional attempt to show a three-dimensional object. Since a
single carbon-carbon covalent bond permits the atoms to rotate freely
around the axis of the bond, the skeleton can be written with bends and
crooks. The important factor is the order in which the carbon atoms
are joined together. Therefore, the formula you have chosen

$$\underset{\text{C—C}}{\overset{\text{C—C—C—C}\ \ \text{C}}{}}$$

is the same as C—C—C—C—C—C—C. Here is another skeleton which
contains the same number of carbon atoms:

$$\underset{\underset{C}{|}}{\overset{\overset{C}{|}}{\text{C—C—C—C—C}}}$$

It cannot be written as a single continuous chain without rearranging the
order of attachment. Do you see the difference? When you do, go back
and select another answer.

You are already familiar with the name of the simplest of the normal alkanes. It is methane (mĕth′ ān), CH_4. The next in the series is ethane (ĕth′ ān), C_2H_6. The alkane family up to ten carbon atoms is shown in this table:

Number of carbon atoms	Name	Structural formula	Molecular formula
1	Methane	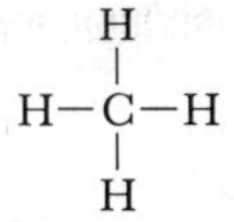	CH_4
2	Ethane	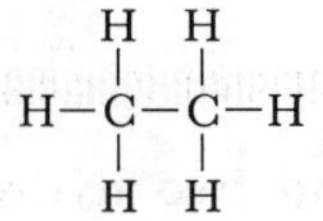	C_2H_6
3	Propane (prō′ pān)	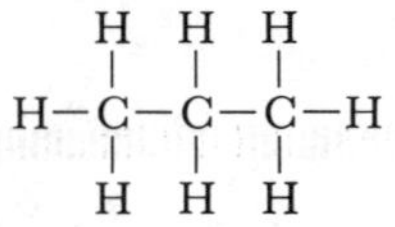	C_3H_8
4	Butane (bū′ tān)	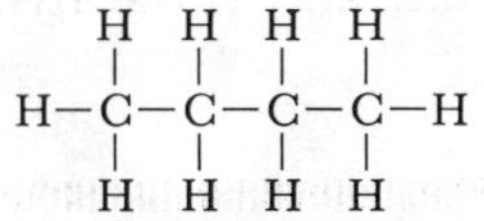	C_4H_{10}
5	Pentane (pĕn′ tān)	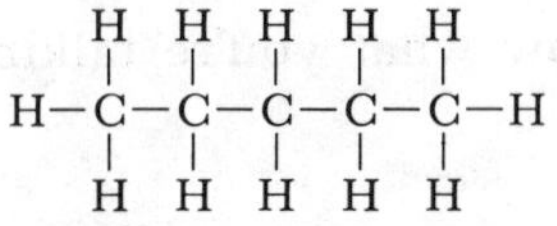	C_5H_{12}
6	Hexane (hĕx ān)	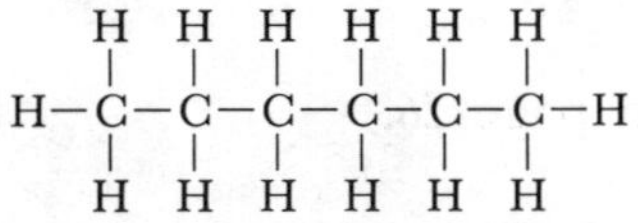	C_6H_{14}
7	Heptane (hĕp tān)	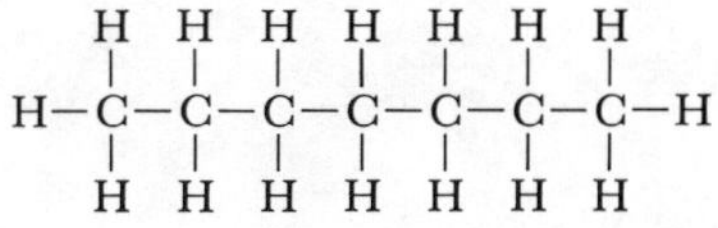	C_7H_{16}
8	Octane (ŏc′ tān)	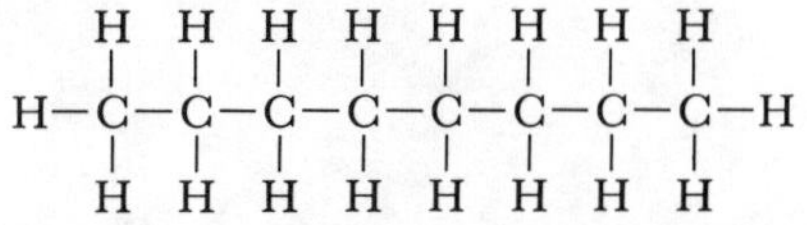	C_8H_{18}
9	Nonane (nō′ nān)	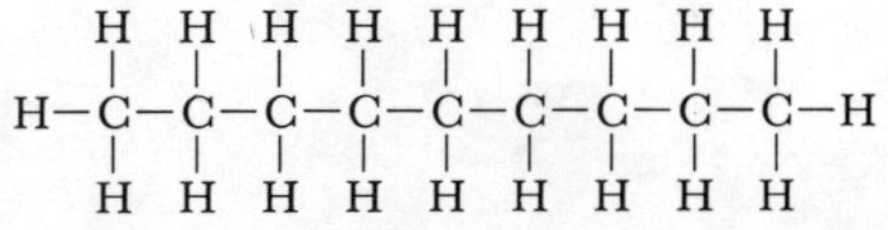	C_9H_{20}
10	Decane (dĕ cān)	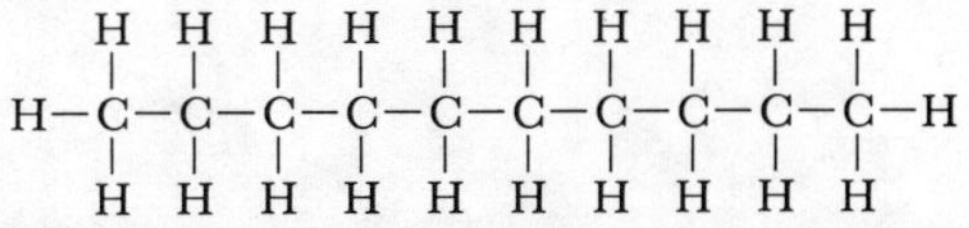	$C_{10}H_{22}$

Although you may not immediately see any regularity to the names, the prefixes from *pent* onward are derived from either the Greek or Latin words for the respective numbers. Memorize this table. It is the basis for the rest of this program.

The family of normal alkanes is known as an homologous (hŏ mŏl′ ō gŭs) series. The compounds in an homologous series differ from one another by a certain specific structural unit.

What is the structural unit that is added to one normal alkane in order to form the next member in the homologous series?

A

One carbon atom

B

One carbon atom and two hydrogen atoms

C

One carbon atom and three hydrogen atoms

D

I don't know what you're talking about

(Answers are on page 26.)

The names of the higher alkanes use the Greek or Latin prefixes to specify the number of carbon atoms.

C_{10} decanes
C_{11} undecanes
C_{12} dodecanes
C_{13} tridecanes
C_{14} tetradecanes
C_{15} pentadecanes
C_{16-19} hexadecanes, etc.
C_{20} eicosanes
C_{21} heneicosanes
C_{22} docosanes
C_{23} tricosanes
C_{24-29} tetracosanes, etc.
C_{30} triacontanes
C_{31} hentriacontanes
C_{32-39} dotriacontanes, etc.
C_{40} tetracontanes
C_{41} hentetracontanes, etc.

A ||||||||||||||||||||||||||||||||||||||||||||||||||||||||||||||||||||||||||||||||||||||||||||||||||||||||||||||||||||||||||||||||||||||||||||

You are partly right. Each member of the series has one more carbon atom than its predecessor. However, it has more hydrogen atoms, too. Compare the molecular formulas to see if you can find how many hydrogen atoms are added along with each carbon atom. Then choose another answer.

B ||||||||||||||||||||||||||||||||||||||||||||||||||||||||||||||||||||||||||||||||||||||||||||||||||||||||||||||||||||||||||||||||||||||||||||

You are right. As the series grows from one member to the next, the

structural unit
$$-\overset{\displaystyle H}{\underset{\displaystyle H}{\overset{|}{\underset{|}{C}}}}-$$
is added each time. Turn to page 27.

C ||||||||||||||||||||||||||||||||||||||||||||||||||||||||||||||||||||||||||||||||||||||||||||||||||||||||||||||||||||||||||||||||||||||||||||

You are on the right track, but not entirely correct. Each member of the homologous series of alkanes has one more carbon than the one before it. Does it also have three more hydrogen atoms? Compare the molecular formulas of propane and butane. Then compare butane with pentane. Then choose another answer.

D ||||||||||||||||||||||||||||||||||||||||||||||||||||||||||||||||||||||||||||||||||||||||||||||||||||||||||||||||||||||||||||||||||||||||||||

Well, let's see if we can help you to understand. If you compare the structural formulas of propane and butane, what is the difference?

$$\overset{\text{H H H}}{\underset{\text{H H H}}{\text{H}-\text{C}-\text{C}-\text{C}-\text{H}}} \qquad \overset{\text{H H H H}}{\underset{\text{H H H H}}{\text{H}-\text{C}-\text{C}-\text{C}-\text{C}-\text{H}}}$$

propane   *butane*

You can see that butane is merely propane with an added

$$-\overset{\displaystyle H}{\underset{\displaystyle H}{\overset{|}{\underset{|}{C}}}}-$$

Now make a similar comparison between butane and the next member of the homologous series, pentane. When you have done this, go back and choose another answer.

Consider another homologous series for a moment. It is series of alcohols as represented by these condensed structural formulas:

CH_3OH, CH_3CH_2OH, $CH_3CH_2CH_2OH$, $CH_3CH_2CH_2CH_2OH$,   etc.

The unit of structural difference in this series is the same as in the normal alkane series. It is CH_2. Each member of the series differs from its predecessor by this unit.

Every member of an homologous series can be represented by a general formula in which a letter substitutes for the number of carbon atoms, and a combination of the letter and a number substitutes for the atoms of the other elements. If the letter "n" is used to represent the number of carbon atoms in one of the alcohols, the number of hydrogen atoms is always "2n + 2." Each alcohol has only one oxygen atom. Therefore, the general formula of the alcohols is $C_nH_{2n+2}O$. Verify this general formula by checking it against the molecular formulas for the alcohols that are shown above. You might say that the general formula is sort of an algebraic equivalent for any one of the series.

The molecular formulas of the first four normal alkanes are CH_4, C_2H_6, C_3H_8, and C_4H_{10}. What is the general formula for the series of normal alkanes?

A ||||||||||||||||||||||||||||||||||||||||||||||||||||||||||||||||||||||||||||||||||||||||||||||||||||||||||||||||||||||||||||

C_nH_{4n}

B ||||||||||||||||||||||||||||||||||||||||||||||||||||||||||||||||||||||||||||||||||||||||||||||||||||||||||||||||||||||||||||

C_nH_{3n+1}

C ||||||||||||||||||||||||||||||||||||||||||||||||||||||||||||||||||||||||||||||||||||||||||||||||||||||||||||||||||||||||||||

C_nH_{4n-2}

D ||||||||||||||||||||||||||||||||||||||||||||||||||||||||||||||||||||||||||||||||||||||||||||||||||||||||||||||||||||||||||||

C_nH_{2n+2}

A ||||||||||||||||||||||||||||||||||||||||||||||||||||||||||||||||||||||||||||||||||||||||||||||||||||||||||||||||||||||||||||||||

You are incorrect. The general formula C_nH_{4n} will work for methane, CH_4, where $n = 1$, but it won't work for ethane, C_2H_6. If your answer were correct, ethane would have to be C_2H_8. A correct general formula must specify the molecular formula for every member of the homologous series if the proper substitutions are made. Turn back and work out another answer.

B ||||||||||||||||||||||||||||||||||||||||||||||||||||||||||||||||||||||||||||||||||||||||||||||||||||||||||||||||||||||||||||||||

You are wrong. The general formula C_nH_{3n+1} works for methane, CH_4, but it does not work for any other member of the series. Suppose you were to use it to predict the formula of propane. If $n = 3$, then $C_nH_{3n+1} = C_3H_{10}$. This is not the right molecular formula for propane. A correct general formula must enable you to determine the molecular formula of any member of the series. Go back and work out the correct answer.

C ||||||||||||||||||||||||||||||||||||||||||||||||||||||||||||||||||||||||||||||||||||||||||||||||||||||||||||||||||||||||||||||||

Your answer is that C_nH_{4n-2} is the general formula for the alkanes. Come on now. This general formula doesn't even work for the first member, methane. Since methane has only one carbon atom, $n = 1$, then $C_nH_{4n-2} = CH_2$. You should know that the correct formula is CH_4, not CH_2. A general formula must allow you to predict the formula for any member of the alkane family. Turn back and work out the right answer.

D ||||||||||||||||||||||||||||||||||||||||||||||||||||||||||||||||||||||||||||||||||||||||||||||||||||||||||||||||||||||||||||||||

You are correct. The general formula for the alkanes is C_nH_{2n+2}. Go on to page 29.

So far you have learned to write four kinds of formulas: molecular, structural, condensed structural, and skeleton. Each has its advantages and disadvantages. The molecular formulas give the composition of the compounds but no information about their structure. The structural formula is a nuisance to write because all the C—H bonds must be shown. Skeleton structural formulas show the important structural features, but they do not represent the entire substance. For this reason skeleton formulas are rarely used except to emphasize a particular feature of the structure. Most textbooks use condensed structural formulas to specify various compounds because they save space as well as give complete information about the structure of the compound.

Whenever a particular structural unit is repeated several times, parentheses can be used to condense the formula even more. A few examples will make this clear to you.

	Molecular formula	*Condensed formula*
Methane	CH_4	CH_4
Ethane	C_2H_6	CH_3CH_3
Propane	C_3H_8	$CH_3CH_2CH_3$
Butane	C_4H_{10}	$CH_3(CH_2)_2CH_3$
Pentane	C_5H_{12}	$CH_3(CH_2)_3CH_3$

Notice that the parentheses have exactly the same meaning as in inorganic compounds. For example, $Ca(OH)_2$ represents 1 Ca^{++} ion and 2 OH^- ions. The $(CH_2)_2$ in the butane formula represents $-CH_2CH_2-$.

Which of the following is a condensed structural formula for octane?

A

$CH_3(CH_2)_8CH_3$

B

$(CH_2)_8$

C

$CH_3(CH_2)_6CH_3$

D

I need help.

A |||||||||||||||||||||||||||||||||||||||||||||||||||||||||||||||||||||||||||||||||||||||||||||||||||||||||||||||||||||||||

You are incorrect. Your answer is that $CH_3(CH_2)_8CH_3$ is a condensed structural formula for octane. Look at the formula carefully. How many carbon atoms are there? There are ten. The prefix *oct-* in the name should tell you that there are eight carbon atoms in octane. You have chosen the condensed formula of decane. Turn back and find the formula for octane.

B |||||||||||||||||||||||||||||||||||||||||||||||||||||||||||||||||||||||||||||||||||||||||||||||||||||||||||||||||||||||||

You are wrong. You have chosen $(CH_2)_8$ as the condensed structural formula of octane. This formula has the correct number of carbon atoms, all right, but what about the hydrogen? If you multiply to remove the parentheses, $(CH_2)_8$ becomes C_8H_{16}. If you substitute n = 8 into the general formula, $C_nH_{2n+2} = C_8H_{18}$. Your answer lacks two hydrogen atoms. If this is not clear to you, try drawing a complete structural formula for $(CH_2)_8$. Compare it with the structural formula for octane on page 23.

C |||||||||||||||||||||||||||||||||||||||||||||||||||||||||||||||||||||||||||||||||||||||||||||||||||||||||||||||||||||||||

Right. The condensed formula $CH_3(CH_2)_6CH_3$ represents octane, C_8H_{18}. You may wish to compare it with the complete structural formula on page 23. Continue on to page 31.

D |||||||||||||||||||||||||||||||||||||||||||||||||||||||||||||||||||||||||||||||||||||||||||||||||||||||||||||||||||||||||

OK, here is some help. The use of parentheses in condensed structural formulas is nothing more than an attempt to save space by not writing repeating structures separately. In inorganic chemistry you write $Mg(NO_3)_2$ instead of $MgNO_3NO_3$. Similarly, in organic chemistry you can write $CH_3(CH_2)_3CH_3$ instead of $CH_3CH_2CH_2CH_2CH_3$. Read page 29 again and choose another answer.

To begin our discussion of branched alkanes, we'll look at their carbon skeletons. You know that a normal alkane is one in which there is a continuous chain containing all the carbon atoms. Although the skeleton may be written with bends and corners, the entire chain can be traced from one end to the other without lifting your pencil or retracing. This is not true for branched alkanes. Compare these two skeletons by tracing the carbon chains with your pencil.

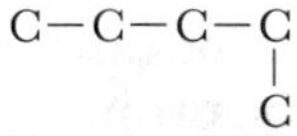

$$C-C-C-C$$
$$|$$
$$C$$

Normal alkane

$$C$$
$$|$$
$$C-C-C-C$$
$$|$$
$$C$$

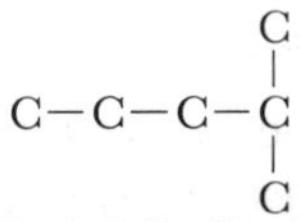

Branched alkane

The skeleton on the right cannot be rearranged to include all of the carbon atoms in a continuous chain without breaking a carbon-carbon bond.

Here is a fairly difficult question for you. What is the minimum number of carbon atoms in a branched alkane?

A

3

B

4

C

5

A ||||||||||||||||||||||||||||||||||||||||||||||||||||||||||||||||||||||||||||||||||||||||||||||||||||||||||||||

You are wrong. No matter how you write the skeleton, three carbon atoms must be in a continuous chain. Here are several ways of depicting a three-carbon chain:

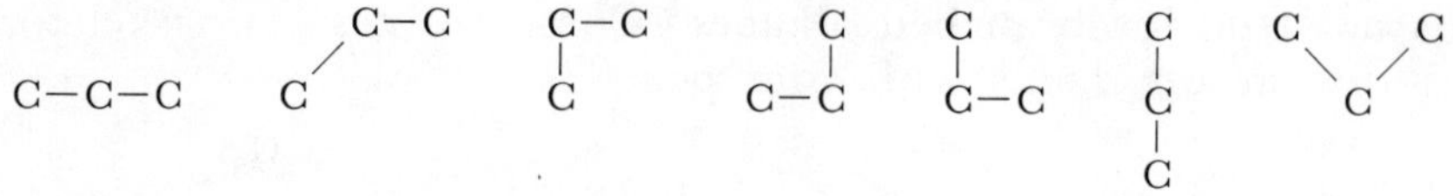

$$
C-C-C \qquad C\!\!\diagup^{\textstyle C-C} \qquad \begin{matrix} C-C \\ | \\ C \end{matrix} \qquad \begin{matrix} C \\ | \\ C-C \end{matrix} \qquad \begin{matrix} C \\ | \\ C-C \end{matrix} \qquad \begin{matrix} C \\ | \\ C \\ | \\ C \end{matrix} \qquad \begin{matrix} C \quad C \\ \diagdown \diagup \\ C \end{matrix}
$$

Since the carbon atoms can rotate freely around the covalent bonds, every one of these skeletons represents ordinary propane.

B ||||||||||||||||||||||||||||||||||||||||||||||||||||||||||||||||||||||||||||||||||||||||||||||||||||||||||||||

Correct. It is possible to write a branched alkane containing only four carbon atoms, but impossible to write one with two or three carbons. Turn to page 33.

C ||||||||||||||||||||||||||||||||||||||||||||||||||||||||||||||||||||||||||||||||||||||||||||||||||||||||||||||

You are incorrect. Suppose that we consider this skeleton for a branched alkane containing five carbon atoms:

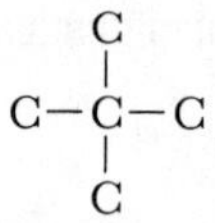

$$
\begin{matrix}
& C & \\
& | & \\
C- & C & -C \\
& | & \\
& C &
\end{matrix}
$$

Try removing any one of the outside carbon atoms. Isn't the remaining skeleton still a branched alkane? Sure it is. Go on to page 33.

There are only two different ways that a carbon skeleton of four atoms can be arranged. They are

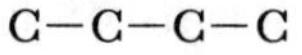

$$C-C-C-C \qquad \text{and} \qquad \begin{matrix} C-C-C \\ | \\ C \end{matrix}$$

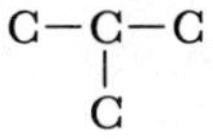

The complete structural formulas of the two compounds are

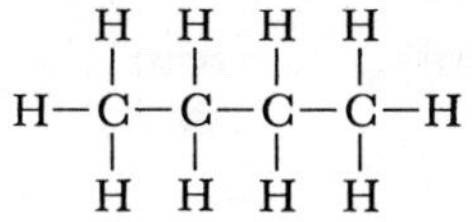

$$\begin{matrix} H & H & H & H \\ | & | & | & | \\ H-C-C-C-C-H \\ | & | & | & | \\ H & H & H & H \end{matrix} \qquad \text{and} \qquad \begin{matrix} H & H & H \\ | & | & | \\ H-C-C-C-H \\ | & | & | \\ H & | & H \\ & H-C-H \\ & | \\ & H \end{matrix}$$

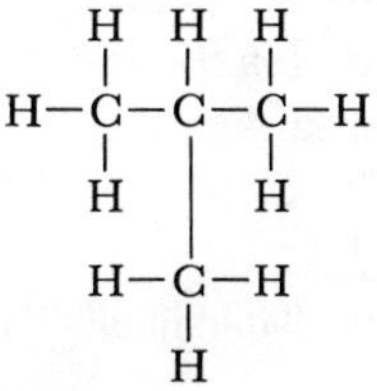

Since both compounds have the same molecular formula, C_4H_{10}, they are isomers. To distinguish between them, the first was named butane (sometimes n-butane for normal butane, the common name) and the second was called isobutane (ī′ sō bū′ tān).

As the number of carbon atoms increases, so does the number of possible structural isomers. How many structural isomers have the formula C_5H_{12}?

A |||||||||||||||||||||||||||||||||||||||||||||||||||||||||||||||||||||||||||||||||||||||||||||||||||||

2

B |||||||||||||||||||||||||||||||||||||||||||||||||||||||||||||||||||||||||||||||||||||||||||||||||||||

3

C |||||||||||||||||||||||||||||||||||||||||||||||||||||||||||||||||||||||||||||||||||||||||||||||||||||

4

D |||||||||||||||||||||||||||||||||||||||||||||||||||||||||||||||||||||||||||||||||||||||||||||||||||||

5

A ||||||||||||||||||||||||||||||||||||||||||||||||||||||||||||||||||||||||||||||||||||||||||||||||||||||||||||||||||

You are incorrect. There are more than two isomeric alkanes that contain five carbon atoms. Here are the skeletons of two of them:

$$
\text{C-C-C-C-C} \qquad\qquad \begin{array}{c} \text{C} \\ | \\ \text{C-C-C-C} \end{array}
$$

Try to find at least one more that is different from these two. Then choose another answer.

B ||||||||||||||||||||||||||||||||||||||||||||||||||||||||||||||||||||||||||||||||||||||||||||||||||||||||||||||||||

You are right. There are three isomeric alkanes that have the formula C_5H_{12}. Their skeletons and common names are on page 35.

C ||||||||||||||||||||||||||||||||||||||||||||||||||||||||||||||||||||||||||||||||||||||||||||||||||||||||||||||||||

You are wrong. There are not four isomers that contain five carbon atoms. Perhaps you have written one skeleton in two different orientations. For instance

$$
\begin{array}{c} \text{C} \\ | \\ \text{C-C-C-C} \end{array} \qquad \begin{array}{c} \text{C-C-C-C} \\ | \\ \text{C} \end{array} \qquad \begin{array}{c} \text{C} \\ | \\ \text{C-C-C-C} \end{array}
$$

All three of these skeletons represent the same compound. They can be superimposed by rotation. Check the skeletons you have written to be sure that they are all different. Then turn back and choose another answer.

D ||||||||||||||||||||||||||||||||||||||||||||||||||||||||||||||||||||||||||||||||||||||||||||||||||||||||||||||||||

You are incorrect. There are not five isomers that contain five carbon atoms. Perhaps you have written the same skeleton in two or more different orientations. For example, all of the skeletons written below have the same structure and represent the same compound. They can be superimposed by rotation.

$$
\begin{array}{c} \text{C} \\ | \\ \text{C-C-C-C} \end{array} \qquad \begin{array}{c} \text{C-C-C-C} \\ | \\ \text{C} \end{array} \qquad \begin{array}{c} \text{C} \\ | \\ \text{C-C-C-C} \end{array} \qquad \begin{array}{c} \text{C-C-C-C} \\ | \\ \text{C} \end{array}
$$

Check the skeletons you have written to see which ones are alike. Then turn back and choose another answer.

The three isomers containing five carbon atoms have these carbon skeletons:

$$C-C-C-C-C \qquad C-C-\overset{\displaystyle C}{\underset{|}{C}}-C \qquad C-\overset{\displaystyle C}{\underset{|}{\underset{\displaystyle C}{\overset{|}{C}}}}-C$$

pentane   *isopentane*   *neopentane*

The name pentane is both a common and the systematic name for the first compound. Isopentane and neopentane are the common names for the latter two, but are allowed by the IUPAC rules.

The number of possible isomers expands quite rapidly for the higher alkanes (i.e., those with more carbon atoms). New prefixes, if coined indefinitely, would soon become impossible to remember. For this reason, the only one in widespread use is *iso-* (ī′ sō). This prefix is retained in the common names for all compounds having a single carbon branch on the carbon atom next to the end of a continuous chain. Thus the skeletons of isohexane and isoheptane are:

$$C-C-C-\overset{\displaystyle C}{\underset{|}{C}}-C \qquad\qquad C-C-C-C-\overset{\displaystyle C}{\underset{|}{C}}-C$$

isohexane   *isoheptane*

Which of these skeletons represents a compound whose common name begins with the prefix *iso-*?

A ||||||||||||||||||||||||||||||||||||||||||||||||||||||||||||||||||||||||||||||||||||||||||||||||||||||

$$C-C-\overset{\displaystyle }{\underset{|}{C}}-C$$
$$\underset{\displaystyle C}{}\quad\underset{\displaystyle C}{}$$

$$C-C-C-C$$
$$\underset{C}{|}\quad\quad\underset{C}{|}$$

B ||||||||||||||||||||||||||||||||||||||||||||||||||||||||||||||||||||||||||||||||||||||||||||||||||||||

$$C-C-C-C$$
$$\underset{C}{|}\quad\quad\quad\underset{C}{|}$$

C ||||||||||||||||||||||||||||||||||||||||||||||||||||||||||||||||||||||||||||||||||||||||||||||||||||||

$$C-C-C-C-C$$
$$\quad\quad\underset{C}{|}$$

D ||||||||||||||||||||||||||||||||||||||||||||||||||||||||||||||||||||||||||||||||||||||||||||||||||||||

$$\overset{\displaystyle C}{\underset{|}{}}$$
$$C-C-C-\overset{\displaystyle C}{\underset{|}{C}}-C$$
$$\underset{C}{|}$$

A ||||||||||||||||||||||||||||||||||||||||||||||||||||||||||||||||||||||||||||||||||||||||||||||||||||||||||||||||||

You are correct. If you straighten out the kink, the skeleton you have chosen can be written

$$C-C-C-\overset{\displaystyle |}{\underset{\displaystyle C}{C}}-C$$

It has a single carbon branch on the carbon atom next to the end of a continuous chain. Therefore, it is an iso- compound, specifically, isohexane. Go on to page 37.

B ||||||||||||||||||||||||||||||||||||||||||||||||||||||||||||||||||||||||||||||||||||||||||||||||||||||||||||||||||

You are incorrect. Perhaps you have forgotten that a single covalent bond between carbon atoms does not restrict the rotation of the atoms. In practical terms, this means that carbon skeleton formulas can be written with crooks that may be straightened out. The formula you have chosen

$$\begin{array}{cccc} C-C-C-C \\ | \qquad\quad | \\ C \qquad\quad C \end{array}$$

can also be written $C-C-C-C-C-C$ and is hexane. With this in mind, turn back and find a skeleton which represents an iso- compound.

C ||||||||||||||||||||||||||||||||||||||||||||||||||||||||||||||||||||||||||||||||||||||||||||||||||||||||||||||||||

You are not correct. An iso- compound has a single carbon branch on the carbon next to the end of a continuous chain. The skeleton you have chosen has either (a) a two-carbon branch on the carbon next to the end of the chain, or (b) a single-carbon branch in the middle. Whether it is (a) or (b) depends on your viewpoint.

Continuous chain in capitals; branch in small letters.

$$\begin{array}{ccc} \text{C—C—C—C—C} & \qquad \text{C—C—C—C} & \qquad \text{C—C—C—C—C} \\ \quad | & \qquad\quad\;\; | & \qquad\qquad\;\; | \\ \quad \text{C} & \qquad\quad\;\; c & \qquad\qquad\;\; c \\ & \qquad\quad\;\; | \\ & \qquad\quad\;\; c \\ \textit{Your Answer} & \qquad\quad (a) & \qquad\qquad (b) \end{array}$$

D ||||||||||||||||||||||||||||||||||||||||||||||||||||||||||||||||||||||||||||||||||||||||||||||||||||||||||||||||||

Wrong. Your answer is that the skeleton

$$C-C-C-\overset{\displaystyle C}{\underset{\displaystyle C}{\overset{\displaystyle |}{\underset{\displaystyle |}{C}}}}-C$$

represents an iso- compound. By definition, an iso- compound has a single carbon branch on the carbon next to the end of a continuous chain. No matter how you choose the continuous chain in this skeleton, there are *two* carbon atoms that cannot be included. Therefore, it does not represent an iso- compound. With this definition of an iso- compound in mind, turn back and select another answer.

The systematic names of all the alkanes are based on the number of carbon atoms in the longest continuous chain of carbon atoms. If the longest chain contains four carbon atoms, the compound is named as a butane. If it has five, it is named as a pentane, and so forth. For an illustration, look at the skeleton of isopentane again.

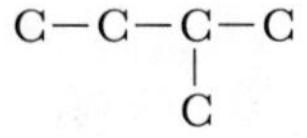

$$C-C-\underset{\displaystyle |}{\overset{\displaystyle }{C}}-C$$
$$C$$

The longest continuous chain has four carbon atoms. Therefore, its systematic name will be based on butane.

The compound represented by this skeleton is named as a propane.

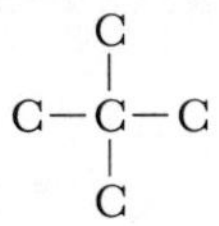

$$C$$
$$|$$
$$C-C-C$$
$$|$$
$$C$$

There are four ways to count a chain of three carbon atoms, but no way to make a chain of four or five.

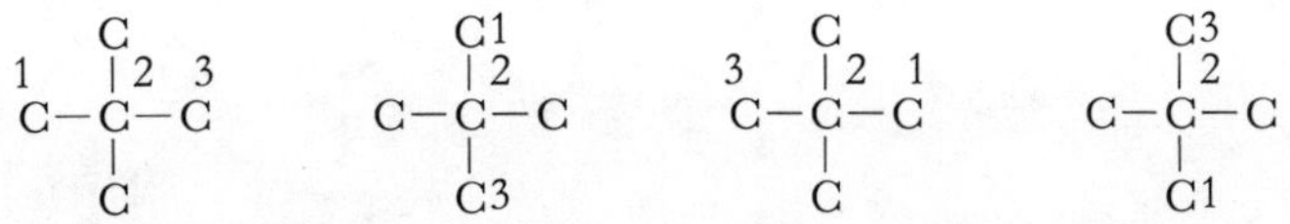

```
      C                  C1               C                   C3
1    | 2  3             | 2            3  | 2  1             | 2
C − C − C           C − C − C           C − C − C           C − C − C
     |                  |                  |                   |
     C                  C3                 C                   C1
```

You have seen this skeleton before. Even though its systematic name is based on propane, another acceptable name is neopentane.

On page 38 are some carbon skeletons. Count the carbon chains in each skeleton, find the longest continuous one, and determine the base name of the compound.

1.

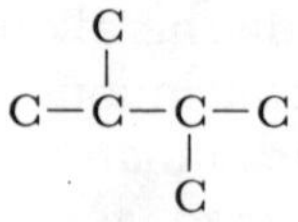

```
        C
        |
    C—C—C—C
        |
        C
```

Four carbon atoms in chain: butane

2.

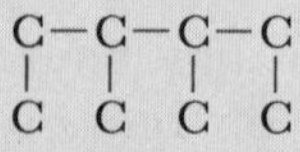

```
    C—C—C—C
    |   |   |   |
    C   C   C   C
```

Six carbon atoms in chain: hexane

3.

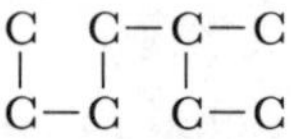

```
    C   C—C—C
    |   |   |
    C—C   C—C
```

Seven carbon atoms in chain: heptane

4.

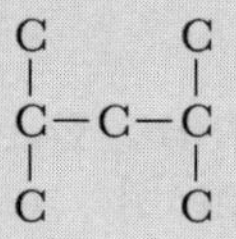

```
    C       C
    |       |
    C—C—C
    |       |
    C       C
```

Five carbon atoms in chain: pentane

5.

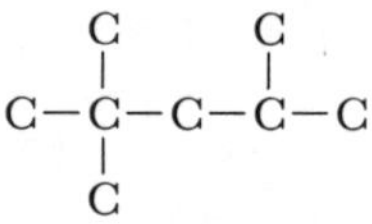

```
        C       C
        |       |
    C—C—C—C—C
        |
        C
```

Five carbon atoms in chain: pentane

Go on to page 39.

Now let's look at two condensed structural formulas:

$$CH_3-CH_2-\overset{*}{C}H-CH_3 \qquad\qquad CH_3-CH_2-\overset{*}{C}H_2-CH_3$$
$$\underset{CH_3}{|}$$

Both have four carbon atoms in the longest chain and are named as butanes. How do they differ? Can you see that the difference is the replacement of one of the H's on the *-marked carbon atom by CH_3—? Replacement of this sort is called substitution, and CH_3— is designated as a substituent group. So the first compound above is a substituted butane. Now we need a way to designate the CH_3—.

Groups of atoms that have an unused valence are called radicals. CH_3— is a radical that might be formed by removing a hydrogen atom from methane, CH_4. Likewise, the radical CH_3CH_2— could be formed from the normal alkane, ethane. A whole series of these radicals can be formed from the normal alkanes. Collectively, they are known as *alkyl* (ăl′ kĭl) *radicals*, or *alkyl groups*. They are named by changing the *-ane* suffix to *-yl*. For example

$$CH_3- \qquad\qquad CH_3CH_2-\text{ or }C_2H_5- \qquad\qquad CH_3CH_2CH_2-\text{ or }C_3H_7-$$
methyl *ethyl* *propyl*

What is the name of the radical represented by all three of these formulas?

$$CH_3CH_2CH_2CH_2- \qquad\qquad CH_3(CH_2)_2CH_2- \qquad\qquad C_4H_9-$$

A ||||||||||||||||||||||||||||||||||||||||||||||||||||||||||||||||||||||||||||||||||||||||||||||||||||||||||||||||||

butyl

B ||||||||||||||||||||||||||||||||||||||||||||||||||||||||||||||||||||||||||||||||||||||||||||||||||||||||||||||||||

pentyl

C ||||||||||||||||||||||||||||||||||||||||||||||||||||||||||||||||||||||||||||||||||||||||||||||||||||||||||||||||||

diethyl

A ||||||||||||||||||||||||||||||||||||||||||||||||||||||||||||||||||||||||||||||||||||||||||||||||||||||||||||||||||||||||||||||||

You are right. All three of the formulas represent the radical which remains when one hydrogen atom is removed from butane. Compare each formula before you go on to page 41.

Butane	$CH_3CH_2CH_2CH_3$	$CH_3(CH_2)_2CH_3$	C_4H_{10}
Butyl radical	$CH_3CH_2CH_2CH_2-$	$CH_3(CH_2)_2CH_2-$	C_4H_9-

B ||||||||||||||||||||||||||||||||||||||||||||||||||||||||||||||||||||||||||||||||||||||||||||||||||||||||||||||||||||||||||||||||

You are incorrect. Perhaps you need to review the names of the alkanes. Here is a list of their names, together with the number of carbon atoms in each:

1	methane	7	heptane
2	ethane	8	octane
3	propane	9	nonane
4	butane	10	decane
5	pentane	11	undecane
6	hexane	12	dodecane

With these clearly in mind, turn back and read page 39 carefully before you select another answer.

C ||||||||||||||||||||||||||||||||||||||||||||||||||||||||||||||||||||||||||||||||||||||||||||||||||||||||||||||||||||||||||||||||

Where did you pick up the term *diethyl*? Certainly not in this program. Turn back and choose an answer that uses something you have seen before in the program.

The radicals derived from isoalkanes are named in the same way as those derived from normal alkanes. The *-ane* suffix of the name is changed to *-yl*. For example

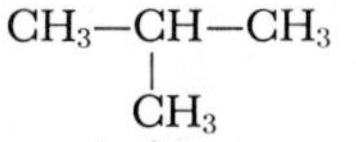

CH$_3$—CH—CH$_3$
|
CH$_3$
isobutane

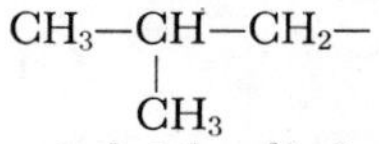

CH$_3$—CH—CH$_2$—
|
CH$_3$
isobutyl radical

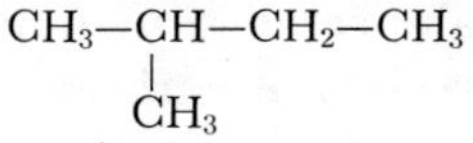

CH$_3$—CH—CH$_2$—CH$_3$
|
CH$_3$
isopentane

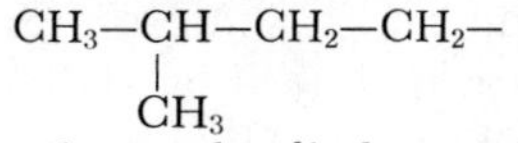

CH$_3$—CH—CH$_2$—CH$_2$—
|
CH$_3$
isopentyl radical

Note carefully that the free valence of the radicals is at the opposite end of the chain from the branch and that the branch, as before, is a single carbon atom attached to the carbon next to the end of the longest continuous chain.

There is one iso- radical that does not have a corresponding isoalkane. Can you guess what it is? It's the isopropyl group. The formula of the isopropyl radical is

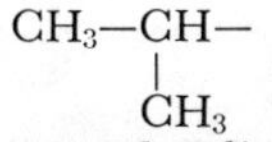

CH$_3$—CH—
|
CH$_3$
isopropyl radical

You can see that the corresponding hydrocarbon is propane.

Which of the following formulas correctly represents the isohexyl radical?

A

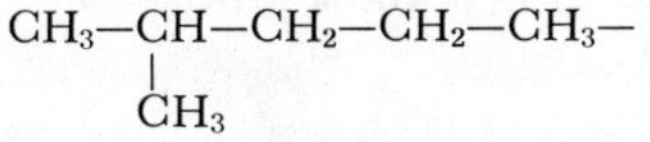

CH$_3$—CH—CH$_2$—CH$_2$—CH$_3$—
|
CH$_3$

B

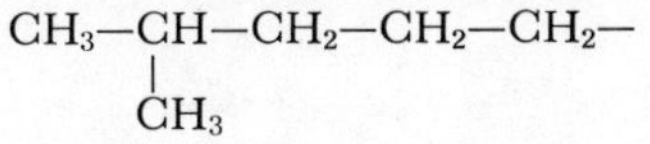

CH$_3$—CH—CH$_2$—CH$_2$—CH$_2$—
|
CH$_3$

C

CH$_3$—CH—CH$_2$—CH—CH$_3$
|
CH$_3$

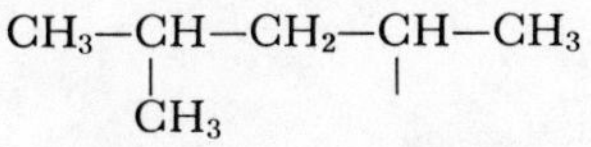

A ||||||||||||||||||||||||||||||||||||||||||||||||||||||||||||||||||||||||||||||||||||||||||||||||||||||||||||||||||||||||||||||||

You made a mistake. Here is the formula you have chosen for the isohexyl radical

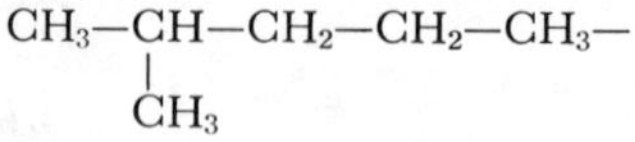

$$CH_3—CH—CH_2—CH_2—CH_3—$$
$$|$$
$$CH_3$$

It has the right skeleton and the free valence is shown on the proper carbon atom, but it is still not right. There is one carbon atom with five covalent bonds. Do you see it? When you do, turn back and find the right answer.

B ||||||||||||||||||||||||||||||||||||||||||||||||||||||||||||||||||||||||||||||||||||||||||||||||||||||||||||||||||||||||||||||||

You are right. Isohexane contains a total of six carbon atoms and the isohexyl radical is formed by removing one hydrogen atom from the carbon atom at the end opposite the branch. Go on to page 43.

C ||||||||||||||||||||||||||||||||||||||||||||||||||||||||||||||||||||||||||||||||||||||||||||||||||||||||||||||||||||||||||||||||

You are wrong. The formula you chose for the isohexyl radical is

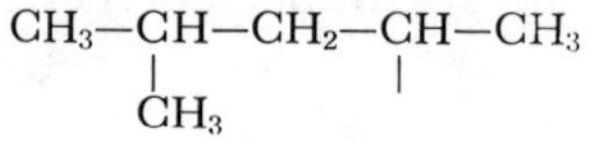

$$CH_3—CH—CH_2—CH—CH_3$$
$$|\qquad\qquad|$$
$$CH_3$$

It has the right skeleton, but the free valence is in the wrong place. The free valence on iso- radicals is located at the terminal (end) carbon atom opposite from the branch. Turn back and select another answer.

The formulas for alkyl radicals can always be recognized by the dash indicating the free valence. Again notice the difference between propane and a propyl group:

$$CH_3CH_2CH_3$$
propane

$$CH_3CH_2CH_2- \text{ or } C_3H_7-$$
propyl group

When radicals or groups of this sort are attached to a carbon atom in a carbon chain, they are written after the carbon atom in the structural formula and enclosed in parentheses if it is needed for clarity.

$$CH_3CH(CH_3)CH_2CH(CH_3)_2 \quad \text{represents}$$

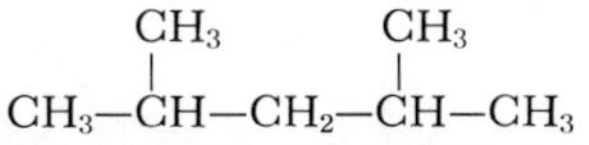

$$\begin{array}{ccccc} & CH_3 & & CH_3 & \\ & | & & | & \\ CH_3- & CH- & CH_2- & CH- & CH_3 \end{array}$$

In checking to make sure that you have interpreted a formula correctly, remember that each carbon atom forms four covalent bonds.

Find the structural formula of the compound represented by this condensed formula: $CH_3C(CH_3)_2CH_3$

A

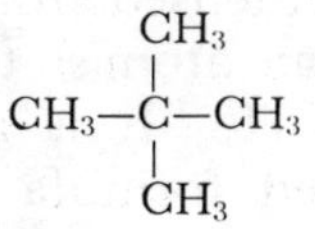

$$\begin{array}{c} CH_3 \\ | \\ CH_3-C-CH_3 \\ | \\ CH_3 \end{array}$$

B

$$\begin{array}{c} CH_3 \\ | \\ CH_3-CH-CH_2-CH_3 \end{array}$$

C

$$\begin{array}{c} CH_3-C-CH_3-CH_3 \\ | \\ CH_3 \end{array}$$

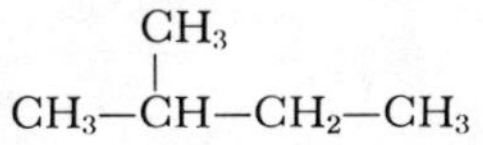

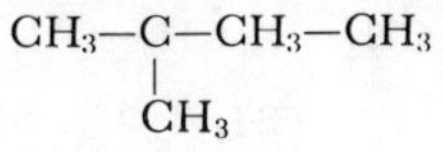

A ||||||||||||||||||||||||||||||||||||||||||||||||||||||||||||||||||||||||||||||||||||||||||||||||||

You are right. Here are the condensed and expanded structural formulas shown side-by-side:

$$CH_3C(CH_3)_2CH_3$$

$$CH_3-\underset{\underset{CH_3}{|}}{\overset{\overset{CH_3}{|}}{C}}-CH_3$$

An acceptable name for the compound is neopentane. Go on to page 45.

B ||||||||||||||||||||||||||||||||||||||||||||||||||||||||||||||||||||||||||||||||||||||||||||||||||

You are incorrect. The expanded formula which you chose does not represent the same compound as $CH_3C(CH_3)_2CH_3$. Let's see how your answer would be condensed. Your answer is

$$CH_3-\underset{\underset{CH_3}{|}}{CH}-CH_2-CH_3$$

Branches are indicated in condensed formulas by enclosing them in parentheses following the carbon atom(s) to which they are attached. In your answer the branch is —CH_3. It is attached to the second carbon atom. Therefore, the condensed formula is $CH_3CH(CH_3)CH_2CH_3$. You might omit the parentheses since it should be clear that the —CH_3 must be a branch. If it were in the chain, the carbon atom would have five covalent bonds: three to hydrogen and two to other carbon atoms. Turn back and select another answer.

C ||||||||||||||||||||||||||||||||||||||||||||||||||||||||||||||||||||||||||||||||||||||||||||||||||

You are wrong. Your answer is

$$CH_3-\overset{\#}{\underset{\underset{CH_3}{|}}{C}}-\overset{*}{CH_3}-CH_3$$

you seem to have forgotten that each carbon atom in an alkane forms four covalent bonds. If you will check your answer, you will see that the carbon atom indicated by # has only three, while the one marked with * has five. Turn back and choose another answer.

Let's get back to isopentane and learn its systematic name. Its structural formula is

$$CH_3-CH_2-\underset{\underset{\displaystyle CH_3}{|}}{CH}-CH_3$$

Have you already guessed that its systematic name is methylbutane? After all, it has a methyl group, CH_3-, substituted on butane, $CH_3CH_2CH_2CH_3$. Note that the methyl group is substituted for one of the hydrogens in the butane molecule. Does the name methylbutane say everything that needs to be said? Is there another compound that could have the same name? What about this one?

$$CH_3-\underset{\underset{\displaystyle CH_3}{|}}{CH}-CH_2-CH_3$$

Although it might appear at first glance to be a different compound, you can see that this formula is the same as the first if you reverse it from left to right. Hence, methylbutane is a unique and satisfactory systematic name for the compound.

What happens when one more carbon atom is added to the end of the methylbutane chain? The new structural formula is

$$CH_3-\underset{\underset{\displaystyle CH_3}{|}}{CH}-CH_2-CH_2-CH_3$$

The longest continuous carbon chain now contains five carbon atoms. Since a methyl group is substituted for one of the hydrogen atoms, the compound must be methylpentane. Is methylpentane a unique name for this compound?

A ||||||||||||||||||||||||||||||||||||||||||||||||||||||||||||||||||||||||||||||||||||||||||||||||||||||||||||||||||||||||

Yes

B ||||||||||||||||||||||||||||||||||||||||||||||||||||||||||||||||||||||||||||||||||||||||||||||||||||||||||||||||||||||||

No

A ||||||||||||||||||||||||||||||||||||||||||||||||||||||||||||||||||||||||||||||||||||||||||||||||||||||||||||||||||||||||||||||||||||||||

You are incorrect. Your answer is that methylpentane is a unique name for

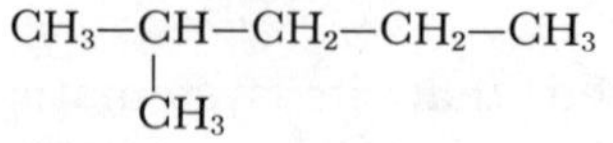

$$CH_3-CH-CH_2-CH_2-CH_3$$
$$|$$
$$CH_3$$

In order for this to be a unique name, there must be no other compound that is a methylpentane. Consider this formula:

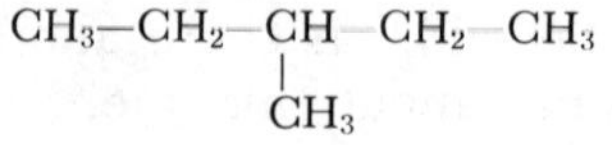

$$CH_3-CH_2-CH-CH_2-CH_3$$
$$|$$
$$CH_3$$

It's methylpentane, too, isn't it? Can you superimpose it on the other formula? No, you cannot. Consequently, methylpentane alone is not a unique name for either one of them. Continue to page 47. to learn how each is named.

B ||||||||||||||||||||||||||||||||||||||||||||||||||||||||||||||||||||||||||||||||||||||||||||||||||||||||||||||||||||||||||||||||||||||||

Correct. Methylpentane is not a unique name for the compound represented by the formula

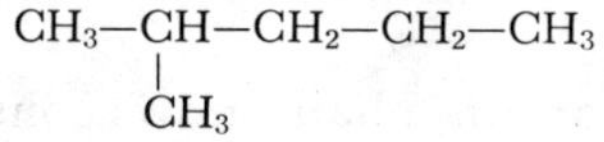

$$CH_3-CH-CH_2-CH_2-CH_3$$
$$|$$
$$CH_3$$

There is a different compound that could also be called methylpentane. Its formula is

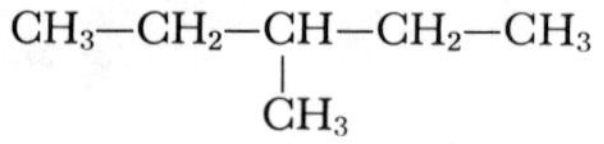

$$CH_3-CH_2-CH-CH_2-CH_3$$
$$|$$
$$CH_3$$

Continue to page 47 to learn how to find a unique name for each of these two compounds.

The skeletons of the two methylpentanes are

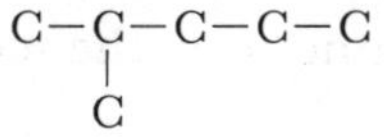

$$
\begin{array}{c}
\text{C--C--C--C--C} \\
\quad\; | \\
\quad\; \text{C}
\end{array}
\quad \text{and} \quad
\begin{array}{c}
\text{C--C--C--C--C} \\
\qquad\quad | \\
\qquad\quad \text{C}
\end{array}
$$

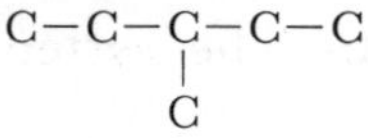

Clearly something more is needed to give each a unique name.

The distinction is made by the use of numbers. The carbon atoms in the chain are numbered consecutively, starting with 1 at the end of the chain nearest the substituent group. Study there examples:

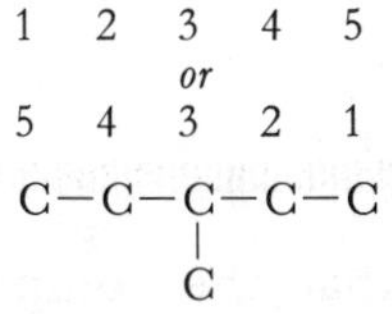

<table>
<tr><td>

1   2   3   4   5
or
5   4   3   2   1

C—C—C—C—C
      |
      C

3-methylpentane

</td><td>

1   2   3   4   5
but not
5   4   3   2   1

C—C—C—C—C
      |
      C

2-methylpentane
but not
4-methylpentane

</td></tr>
</table>

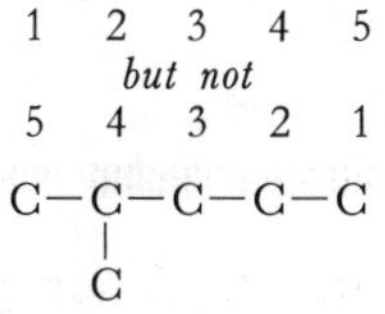

The numbers are used to locate the position of the methyl group on the pentane chain. Numbering begins at the end nearest the branch so that the lowest number(s) will be used.

What is the systematic name for this compound?

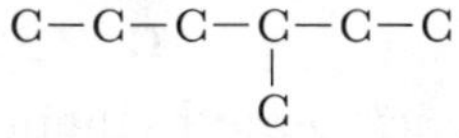

$$
\begin{array}{c}
\text{C--C--C--C--C--C} \\
\qquad\quad | \\
\qquad\quad \text{C}
\end{array}
$$

A

3-methylhexane

B

4-methylhexane

C

isoheptane

A ||||||||||||||||||||||||||||||||||||||||||||||||||||||||||||||||||||||||||||||||||||||||||||||||||||||||||||||||

You are right. The systematic name for the compound with the skeleton

$$C-C-C-\overset{\displaystyle |}{\underset{\displaystyle C}{C}}-C-C$$

is 3-methylhexane. The carbon chain is numbered from the end nearest the branch. Carry on to page 49.

B ||||||||||||||||||||||||||||||||||||||||||||||||||||||||||||||||||||||||||||||||||||||||||||||||||||||||||||||||

You are incorrect. Your answer is that the compound having the skeleton

$$C-C-C-\overset{\displaystyle |}{\underset{\displaystyle C}{C}}-C-C$$

is 4-methylhexane. You have numbered the carbon chain from the wrong end. Always start at the end nearest the branch. For example

$$C-C-C-C-\overset{\displaystyle |}{\underset{\displaystyle C}{C}}-C-C$$

represents 3-methylheptane, *not* 5-methylheptane. Turn back and select another answer.

C ||||||||||||||||||||||||||||||||||||||||||||||||||||||||||||||||||||||||||||||||||||||||||||||||||||||||||||||||||||||

You are wrong. Isoheptane is not the name of the compound represented by the skeleton

$$C-C-C-\overset{\displaystyle |}{\underset{\displaystyle C}{C}}-C-C$$

Let's see why. You should recall that iso- compounds have a branch at the carbon atom next to the end of the carbon chain. The skeleton of isoheptane is

$$C-C-C-C-\overset{\displaystyle |}{\underset{\displaystyle C}{C}}-C$$

How would you name isoheptane systematically? If the carbon chain is numbered consecutively from the end nearest the branch, the branch is seen to be attached to the number 2 carbon atom in the chain. Isoheptane is 2-methylhexane. Turn back and pick another answer.

You may think that you have spent a long time learning to count carbon chains and number them. Nevertheless, this ability is vital to success in learning the nomenclature of other families of organic compounds. Your progress should accelerate from this point onward.

Now you need some practice in naming substituted or branched alkanes. Remember the three steps you have learned:

1. Find the longest continuous carbon chain.

2. Number the carbon atoms consecutively from the end nearest the branch.

3. Locate the position of the substituent group by number and name it according to the number of carbon atoms it contains.

On the next page are five carbon skeletons. The correct name of the compound is below each skeleton. Expose the names only after you have worked out the name yourself. If you miss more than one, you should go back and review.

1. 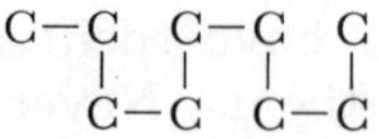
$$
\begin{array}{ccccc}
\text{C}-\text{C} & \text{C}-\text{C} & \text{C} \\
| & | & | \\
\text{C}-\text{C} & \text{C}-\text{C}
\end{array}
$$

nonane

2. 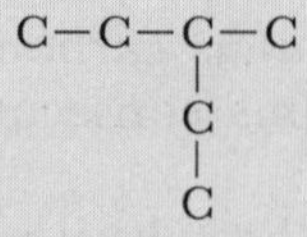
$$
\begin{array}{c}
\text{C}-\text{C}-\text{C}-\text{C} \\
| \\
\text{C} \\
| \\
\text{C}
\end{array}
$$

3-methylpentane

3. 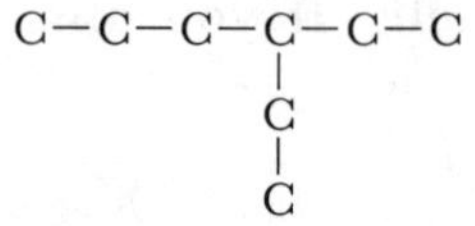
$$
\begin{array}{c}
\text{C}-\text{C}-\text{C}-\text{C}-\text{C}-\text{C} \\
| \\
\text{C} \\
| \\
\text{C}
\end{array}
$$

3-ethylhexane

4. 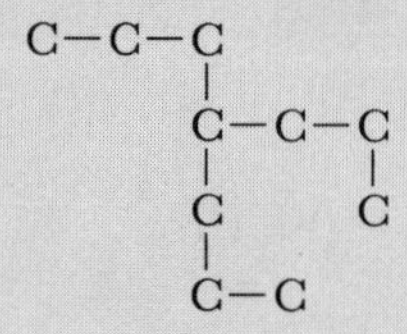
$$
\begin{array}{c}
\text{C}-\text{C}-\text{C} \\
| \\
\text{C}-\text{C}-\text{C} \\
| \quad\quad | \\
\text{C} \quad\quad \text{C} \\
| \\
\text{C}-\text{C}
\end{array}
$$

4-propylheptane (Note: There are three different ways to number the chain. Each leads to the same answer.)

5. 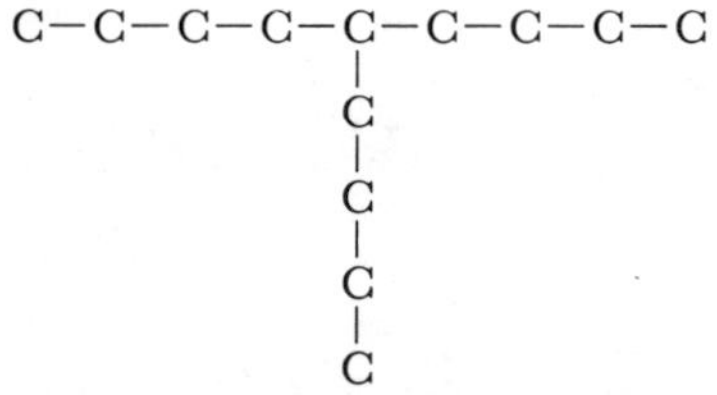
$$
\begin{array}{c}
\text{C}-\text{C}-\text{C}-\text{C}-\text{C}-\text{C}-\text{C}-\text{C}-\text{C} \\
| \\
\text{C} \\
| \\
\text{C} \\
| \\
\text{C} \\
| \\
\text{C}
\end{array}
$$

5-butylnonane (Note: There are three ways to number the chain. All three lead to the same name.)

Turn to page 51.

Suppose you encounter an alkane with two branches. Like this one, for instance:

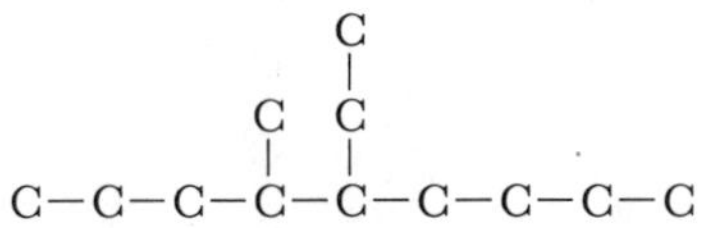

```
              C
              |
          C   C
          |   |
  C—C—C—C—C—C—C—C—C
```

Begin the same way. Find the longest carbon chain and number it from the end nearest to any branch. Thus

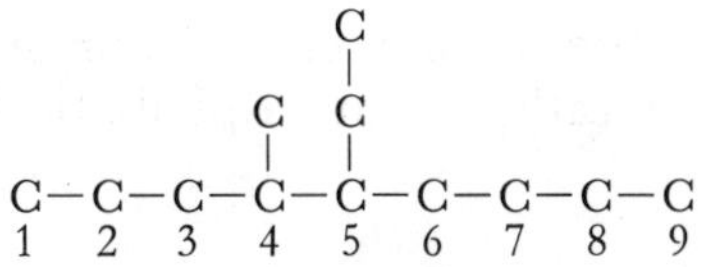

```
              C
              |
          C   C
          |   |
  C—C—C—C—C—C—C—C—C
  1 2 3 4 5 6 7 8 9
```

This compound is a substituted nonane. Now name and locate each of the substituent groups. This is 5-ethyl-4-methylnonane. Why isn't it 4-methyl-5-ethylnonane? Only because the American custom established by *Chemical Abstracts* is to name branches in alphabetical order according to the names of the substituent groups. Occasionally you will find them named in order of increasing size of the substituent groups. Either way gives a unique name to the compound. That is what we are after.

How would you name this compound?

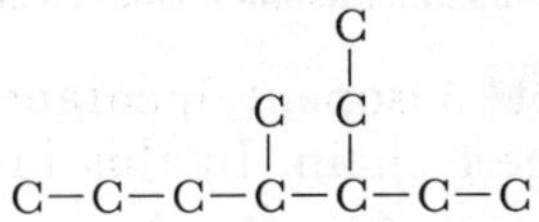

```
          C
          |
      C   C
      |   |
  C—C—C—C—C—C—C
```

A ||||||||||||||||||||||||||||||||||||||||||||||||||||||||||||||||||||||||||||||||||||||||||||||||||

4-methyl-5-ethylheptane

B ||||||||||||||||||||||||||||||||||||||||||||||||||||||||||||||||||||||||||||||||||||||||||||||||||

3-ethyl-4-methylheptane

C ||||||||||||||||||||||||||||||||||||||||||||||||||||||||||||||||||||||||||||||||||||||||||||||||||

3-isopentylpentane

D ||||||||||||||||||||||||||||||||||||||||||||||||||||||||||||||||||||||||||||||||||||||||||||||||||

isodecane

A ||||||||||||||||||||||||||||||||||||||||||||||||||||||||||||||||||||||||||||||||||||||||||||||||||||||||||||||||||||||||||

You are wrong. Your name for the skeleton

$$\begin{array}{ccccccc} & & & & \overset{\displaystyle C}{|} & & \\ & & & \overset{\displaystyle C}{|} & \overset{\displaystyle C}{|} & & \\ C-C-C-C-C-C-C & & & & & & \end{array}$$

is 4-methyl-5-ethylheptane. Most of your answer is right. It is a heptane and the branches are methyl and ethyl. Your first error was to number the heptane chain from the wrong end. Your second was to name the branches in order of size rather than alphabetically. Correct these two mistakes and try again.

B ||||||||||||||||||||||||||||||||||||||||||||||||||||||||||||||||||||||||||||||||||||||||||||||||||||||||||||||||||||||||||

Right you are. The name is 3-ethyl-4-methylheptane. The longest chain contains seven carbon atoms; the branches are an ethyl and a methyl group. They are located on the number 3 and 4 carbon atoms. Ethyl precedes methyl alphabetically and is named first. Go on to page 53.

C ||||||||||||||||||||||||||||||||||||||||||||||||||||||||||||||||||||||||||||||||||||||||||||||||||||||||||||||||||||||||||

No. The name is not 3-isopentylpentane. You need some more practice in finding the longest chain. In this instance there are two ways to number a chain of seven carbon atoms:

$$\begin{array}{cccccccc} & & & & C & & & \\ & & & C & C & & & \\ & C-C-C-C-C-C-C & & & & & & \\ & 7 \; 6 \; 5 \; 4 \; 3 \; 2 \; 1 & & & & & & \end{array} \qquad \begin{array}{cccccc} & & & C1 & & \\ & & C & C2 & & \\ & C-C-C-C-C-C-C & & & & \\ & 7 \; 6 \; 5 \; 4 \; 3 & & & & \end{array}$$

Turn back and read page 51 carefully before you choose another answer.

D ||||||||||||||||||||||||||||||||||||||||||||||||||||||||||||||||||||||||||||||||||||||||||||||||||||||||||||||||||||||||||

You are wrong. First of all, an iso- compound is a singly branched compound with a methyl group substituted on the carbon atom next to the end of the chain. Isodecane has a total of ten carbon atoms with this skeleton:

$$\begin{array}{ccccccccc} C-C-C-C-C-C-C-C-C \\ \qquad\qquad\qquad\qquad\qquad | \\ \qquad\qquad\qquad\qquad\qquad C \end{array}$$

Read page 51 carefully again before choosing another answer.

Learn one last point and you will be able to name alkanes with the experts. Whenever there are two or more of the same groups (radicals) substituted on the longest chain, the fact is indicated by the appropriate prefix: *di-* for two of them, *tri-* for three of them, *tetra-* for four, *penta-* for five, and so on. To illustrate, consider the compound generally called "isooctane." It is used as an antiknocking additive in gasoline. Its carbon skeleton is

```
        C       C
        |       |
    C — C — C — C — C
        |
        C
```

According to our system, it is 2,2,4-trimethylpentane. The "tri-" indicates three methyl groups and the "2,2,4-" show where they are. Notice, too, that commas are used to separate numbers from numbers while hyphens are used to separate numbers from words. You can find several ways to number a five-carbon chain in "isooctane." Once you have made a choice of numbers, you must stick with it. Don't use one set to locate one branch and another set for a second branch. Here is another skeleton for you to name.

```
                C
                |
        C       C   C
        |       |   |
    C — C — C — C — C — C — C
```

It is 5-ethyl-2,4-dimethylheptane. Right? Note that the prefixes such as *di-* and *tri-* are *not* considered to be part of the group names when determining the proper alphabetical order.

What name would you give to this alkane?

```
                C
                |
            C   C           C
            |   |           |
        C   C   C           C
        |   |   |           |
    C — C — C — C — C — C — C — C — C
        |
        C
```

A |||||||||||||||||||||||||||||||||||||||||||||||||||||||||||||||||||||||||||||||||||||||||||||||||||||||||||||||

3,7-ethyl-2,2-methyl-4-propylnonane

B |||||||||||||||||||||||||||||||||||||||||||||||||||||||||||||||||||||||||||||||||||||||||||||||||||||||||||||||

3,7-diethyl-2,2-dimethyl-4-propylnonane

C |||||||||||||||||||||||||||||||||||||||||||||||||||||||||||||||||||||||||||||||||||||||||||||||||||||||||||||||

3,7-diethyl-8,8-dimethyl-6-propylnonane

A ||||||||||||||||||||||||||||||||||||||||||||||||||||||||||||||||||||||||||||||||||||||||||||||||||||||||||||||||||||||||||||||||||||||||||||

Close but no cigar. You missed the important point on the previous page. If there are two or more identical substituent groups, you must signal the fact with a prefix. For example

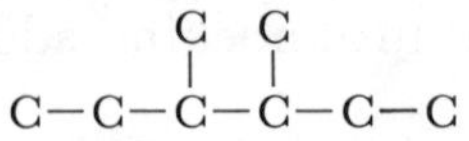

$$
\begin{array}{c}
\quad\ \ \text{C}\quad\text{C} \\
\quad\ \ |\quad\ | \\
\text{C}-\text{C}-\text{C}-\text{C}-\text{C}-\text{C}
\end{array}
$$

This is 3,4-dimethylhexane, *not* just 3,4-methylhexane. The *di-* indicates that there are two methyl groups. Turn back to page 53 and choose the correct answer.

B ||||||||||||||||||||||||||||||||||||||||||||||||||||||||||||||||||||||||||||||||||||||||||||||||||||||||||||||||||||||||||||||||||||||||||||

You are correct. You can have confidence now that you can name just about any alkane. Turn to page 55.

C ||||||||||||||||||||||||||||||||||||||||||||||||||||||||||||||||||||||||||||||||||||||||||||||||||||||||||||||||||||||||||||||||||||||||||||

Come on now. Once you have located the longest carbon chain, number it from the end *nearest any branch*. You did not do this.

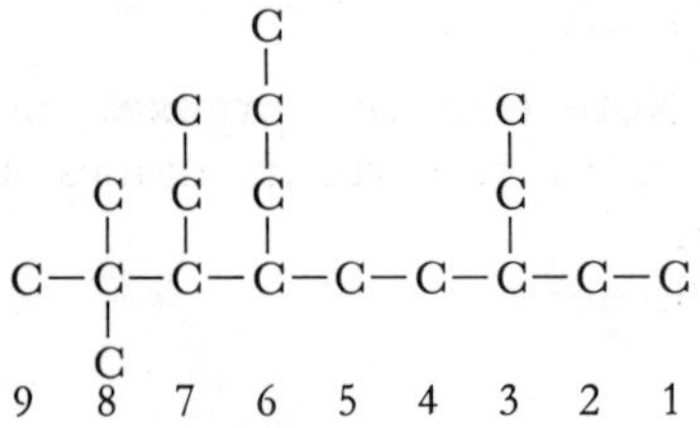

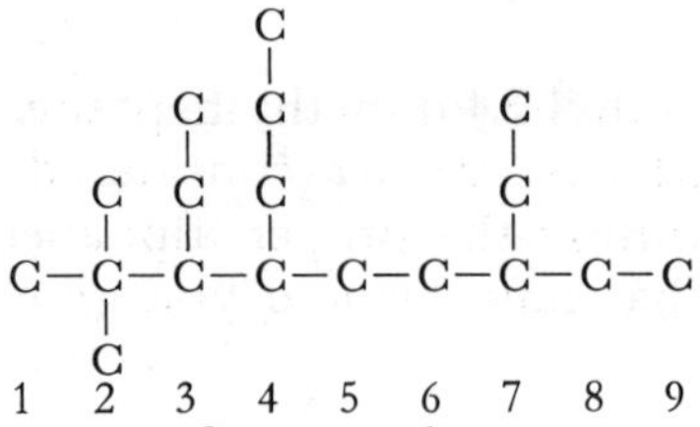

Can you see your mistake? The two methyl groups are closer to the end than the ethyl group. Turn back and select another answer.

There is an easy way to check names to see if they are complete. Just add the number of carbon atoms specified by the name and see if it is the same as the total number in the formula. Let's return to a compound you saw a couple of pages back. Its skeleton was

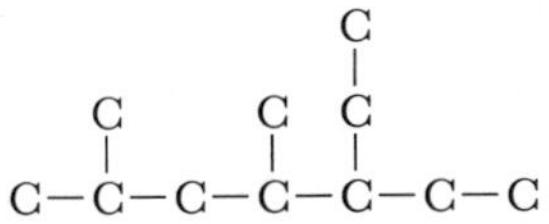

$$
\begin{array}{ccccccc}
 & & & & C & & \\
 & & & & | & & \\
 & & C & & C & C & \\
 & & | & & | & | & \\
C-&C-&C-&C-&C-&C-&C \\
\end{array}
$$

You named it 5-ethyl-2,4-dimethylheptane. Here is the way to check it:

Fragment of name	Number of carbon atoms
5-ethyl	2
2,4-dimethyl	2 (1 for each methyl)
heptane	7
	11

There are 11 carbon atoms in the skeleton, too.

A final note about writing names. All numbers are set off from group names by hyphens. Consecutive numbers are separated by commas. The last-named radical and the base name are combined into one word.

So far we have concentrated on figuring out the names from given formulas. It ought to be easy for you to reverse the process now. Which of these skeletons represents 5-ethyl-2,4-dimethyloctane?

A

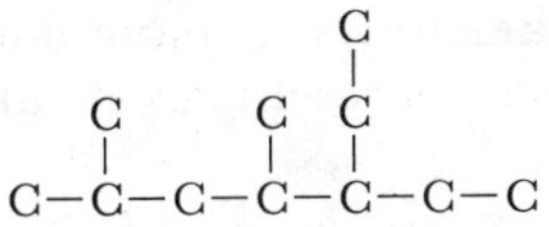

$$
\begin{array}{ccccccc}
 & & & & C & & \\
 & & & & | & & \\
 & & C & & C & C & \\
 & & | & & | & | & \\
C-&C-&C-&C-&C-&C-&C \\
\end{array}
$$

B

$$
\begin{array}{cccccc}
 & & & C & & \\
 & & & | & & \\
C-&C-&C-&C-&C-&C \\
 & & & | & & | \\
 & & & C & & C-C \\
 & & & | & & | \\
 & & & C & & C \\
\end{array}
$$

C

$$
\begin{array}{ccccc}
 & & & C & \\
 & & & | & \\
C-C-C & & C-C-C \\
 & | & & | & | \\
C-C-C-C & & C \\
\end{array}
$$

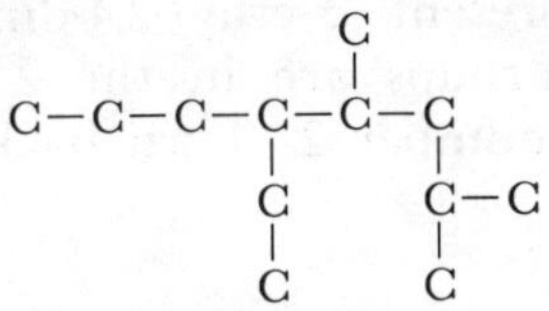

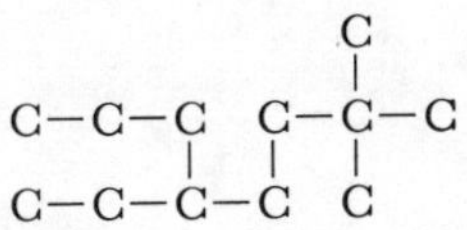

A ||||||||||||||||||||||||||||||||||||||||||||||||||||||||||||||||||||||||||||||||||||||||||||||||||||||||||||||||||||||||||||

You are incorrect. From the name 5-ethyl-2,4-dimethyloctane you know that the longest carbon chain must have eight atoms. What is the longest chain in your answer?

```
                  C
                  |
        C     C   C
        |     |   |
    C—C—C—C—C—C—C
```

Only seven. This is the skeleton of 5-ethyl-2, 4-dimethylheptane. Do you agree? When you do, turn back and work out another answer.

B ||||||||||||||||||||||||||||||||||||||||||||||||||||||||||||||||||||||||||||||||||||||||||||||||||||||||||||||||||||||||||||

Right. The skeleton has a carbon chain of eight carbon atoms and the branches are of the proper size and location to represent 5-ethyl-2, 4-dimethyloctane. Note that the consecutive numbers are separated by commas, but that numbers are separated from group names by hyphens. The final radical and the base name are combined into one word (dimethyloctane). Go on to page 57.

C ||||||||||||||||||||||||||||||||||||||||||||||||||||||||||||||||||||||||||||||||||||||||||||||||||||||||||||||||||||||||||||

You are wrong. The skeleton you have chosen does have a chain of eight carbon atoms and does represent an octane.

```
                      C
      8   7   6   3   |2  1
      C—C—C   C—C—C
              |   |   |
      C—C—C—C   C
              5   4
```

However, it does not represent 5-ethyl-2,4-dimethyloctane. The name specifies that the methyl groups are in the 2 and 4 positions. In this skeleton they are both on number 2. Turn back and find the completely correct answer.

On the next page are some drill exercises for you. The correct answer is below each one. Do not expose it until you have decided on your own answer. Turn to the other side.

Where a formula is given, write the name of the alkane. Where a name is given, write the skeleton formula.

1. 2-methylhexane

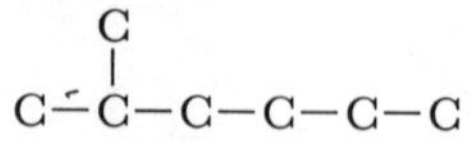

```
        C
        |
  C─C─C─C─C─C
```

2.

```
        C
        |
  C─C─C
        |
        C
```

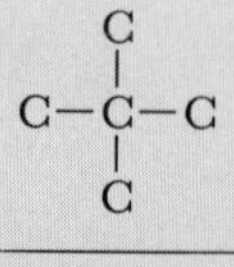

2,2-dimethylpropane, or neopentane

3.

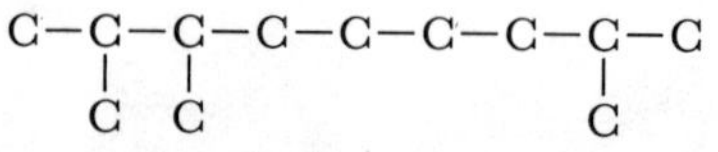

```
  C─C─C─C─C─C─C─C─C
     |  |           |
     C  C           C
```

2,3,8-trimethylnonane, *not* 2,7,8-trimethylnonane

4. 5-methyl-4-propylnonane

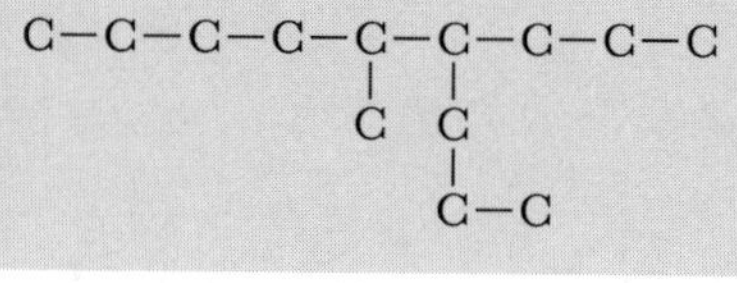

```
  C─C─C─C─C─C─C─C─C
           |  |
           C  C
              |
              C─C
```

5. $CH_3(CH_2)_3CH(CH_3)_2$

2-methylhexane or isoheptane. The skeleton is

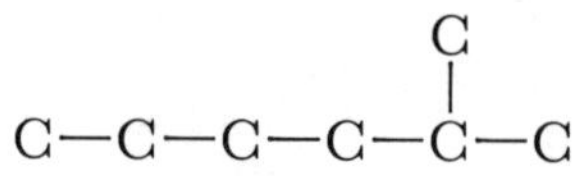

```
              C
              |
  C─C─C─C─C─C
```

Go on to page 59.

Summary: Naming of Alkanes

Alkanes are saturated aliphatic hydrocarbons. When two or more different compounds have the same molecular formula, they are called isomers. Alkanes with four or more carbon atoms have isomers that differ in structure. These are known as structural isomers. Each has its own chemical and physical properties.

The general formula for the alkanes is C_nH_{2n+2}. The names of the first 10 members of the homologous series are methane, ethane, propane, butane, pentane, hexane, heptane, octane, nonane, and decane. All alkanes have names ending with the suffix -*ane*.

When one hydrogen atom is removed from an alkane, the resulting univalent radical is named by substituting the suffix -*yl* for the -*ane* in the name of the alkane. Collectively, these are known as alkyl radicals or alkyl groups.

Unbranched alkanes are known as normal alkanes. Names for branched alkanes are determined by following four steps:

1. Find the longest continuous chain of carbon atoms and name it according to the basic alkane names.

2. Number the carbon atoms in the longest chain consecutively from the end nearest a branch.

3. Name the branching alkyl groups according to the number of carbon atoms each contains, list the names alphabetically, and specify the location of each group by the number of the atom to which it is attached.

4. When two or more of the same alkyl groups appear, indicate the fact by means of a prefix; the location of *each* group is shown by a number.

ALKANES

General formula: C_nH_{2n+2} Series name: -*ane*

When you are ready, turn to page 60 to begin a short test.

Answer these questions one at a time and check your answers on pages 61 and 62.

1. One formula for 2,2,4-trimethylpentane is

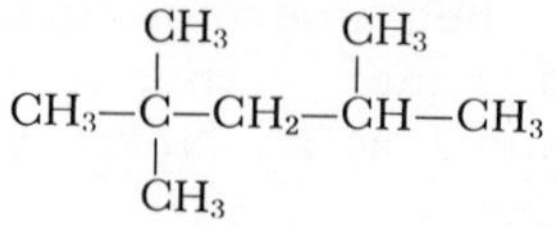

$$CH_3-\underset{\underset{CH_3}{|}}{\overset{\overset{CH_3}{|}}{C}}-CH_2-\underset{}{\overset{\overset{CH_3}{|}}{C}}H-CH_3$$

It is an isomer of

1A

2-ethylpentane

1B

octane

1C

2,2,3-trimethylhexane

_____

2. What is the name of the alkane represented by this skeleton:

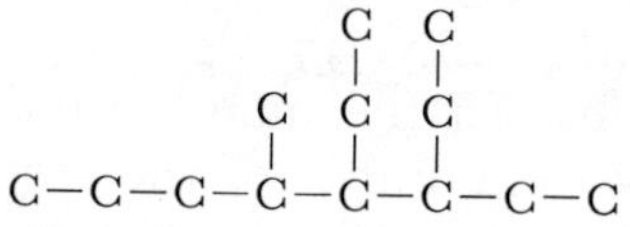

$$\begin{array}{ccccccc}
 & & & & C & C & \\
 & & & C & C & C & \\
 & & & | & | & | & \\
C-C-C-C-C-C-C-C
\end{array}$$

2A

5,6-ethyl-4-methyloctane

2B

3,4-diethyl-5-methyloctane

2C

5-methyl-3,4-diethyloctane

_____

3. Name the alkane that has this skeleton:

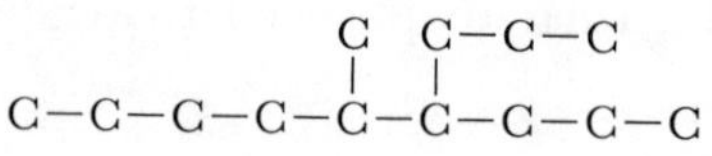

$$\begin{array}{cc}
C & C-C-C \\
| & | \\
C-C-C-C-C-C-C-C-C
\end{array}$$

3A

5-methyl-6-propylnonane

3B

4-isohexylheptane

3C

5-methyl-4-propylnonane

_____

4. Write as many different kinds of formulas for 2,2,3,3-tetramethylbutane as you can. You should be able to write at least three.

_____

1A ‖‖‖

You are incorrect. The isomer you seek must have the same number of carbon atoms as 2,2,4-trimethylpentane Let's check the number.

Fragment of name	Number of carbons
2,2,4-trimethyl	3
pentane	5
	8

You chose 2-ethylpentane as an isomer. Checking it, we find:

2-ethyl	2
pentane	5
	7

Turn back and choose another answer.

1B ‖‖

You are right. Both 2,2,4-trimethylpentane and octane are alkanes containing eight carbon atoms. Their molecular formulas are C_8H_{18}. Therefore they are isomers.

1C ‖‖

Wrong. Any isomer must have the same number of carbon atoms as the compound in question, 2,2,4-trimethylpentane. Let's check:

Fragment of name	Number of carbons
2,2,4-trimethyl	3
pentane	5
	8

Now let's check your answer, 2,2,3-trimethylhexane

2,2,3-trimethyl	3
hexane	6
	9

These cannot be isomers. Go back and choose another answer.

2A ‖‖

You are wrong. The skeleton does represent an octane. But you have numbered the chain from the wrong end. Always start your numbers at the end nearest a branch. One more thing: if there are more than one of the same branching group, show this by means of a prefix (*di-*, *tri-*, etc.). Go back and choose another answer.

2B ‖‖

You are right. The skeleton represents 3,4-diethyl-5-methyloctane.

2C ‖‖

Incorrect. You have named the compound correctly as an octane and identified the substituent groups. You also numbered the chain from the proper end. Your only error was not to name the groups alphabetically. Choose another answer.

3A ||||||||||||||||||||||||||||||||||||||||||||||||||||||||||||||||||||||||||||||||||||||||||||||||||||||||||||||||||||||

Incorrect. You are still having trouble assigning numbers to the carbon atoms in the longest chain. Always begin at the end nearest a substituent or branching group. Turn back and choose another answer carefully.

3B |||||||||||||||||||||||||||||||||||||||||||||||||||||||||||||||||||||||||||||||||||||||||||||||||||||||||||||||||

You are wrong. The skeleton does not represent a heptane. Turn back and find a continuous carbon chain that has more than seven carbon atoms.

3C |||||||||||||||||||||||||||||||||||||||||||||||||||||||||||||||||||||||||||||||||||||||||||||||||||||||||||||||||

You are right. The skeleton represents 5-methyl-4-propylnonane. You correctly remembered to name the branches in alphabetical order.

4. Here are several kinds of formula for 2,2,3,3-tetramethylbutane:

Molecular formula C_8H_{18}

Structural formula

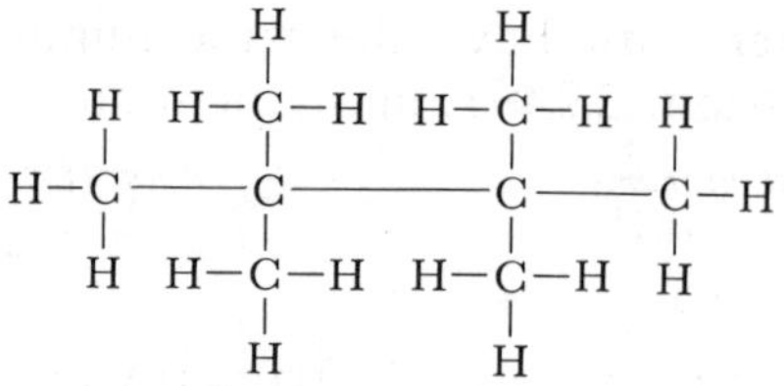

Condensed structural formulas

$CH_3C(CH_3)_2C(CH_3)_2CH_3$ or

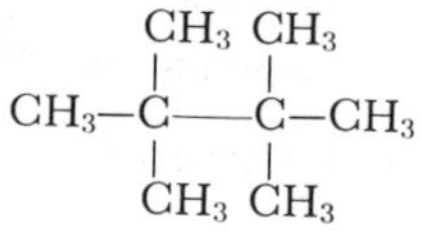

Skeleton formula

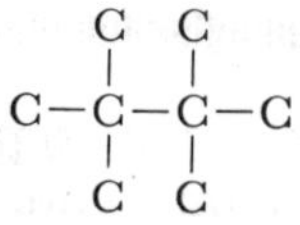

Go on to page 63.

1.3 ALKENES

Once you have learned to name alkanes, the rest of your introduction to the Geneva system of organic nomenclature is easy. Many of the common organic compounds are derived from alkanes. The next family we will consider is the *alkenes*. Alkenes are unsaturated aliphatic hydrocarbons that contain one carbon-carbon double bond. They are sometimes called olefins (ō′ lĕ fĭnz), too. You can think of them as the product resulting from the removal of a molecule of hydrogen from an alkane. For example

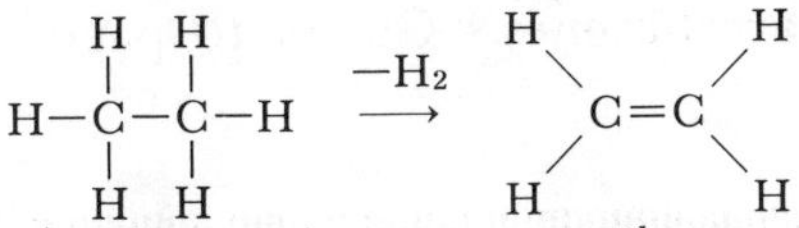

$$H-\underset{\underset{H}{|}}{\overset{\overset{H}{|}}{C}}-\underset{\underset{H}{|}}{\overset{\overset{H}{|}}{C}}-H \quad \overset{-H_2}{\longrightarrow} \quad \underset{\underset{H}{\diagup}}{\overset{\overset{H}{\diagdown}}{C}}=\underset{\underset{H}{\diagdown}}{\overset{\overset{H}{\diagup}}{C}}$$

ethane   *ethene*

The names of the alkenes are formed by changing the *-ane* ending of the parent alkane to *-ene*. As you can see above, ethane becomes ethene. Obviously, there is no alkene corresponding to the simplest of the alkanes, methane.

What is the name of an alkene derived from this alkane?

$$CH_3(CH_2)_2CH_3$$

A ‖‖

propene

B ‖‖

butene

C ‖‖

pentene

D ‖‖

hexene

A ||||||||||||||||||||||||||||||||||||||||||||||||||||||||||||||||||||||||||||||||||||||||||||||||||||||||||||||||||

Incorrect. Perhaps you did not look carefully at the condensed structural formula: $CH_3(CH_2)_2CH_3$. When written out fully, it is $CH_3CH_2CH_2CH_3$, butane. If hydrogen is removed to give it a double bond, it becomes butene. Go on to page 65.

B ||||||||||||||||||||||||||||||||||||||||||||||||||||||||||||||||||||||||||||||||||||||||||||||||||||||||||||||||||

You are right. The condensed structural formula is butane. Alkenes derived from butane are butenes. Go on to page 65.

C ||||||||||||||||||||||||||||||||||||||||||||||||||||||||||||||||||||||||||||||||||||||||||||||||||||||||||||||||||

You are wrong. Look carefully at the condensed structural formula again. Does it have five carbon atoms? If not, an alkene derived from it will not be called pentene. Go back and choose another answer.

D ||||||||||||||||||||||||||||||||||||||||||||||||||||||||||||||||||||||||||||||||||||||||||||||||||||||||||||||||||

Wrong. Does the structural formula have a carbon chain of six carbon atoms? If not, an unsaturated derivative will not be a hexene. Go back and choose another answer.

Since they result from the removal of hydrogen from alkanes, the alkenes have the general formula C_nH_{2n}. Of course, n must have a value of 2 or more.

There is no chance for ambiguity in naming the first two members of the homologous series of alkenes. Ethene and propene can have only the formulas $CH_2{=}CH_2$ and $CH_3{-}CH{=}CH_2$. Butene and all higher members of the series have isomers which differ in the location of the double bond. Let's look at the possibilities for butene. Both of the skeletons shown here represent butene:

$$C-C-C=C \qquad\qquad C-C=C-C$$

The solution to the problem again lies with numbering the carbon atoms. Assign numbers consecutively from the end of the chain nearest the double bond. In this case

$$\begin{matrix} C-C-C=C \\ 4 \quad 3 \quad 2 \quad 1 \end{matrix} \qquad\qquad \begin{matrix} C-C=C-C \\ 4 \quad 3 \quad 2 \quad 1 \end{matrix}$$

The location of the double bond is given by writing the lower number of the two carbon atoms joined by the double bond, as shown here.

$$\begin{matrix} C-C-C=C \\ \textit{1-butene} \end{matrix} \qquad\qquad \begin{matrix} C-C=C-C \\ \textit{2-butene} \end{matrix}$$

Which of these skeletons represents 3-heptene?

A ‖‖

$$C-C=C-C-C-C-C$$

B ‖‖

$$C-C-C=C-C-C$$

C ‖‖

$$C-C-C=C-C-C-C$$

A ||||||||||||||||||||||||||||||||||||||||||||||||||||||||||||||||||||||||||||||||||||||||||||||||||||||||||||||||||

Incorrect. The skeleton does represent a heptene. Look at it again.

$$C-C=C-C-C-C-C$$
$$1 \quad 2 \quad 3 \quad 4 \quad 5 \quad 6 \quad 7$$

The double bond is between the carbon atoms numbered 2 and 3. Positions of double bonds are always indicated by giving the *lower* number of the atoms which it joins. Hence, this skeleton represents 2-heptene. Turn back and choose another answer.

B ||||||||||||||||||||||||||||||||||||||||||||||||||||||||||||||||||||||||||||||||||||||||||||||||||||||||||||||||||

You are wrong. Your answer is that this skeleton represents 3-heptene:

$$C-C-C=C-C-C$$

The double bond is in the 3-4 position and should be designated by the number 3, but how long is the chain? Only six carbons. Doesn't that make it the skeleton of 3-hexene? Sure. Now go back and choose another answer.

C ||||||||||||||||||||||||||||||||||||||||||||||||||||||||||||||||||||||||||||||||||||||||||||||||||||||||||||||||||

Right. The skeleton

$$C-C-C=C-C-C-C$$

represents a heptene since there are seven carbon atoms in the chain. The double bond joins the third and fourth atoms and is designated by the number 3 in the name 3-heptene. Go on to page 67.

Hydrocarbons that contain more than one double bond are known as alkadienes, alkatrienes, alkatetraënes, etc. The prefixes *di-*, *tri-*, *tetra-*, etc., are used to specify the number of double bonds. The location of each double bond is specified by giving the lower number of the two carbon atoms joined by each double bond. A couple of examples will serve to make this clear:

C=C—C=C 1 2 3 4	1,3-butadiene (an ingredient of some synthetic rubbers)
C=C—C—C=C 1 2 3 4 5	1,4-pentadiene
C—C=C=C—C—C 1 2 3 4 5 6	2,3-hexadiene (*not* 3,4-hexadiene)

Notice that the carbons are always numbered from the end of the chain nearest to a double bond.

Branched, or substituted, alkenes are named in a manner similar to the alkanes. The carbon atoms are numbered, substituent groups are located and named, the double bonds are located, and the main chain is named. For example

$$\begin{array}{c} \text{C} \\ | \\ \text{C—C—C—C=C} \end{array}$$ 2-methyl-1-pentene

$$\begin{array}{c} \text{C} \\ | \\ \text{C—C=C—C=C} \end{array}$$ 2-methyl-1,3-pentadiene

What is the correct name for the alkene represented by this skeleton?

$$\begin{array}{c} \text{C—C—C—C=C—C—C} \\ | \\ \text{C} \end{array}$$

A ||||||||||||||||||||||||||||||||||||||||||||||||||||||||||||||||||||||||||||||||||||||||||||||||||||||||||||||||||||||

5-methyl-3-heptene

B ||||||||||||||||||||||||||||||||||||||||||||||||||||||||||||||||||||||||||||||||||||||||||||||||||||||||||||||||||||||

3-methyl-4-heptene

C ||||||||||||||||||||||||||||||||||||||||||||||||||||||||||||||||||||||||||||||||||||||||||||||||||||||||||||||||||||||

Help!

A ||||||||||||||||||||||||||||||||||||||||||||||||||||||||||||||||||||||||||||||||||||||||||||||||||||||||||||||||||||||||||||||||||||||||||||||||

You are right. The carbon chain is numbered from the end nearest the double bond. Then any substituent groups are located. Consequently

$$\underset{C}{\overset{7\quad6\quad5\quad4\quad3\quad2\quad1}{C-C-C-C=C-C-C}}$$

is the skeleton for 5-methyl-3-heptene. Numbering of the chain is shown. Go on to page 69.

B ||||||||||||||||||||||||||||||||||||||||||||||||||||||||||||||||||||||||||||||||||||||||||||||||||||||||||||||||||||||||||||||||||||||||||||

Incorrect. You have numbered the carbon atoms incorrectly. Always number the chain from the end nearest the double bond as shown here.

$$\underset{C}{\overset{7\quad6\quad5\quad4\quad3\quad2\quad1}{C-C-C-C=C-C-C}}$$

Then name and locate the substituent groups. Turn back and choose another answer.

C ||||||||||||||||||||||||||||||||||||||||||||||||||||||||||||||||||||||||||||||||||||||||||||||||||||||||||||||||||||||||||||||||||||||||||||||||

So you need help in naming the compound by the skeleton

$$\underset{C}{\overset{7\quad6\quad5\quad4\quad3\quad2\quad1}{C-C-C-C=C-C-C}}$$

First of all, you can see that this is an alkene since it has a double bond. The last syllable of the name will be *-ene*. There are seven carbon atoms in the longest chain which includes the double bond, so it is a derivative of heptane. First number the chain from the end nearer the double bond and then locate the double bond and substituent group. The double bond joins the number 3 and 4 carbon atoms and its location is specified by the 3 in the name. Finally, there is a methyl group on carbon number 5. Put all of these together and you have the name. Turn back and see if the name you chose is one of the answers on page 67.

Whenever there are two carbon chains of equal length, choose the one containing the maximum number of double bonds as the basis of the name. This skeleton should be named as a pent*ene* rather than a pentane:

$$C-C-C=C-C$$
$$|$$
$$C$$
$$|$$
$$C$$

There are only a few alkenes that have common names worth remembering. They are shown in this table.

Formula	Systematic name	Common name
$CH_2=CH_2$	ethene	ethylene (also an acceptable systematic name)
$CH_3CH=CH_2$	propene	propylene
$CH_3\overset{\textstyle CH_3}{\underset{\textstyle |}{C}}=CH_2$	methylpropene	isobutylene
$CH_3CH_2CH=CH_2$	1-butene	α-butylene
$CH_3CH=CHCH_3$	2-butene	β-butylene

Natural rubber is a polymer of an alkadiene. The common name of the monomer, or basic unit, of natural rubber is isoprene. Its skeleton is shown below. What is its preferred systematic name?

$$\overset{\textstyle C}{\underset{\textstyle |}{}}$$
$$C=C-C=C$$

A ‖‖‖

2-methylbutadiene

B ‖‖‖

2-methyl-1,3-butadiene

C ‖‖‖

3-methyl-1,3-butadiene

One of the ingredients of the textile polymers Acrilan and Orlon is acrylonitrile.

$$CH_2=CHCN$$

It is prepared from ethene or ethyne.

A |||||||||||||||||||||||||||||||||||||||||||||||||||||||||||||||||||||||||||||||||||||||||||||||||||||||||||||||||||||||||||||||||||

Incorrect. Your answer is that the skeleton

$$C=C-\overset{\overset{\displaystyle C}{|}}{C}=C$$

represents 2-methylbutadiene. Everything you have written is correct; but you do not have enough. Couldn't you also call the compound represented by this skeleton by the same name?

$$C=C=\overset{\overset{\displaystyle C}{|}}{C}-C$$

The positions of the double bonds need to be specified. When you have done this, turn back and choose another answer.

B |||||||||||||||||||||||||||||||||||||||||||||||||||||||||||||||||||||||||||||||||||||||||||||||||||||||||||||||||

You are right. The systematic name for isoprene is 2-methyl-1, 3-butadiene. Isoprene as well as 1,3-butadiene is used in some synthetic rubbers. Go on to page 71.

C |||||||||||||||||||||||||||||||||||||||||||||||||||||||||||||||||||||||||||||||||||||||||||||||||||||||||||||||||||||||||||||

You are wrong. It appears that you numbered the carbon chain from the wrong end. Here is the skeleton again:

$$C=C-\overset{\overset{\displaystyle C}{|}}{C}=C$$

As far as the double bonds are concerned, it makes no difference about the numbers. It would be 1,3-butadiene either way. The presence of the methyl group, however, requires that you number from the end nearer to the methyl group. When you have determined the correct name, turn back and choose it as your answer.

Condensed formulas for alkenes usually show double bonds by means of a double dash ($=$). Some books use a colon for the same purpose. Thus, both

$$CH_2=CHCH(CH_3)CH_2CH_3 \quad \text{and} \quad C=C-\overset{\displaystyle C}{\underset{|}{C}}-C-C$$

represent 3-methyl-1-pentene. As always, the key is to make sure that each carbon atom has four covalent bonds.

What is the correct condensed structural formula for 3-ethyl-1, 4-pentadiene?

A

$$CH_3=CHCH(C_2H_5)CH=CH_3$$

B

$$CH_2=CHCH(C_2H_5)CH=CH_2$$

C

$$CH_2CHCH(C_2H_5)CHCH_2$$

A ||||||||||||||||||||||||||||||||||||||||||||||||||||||||||||||||||||||||||||||||||||||||||||||||||||||||||||||||||||||||||||||||||||||||||||||||||||||||||||||||||

Incorrect. Perhaps you did not examine the formula carefully enough. The answer you chose is $CH_3=CHCH(C_2H_5)CH=CH_3$. It fits all the requirements for 3-ethyl-1,4-pentadiene except one. Check the number of bonds on the number 1 and number 5 carbon atoms. They would be like this:

$$H-\overset{\overset{\textstyle H}{|}}{\underset{\underset{\textstyle H}{|}}{C}}=$$

This is one too many. Turn back and choose another answer.

B ||||||||||||||||||||||||||||||||||||||||||||||||||||||||||||||||||||||||||||||||||||||||||||||||||||||||||||||||||||||||||||||||||||||||||||||||||||||||||||||||||

Right. $CH_2=CHCH(C_2H_5)CH=CH_2$ is the condensed one-line formula for 3-ethyl-1,4-pentadiene. Pay particular attention to the fact that each carbon atom has four and only four covalent bonds. This can be shown more clearly by writing the full structural formula.

$$\begin{array}{c} \overset{\textstyle H}{|}\;\overset{\textstyle H}{|} \\ H-C-C-H \\ |\quad | \\ H\quad H \end{array}$$

C ||||||||||||||||||||||||||||||||||||||||||||||||||||||||||||||||||||||||||||||||||||||||||||||||||||||||||||||||||||||||||||||||||||||||||||||||||||||||||||||||||

You are wrong. You want the condensed structural formula for 3-ethyl-1,4-pentadiene. The *-diene* portion of the name is a signal that there should be two double bonds in the formula. The answer you have chosen, $CH_2CHCH(C_2H_5)CHCH_2$, has none at all. You can see the location of the double bonds more clearly if you write the full structural formula

Where should the double bonds be placed in order to have four bonds on each carbon atom? When you have decided, go back and choose another answer.

Except for the radical derived from ethylene, radicals derived from alkenes are named in the same fashion as those derived from alkanes. The *-ene* ending of the name is changed to *-enyl*. This table illustrates the general rule as well as the exception:

Systematic name	Formula
vinyl radical	$CH_2=CH-$
2-propenyl radical	$CH_2=CHCH_2-$
2-butenyl radical	$CH_3CH=CHCH_2-$
1,3-butadienyl radical	$CH_2=CHCH=CH-$

The carbon atoms must be numbered for all but the vinyl radical. The carbon atom with the free valence is always number 1.

Even though you know how to name unsaturated radicals, you should name hydrocarbons in such a way as to include any double bonds in the base name if you can. For example, the compound represented by this skeleton should be named 3-ethyl-1-pentene rather than 3-vinylpentane.

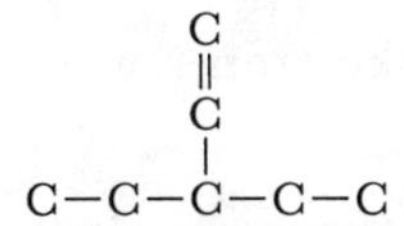

```
      C
      ‖
      C
      |
C—C—C—C—C
```

What is the preferred systematic name for this compound?

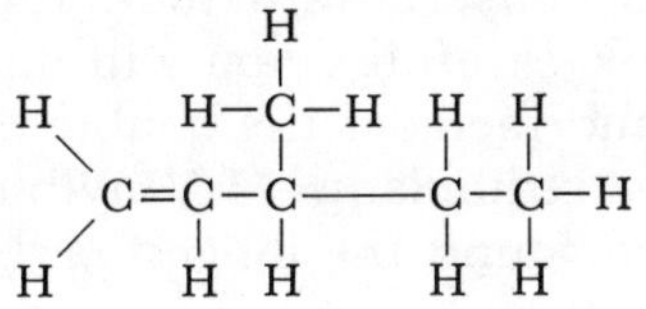

```
           H
           |
 H    H—C—H  H  H
  \        |   |  |
   C=C—C——C—C—H
  /    |  |   |  |
 H    H  H   H  H
```

A |||||||||||||||||||||||||||||||||||||||||||||||||||||||||||||||||||||||||||||||||

vinylbutane

B |||||||||||||||||||||||||||||||||||||||||||||||||||||||||||||||||||||||||

2-vinylbutane

C |||||||||||||||||||||||||||||||||||||||||||||||||||||||||||||||||||||||||||||||||||

3-methyl-1-pentene

A ||||||||||||||||||||||||||||||||||||||||||||||||||||||||||||||||||||||||||||||||||||||||||||||||||||||||||||||||

Incorrect. The preferred name for the compound represented by the skeleton

$$\begin{array}{c} C \\ | \\ C=C-C-C-C \end{array}$$

is not vinylbutane, although this name does describe it adequately. The name violates our first rule: find the longest continuous carbon chain. There is a carbon chain that includes more than four carbon atoms and the double bond as well. Look at the skeleton above until you find it. Then turn back and choose another answer.

B ||||||||||||||||||||||||||||||||||||||||||||||||||||||||||||||||||||||||||||||||||||||||||||||||||||||||||||||||

You are incorrect. The skeleton for the compound in question is

$$\begin{array}{c} C \\ | \\ C=C-C-C-C \end{array}$$

The name you chose is 2-vinylbutane. You have failed to apply the first rule for naming hydrocarbons: always look for the longest continuous carbon chain. If you look carefully, you will find a chain that has more than four carbon atoms and includes the double bond as well. You should also note that the 2 is redundant. "1-Vinylbutane" would be simply 1-hexene. When you have found the longest carbon chain which includes the double bond, turn back and choose another answer.

C ||||||||||||||||||||||||||||||||||||||||||||||||||||||||||||||||||||||||||||||||||||||||||||||||||||||||||||||||

Correct. The skeleton formula for the compound in question is

$$\begin{array}{c} C \\ | \\ C=C-C-C-C \end{array}$$

The longest carbon chain contains five carbon atoms and includes the double bond. The preferred systematic name is 3-methyl-1-pentene. Go on to page 75.

Now you need practice to make sure that you have the system down pat. Give the preferred name for the compound represented by each of these formulas. The correct answer appears below each one. Do not uncover an answer until you have worked out your own.

1.

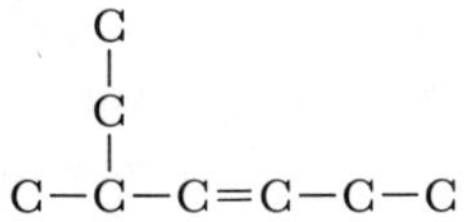

$$\begin{array}{c} C \\ | \\ C \\ | \\ C-C-C=C-C-C \end{array}$$

5-methyl-3-heptene (See reverse side if you chose any other.)

2. $CH_3CH_2CH_2-$

propyl radical or group (See reverse side if you chose a different answer.)

3.

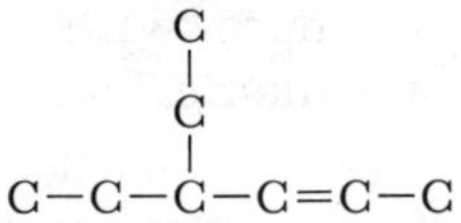

$$\begin{array}{c} C \\ | \\ C \\ | \\ C-C-C-C=C-C \end{array}$$

4-ethyl-2-hexene (See reverse side if you chose 3-ethyl-4-hexene.)

4.

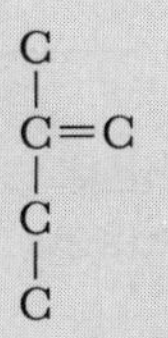

$$\begin{array}{c} C \\ | \\ C=C \\ | \\ C \\ | \\ C \end{array}$$

2-methyl-1-butene (See reverse if you chose 1-methyl-1-ethylethene.)

5.

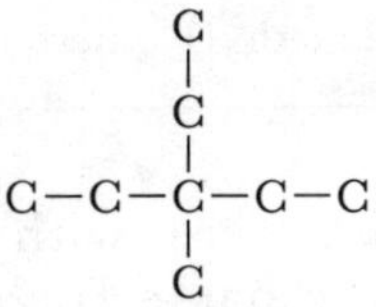

$$\begin{array}{c} C \\ | \\ C \\ | \\ C-C-C-C-C \\ | \\ C \end{array}$$

3-ethyl-3-methylpentane

6.

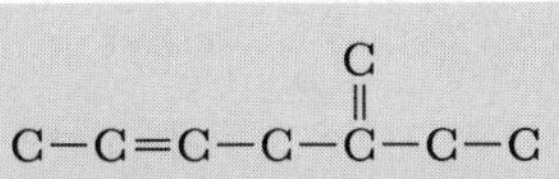

$$\begin{array}{c} C \\ \| \\ C-C=C-C-C-C-C \end{array}$$

2-ethyl-1,4-hexadiene (See reverse for explanation of answer.)

7. $C=C-$

vinyl radical

If you named all of these correctly, go on to page 77. If you made more than one error, you should review the section on alkenes.

Answers

1. The skeleton with the proper numbering is shown here. The meanings of the different parts of the name are:

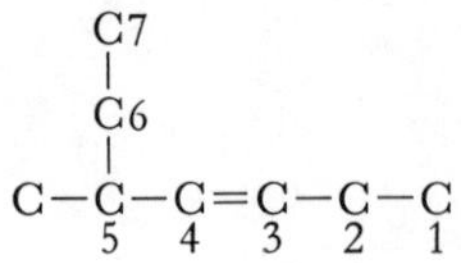

$$
\begin{array}{c}
\text{C7} \\
| \\
\text{C6} \\
| \\
\text{C}-\text{C}-\text{C}=\text{C}-\text{C}-\text{C} \\
\phantom{\text{C}-}54321
\end{array}
$$

-ene	one double bond
hept-	seven C's in chain
-3-	double bond between numbers 3 and 4
5-methyl-	methyl group on number 5

2. This radical, $CH_3CH_2CH_2-$, is formed by the removal of one hydrogen atom from $CH_3CH_2CH_3$, propane. The name follows the general rule for radicals: Change the *-ane* to *-yl*.

3. The skeleton is shown here with the carbon atoms numbered properly. The meanings of the name fragments are:

$$
\begin{array}{c}
\text{C6} \\
| \\
\text{C5} \\
| \\
\text{C}-\text{C}-\text{C}-\text{C}=\text{C}-\text{C} \\
\phantom{\text{C}-\text{C}-}4321
\end{array}
$$

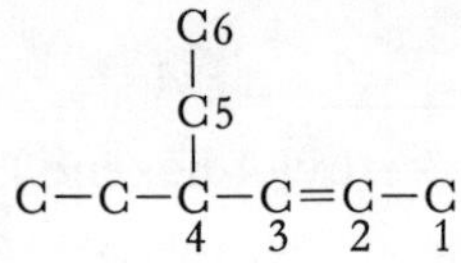

-ene	one double bond
hex-	six C's in chain
-2-	double bond between numbers 2 and 3
4-ethyl-	ethyl group on number 4

4. The skeleton is shown here with the carbon atoms numbered properly. The meanings of the name fragments are:

$$
\begin{array}{c}
\text{C} \\
| \quad 1 \\
2\text{C}=\text{C} \\
| \\
3\text{C} \\
| \\
4\text{C}
\end{array}
$$

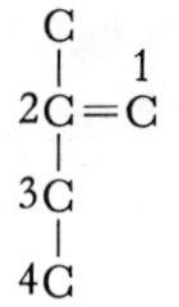

-ene	one double bond
but-	four C's in chain
-1-	double bond between numbers 1 and 2
2-methyl	methyl group on number 2

5. The skeleton is shown here with the carbon atoms numbered properly. The meanings of the name fragments are:

$$
\begin{array}{c}
\text{C1} \\
|| \\
\text{C}-\text{C}=\text{C}-\text{C}-\text{C}-\text{C}-\text{C} \\
65432
\end{array}
$$

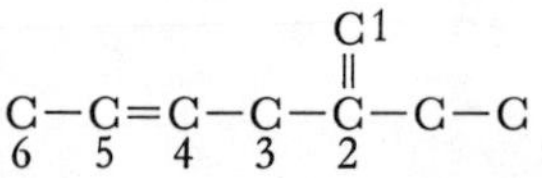

-diene	two double bonds
hexa-	six C's in chain
-1, 4-	double bonds in 1-2 and 4-5 positions
2-ethyl	ethyl group on number 2

ALKANES

General formula: C_nH_{2n+2} Series name: *-ane*

ALKENES

General formula: C_nH_{2n} Series name: *-ene*

1.4 ALKYNES

A third family of hydrocarbons is the *alkynes* (ăl' kīnz). These are unsaturated hydrocarbons containing a carbon-carbon triple bond. The simplest and only common alkyne is ethyne (ĕth' īne). Its formula is

$$H-C \equiv C-H$$

You may recognize its common name, acetylene. Since the alkynes could result from the removal of two molecules of hydrogen from the alkanes, their general molecular formula is C_nH_{2n-2}.

The names of the alkynes are formed by changing the *-ane* ending of the parent alkane to *-yne*. All of the rules you have learned for alkenes apply also to alkynes. Number the carbon atoms, if necessary, from the end of the chain nearest the triple bond. Locate the triple bond by the lower number of the two carbon atoms joined.

What is the name of the alkyne represented by this skeleton?

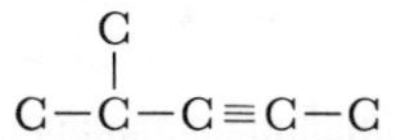

$$
\begin{array}{c}
\overset{\displaystyle C}{\underset{\displaystyle |}{}} \\
C-C-C \equiv C-C
\end{array}
$$

A |||||||||||||||||||||||||||||||||||||||||||||||||||||||||||||||||||||||||||||||||||||||||||||||||||||||||||||||

4-methyl-2-pentyne

B |||||||||||||||||||||||||||||||||||||||||||||||||||||||||||||||||||||||||||||||||||||||||||||||||||||||||||||||

2-methyl-3-pentyne

C |||||||||||||||||||||||||||||||||||||||||||||||||||||||||||||||||||||||||||||||||||||||||||||||||||||||||||||||

4-methyl-3-pentyne

D |||||||||||||||||||||||||||||||||||||||||||||||||||||||||||||||||||||||||||||||||||||||||||||||||||||||||||||||

Help!

A ||||||||||||||||||||||||||||||||||||||||||||||||||||||||||||||||||||||||||||||||||||||||||||||||||||||||||||||||||||||||||

You are correct. This skeleton represents 4-methyl-2-pentyne.

$$\begin{array}{c} C \\ | \\ C-C-C\equiv C-C \end{array}$$

Since it contains a triple carbon-carbon bond, the suffix on the name is *-yne*. Write the complete structural formula and check to be certain that it obeys the general formula C_nH_{2n-2}. Go to page 79.

B ||||||||||||||||||||||||||||||||||||||||||||||||||||||||||||||||||||||||||||||||||||||||||||||||||||||||||||||||||||||||

Incorrect. You numbered the carbon chain from the wrong end. The carbon chain in alkynes must be numbered from the end nearest the triple bond. Turn back and study the skeleton again carefully before you choose another answer.

C ||||||||||||||||||||||||||||||||||||||||||||||||||||||||||||||||||||||||||||||||||||||||||||||||||||||||||||||||||||||||

You are so close to right that your error may only be a careless one. Remember that the location of double and triple bonds is specified by the lower number of the two carbon atoms joined. Study the skeleton again before you turn back to pick another answer.

$$\begin{array}{c} C \\ | \\ C-C-C\equiv C-C \end{array}$$

D ||||||||||||||||||||||||||||||||||||||||||||||||||||||||||||||||||||||||||||||||||||||||||||||||||||||||||||||||||||||||

Here is a bit of help for you. Hydrocarbon names are most readily put together from back to front. The steps are:

1. Determine suffix (*-yne* here because of triple bond).
2. Find base name by locating longest carbon chain.
3. Number chain from end nearest triple bond and specify the location of the triple bond.
4. Name and locate, by means of a number, any substituent groups. Turn back and work out an answer.

Radicals derived from the alkynes are named in a manner similar to the radicals derived from alkanes and alkenes. The final -*e* in the name is replaced by -*yl*. Hence, the radical

$$HC \equiv C-$$

is the ethynyl radical.

Before we go on to some derivatives of the hydrocarbons that contain elements other than carbon and hydrogen, let's practice a little more. The answers to each of the following questions is just below the question. Cover each one until you have decided on your own answer.

1. Give the name of

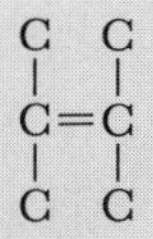

```
    C   C
    |   |
    C = C
    |   |
    C   C
```

2,3-dimethyl-2-butene

2. Write the skeleton of 3-ethyl-2-methyl-1,3-pentadiene.

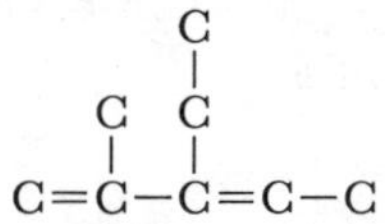

```
            C
            |
        C   C
        |   |
    C = C - C = C - C
```

3. Give the name of $CH_3CH = C(CH_3)_2$. Hint: Write a structural formula.

2-methyl-2-butene

4. Write a condensed structural formula for 2,3-dimethyl-1,3-butadiene.

$$CH_2 = C(CH_3)C(CH_3) = CH_2$$

5. Write the skeleton of 3,3,4,4-tetramethyl-1-pentyne.

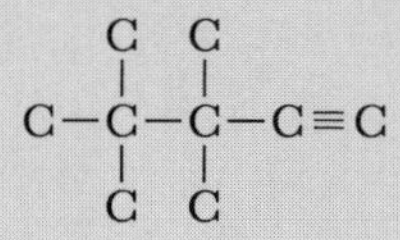

```
        C   C
        |   |
    C - C - C - C ≡ C
        |   |
        C   C
```

6. Write the molecular formula for 6-methyl-3-nonyne.

$$C_{10}H_{18}$$

If you answered all these questions correctly, go on to the next chapter. If you made errors or are unsure of yourself, review page 59 and pages 68 through 77.

ALKANES

General formula: C_nH_{2n+2} Series name: *-ane*

ALKENES

General formula: C_nH_{2n} Series name: *-ene*

ALKYNES

General formula: C_nH_{2n-2} Series name: *-yne*

2

Cyclic Hydrocarbons And Substituted Hydrocarbons

The two general classes of organic compounds are aliphatic and cyclic. Cyclic compounds are further subdivided into homocyclic and heterocyclic, depending on whether the closed ring contains only carbon atoms or atoms of carbon and one or more other elements. The homocyclic group is further divided into aromatic and alicyclic compounds. The classification is summarized in this diagram:

Organic compounds

Aliphatic — *Cyclic*

Homocyclic — *Heterocyclic*

Alicyclic — *Aromatic*

The nomenclature of alicyclic hydrocarbons will be discussed in this section. Aromatic hydrocarbons will be the subject of the following section.

2.1 ALICYCLIC HYDROCARBONS

Alicyclic hydrocarbons resemble the corresponding aliphatic or open-chain hydrocarbons in many ways, including their nomenclature. The names are derived from the systematic names of the aliphatic hydrocarbons that have the same number of carbon atoms. The prefix *cyclo-* (sī′ klŏ) is attached. Here are some examples:

$$CH_2 \diagdown \atop CH_2 \diagup CH_2$$
cyclopropane

$$CH_2 - CH_2 \atop | \quad | \atop CH_2 - CH_2$$
cyclobutane

$$CH_2 - CH_2 \diagdown \atop | \qquad CH_2 \atop CH_2 - CH_2 \diagup$$
cyclopentane

What is the general formula for the cycloalkanes?

A ||||||||||||||||||||||||||||||||||||||||||||||||||||||||||||||||||||||||||||||||||||||||||||||||||||||||||||||||||||||||||||||||||||||

C_nH_{2n}

B ||||||||||||||||||||||||||||||||||||||||||||||||||||||||||||||||||||||||||||||||||||||||||||||||||||||||||||||||||||||||||||||||||||||

C_nH_{2n+2}

C ||||||||||||||||||||||||||||||||||||||||||||||||||||||||||||||||||||||||||||||||||||||||||||||||||||||||||||||||||||||||||||||||||||||

C_nH_{2n} with $n \geq 3$

A |||||||||||||||||||||||||||||||||||||||||||||||||||||||||||||||||||||||||||||||||||||||||||||||||||||||||||||||||||||||||||||||

You are close, but not entirely correct. Cycloalkanes do have two fewer hydrogen atoms than the aliphatic alkane with the same number of carbon atoms. Consequently, if the general formula for aliphatic alkanes is C_nH_{2n+2}, the general formula for the cycloalkanes ought to be C_nH_{2n}. But shouldn't there be a further limitation? Suppose that $n=1$. Is there a cycloalkane with the molecular formula CH_2? No, there isn't. Turn back for another answer.

B |||||||||||||||||||||||||||||||||||||||||||||||||||||||||||||||||||||||||||||||||||||||||||||||||||||||||||||||||||||||||||||||||||||

Incorrect. The general formula C_nH_{2n+2} is correct for aliphatic alkanes, but not for the cycloalkanes. For instance, here are the structural and molecular formulas for the compounds with $n = 4$.

$$
\begin{array}{cc}
\begin{array}{c}
\;\;\text{H}\;\;\text{H}\\
\;\;\vert\;\;\;\vert\\
\text{H}-\text{C}-\text{C}-\text{H}\\
\;\;\vert\;\;\;\vert\\
\text{H}-\text{C}-\text{C}-\text{H}\\
\;\;\vert\;\;\;\vert\\
\;\;\text{H}\;\;\text{H}\\
\textit{cyclobutane, } C_4H_8
\end{array}
&
\begin{array}{c}
\;\;\text{H}\;\;\text{H}\;\;\text{H}\;\;\text{H}\\
\;\;\vert\;\;\;\vert\;\;\;\vert\;\;\;\vert\\
\text{H}-\text{C}-\text{C}-\text{C}-\text{C}-\text{H}\\
\;\;\vert\;\;\;\vert\;\;\;\vert\;\;\;\vert\\
\;\;\text{H}\;\;\text{H}\;\;\text{H}\;\;\text{H}\\
\textit{butane, } C_4H_{10}
\end{array}
\end{array}
$$

If comparison of these two formulas doesn't lead you to the correct general formula for the cycloalkanes, try writing one or two more similar pairs. Then turn back and choose another answer.

C ||||||||||||||||||||||||||||||||||||||||||||||||||||||||||||||||||||||||||||||||||||||||||||||||||||||||||||||||||||||||||||||||||||

Right. A cycloalkane has two fewer hydrogen atoms than the aliphatic alkane with the same number of carbon atoms. Therefore, the general formula is C_nH_{2n}. Since there are no cycloalkanes with 1 or 2 carbon atoms, there must be the further statement that n is equal to or greater than 3. Go on to page 83.

The number of carbon atoms in the rings of known cycloalkanes ranges from 3 to 34. Cyclohexane and its substituted derivatives are the most important. Cyclohexane is used as a solvent and as an intermediate in organic synthesis. Cyclopropane is a widely used anesthetic.

The unsaturated cycloalkenes are named by adding the prefix *cyclo-* to the name of the corresponding alkene. Two examples are

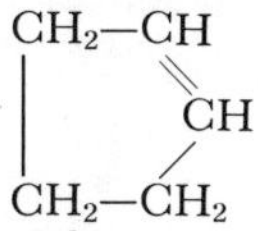

$$CH_2—CH$$
$$\qquad \diagdown CH$$
$$CH_2—CH_2$$
cyclopentene

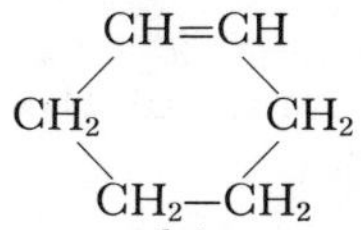

$$CH=CH$$
$$CH_2 \qquad CH_2$$
$$CH_2—CH_2$$
cyclohexene

When there is more than one double bond, numbers are needed to specify their location. Begin numbering so that one of the double bonds joins the number 1 and 2 carbon atoms. Study these two examples

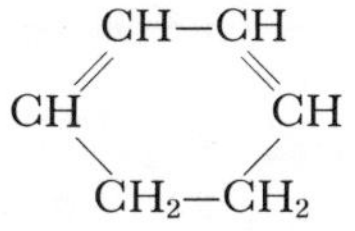

$$CH—CH$$
$$CH \qquad CH$$
$$CH_2—CH_2$$
1,3-*cyclohexadiene*

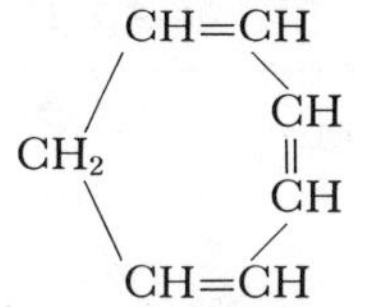

$$CH=CH$$
$$CH_2 \qquad CH$$
$$\qquad\qquad \| CH$$
$$CH=CH$$
1,3,5-*cycloheptatriene*

Substituted cycloalkanes and cycloalkenes are named with the same prefixes that are used for aliphatic compounds. Here are the formulas of methylcyclohexane and 3-methylcyclohexene.

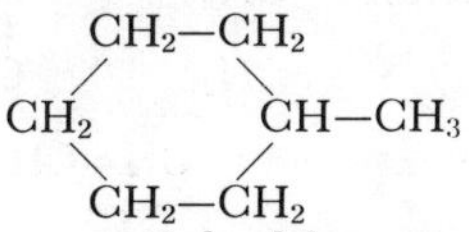

$$CH_2—CH_2$$
$$CH_2 \qquad CH—CH_3$$
$$CH_2—CH_2$$
methylcyclohexane

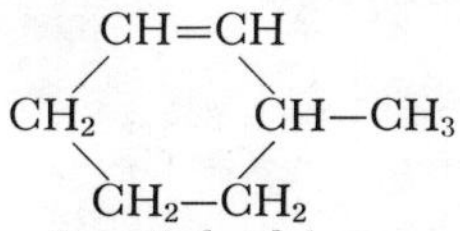

$$CH=CH$$
$$CH_2 \qquad CH—CH_3$$
$$CH_2—CH_2$$
3-*methylcyclohexene*

On the next page are four questions concerning alicyclic compounds. The answer is below each question. Cover it until you have worked out your own answer.

1. Write the carbon skeleton for cycloheptene.

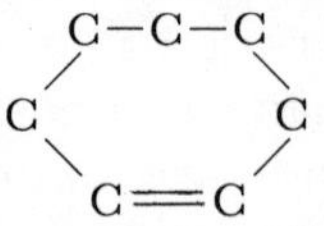

$$\begin{array}{c} C-C-C \\ C \qquad C \\ C=C \end{array}$$

2. What is the name of this compound?

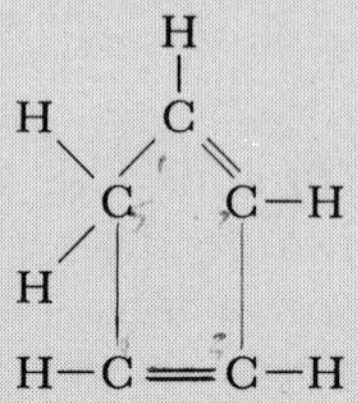

$$\begin{array}{c} H \\ | \\ H \qquad C \\ \backslash \quad \diagup \diagup \\ C \quad C-H \\ H \quad | \quad | \\ H-C=C-H \end{array}$$

1,3-cyclopentadiene

3. Write the formula for 1,4-cyclooctadiene.

Molecular $\quad C_8H_{12}$

Skeleton
$$\begin{array}{c} C-C \\ C \qquad C \\ C \qquad C \\ C=C \end{array}$$

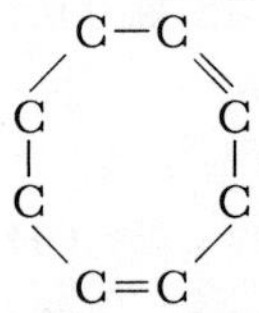

Structural
$$\begin{array}{c} CH_2-CH \\ CH_2 \qquad CH \\ CH_2 \qquad CH_2 \\ CH=CH \end{array}$$

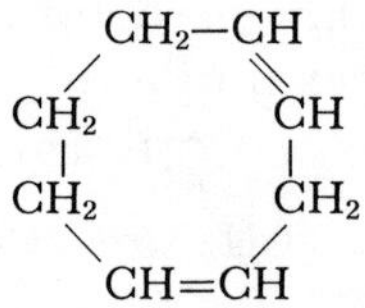

4. Write the carbon skeleton for 1,3-dimethylcyclohexane.

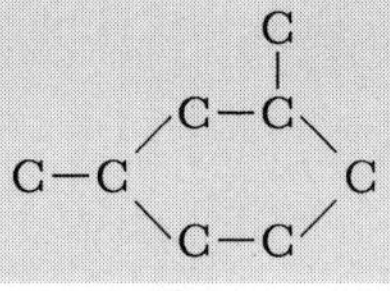

$$\begin{array}{c} C \\ | \\ C-C \\ C-C \qquad C \\ C-C \end{array}$$

A number of important biological compounds such as Vitamin A and Vitamin D are alicyclic compounds. Their structures, however, are too complicated for consideration here. If you answered these four questions to your satisfaction, go on to page 85.

ALKANES
General formula: C_nH_{2n+2} Series name: *-ane*
ALKENES
General formula: C_nH_{2n} Series name: *-ene*
ALKYNES
General formula: C_nH_{2n-2} Series name: *-yne*
ALICYCLIC HYDROCARBONS
     Series name: *cyclo-*

2.2 AROMATIC HYDROCARBONS

The addition of the aromatic series, compounds which have special characteristics to distinguish them from the alicyclic series, completes the classification shown on page 81. The simplest aromatic hydrocarbon is benzene, and the term aromatic is applied to compounds having chemical properties similar to benzene. Most of them contain six-membered rings but some have five or seven. The rings are unsaturated, but not in the same sense that alkenes, alkynes, and cycloalkenes are unsaturated. Benzene and the rest of the aromatic series are examples of resonant compounds that cannot be represented adequately by a single structural formula. The generic name for these compounds is *arene*.

In formula writing benzene is usually represented by a hexagon. The six hydrogen atoms are not shown.

benzene *benzene*

The double bonds or circle specify the aromatic character of the ring and the circle will be used in this program.

When a hydrogen atom is removed from one of the carbon atoms, the radical that is formed has the formula C_6H_5- and may be shown as:

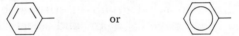

or

It is called a *phenyl* (fĕn′ ĭl) *group*. Since all of the carbon atoms are the same chemically, the free valence can be shown on any one of them. Collectively, radicals derived from aromatic compounds are known as *aryl* (âr′ ĭl) groups.

When alkyl radicals are joined to a phenyl group, the resulting compound is named as a substituted benzene. For example,

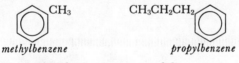

methylbenzene *propylbenzene*

How would you name these compounds?

A ||||||||||||||||||||||||||||||||||||||||||||||||||||||||||||||||||||||||||||||||||||||||||||||||||||||||||||||

ethylbenzene and phenylethane

B ||||||||||||||||||||||||||||||||||||||||||||||||||||||||||||||||||||||||||||||||||||||||||||||||||||||||||||||

ethylbenzene and 1-phenylethane

C ||||||||||||||||||||||||||||||||||||||||||||||||||||||||||||||||||||||||||||||||||||||||||||||||||||||||||||||

Both are ethylbenzene

D ||||||||||||||||||||||||||||||||||||||||||||||||||||||||||||||||||||||||||||||||||||||||||||||||||||||||||||||

None of the above is correct

A ||||||||||||||||||||||||||||||||||||||||||||||||||||||||||||||||||||||||||||||||||||||||||||||||||||||||||||||||||||||

Incorrect. The two formulas in question are

One of the characteristics of the aromatic ring is that all its carbon atoms have the same chemical reactivity. Therefore, both of these formulas represent the same compound. Read page 85 again and choose another answer.

B ||||||||||||||||||||||||||||||||||||||||||||||||||||||||||||||||||||||||||||||||||||||||||||||||||||||||||||||||||||||

Wrong. The two formulas in question are

One of the characteristics of the aromatic ring is that all its carbons have the same chemical reactivity. There is no need to number the carbon atoms in a mono-substituted benzene. Moreover, since both of these compounds have an ethyl group substituted on the benzene ring, they are identical. Read page 85, again and select another answer.

C ||||||||||||||||||||||||||||||||||||||||||||||||||||||||||||||||||||||||||||||||||||||||||||||||||||||||||||||||||||||

Correct. Since all the carbon atoms in the benzene ring have the same chemical reactivity, the two formulas represent the same compound, ethylbenzene. Go on to page 87.

D ||||||||||||||||||||||||||||||||||||||||||||||||||||||||||||||||||||||||||||||||||||||||||||||||||||||||||||||||||||||

You are wrong. One of the answers is all right. First, let's examine the two formulas carefully. They are

One of the properties of the benzene ring is that all of the carbons have the same reactivity. Both of these compounds have an ethyl group substituted on one carbon. Turn back and choose another answer.

Two mono-substituted benzenes with other names that you need to remember are toluene (tŏl′ ŭ ēn) and styrene (stī′ rēn). The common names toluene and styrene are both accepted for use in the IUPAC system and are indexed in *Chemical Abstracts*. Toluene is methylbenzene; styrene is vinylbenzene.

toluene   *styrene*

The location of substituent groups on a benzene ring becomes important when two or more groups are substituted on the benzene ring. There are three dimethylbenzenes. Their formulas are

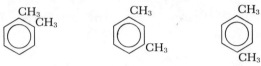

How can they be distinguished? There are two systems. One involves numbers and the other uses a special set of prefixes. In the first system a carbon atom bearing a substituent is given the number 1 and the rest are numbered consecutively around the ring in the direction that will give the smallest set of numbers when all of the substituents are located. For example

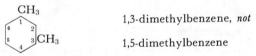

1,3-dimethylbenzene, *not*

1,5-dimethylbenzene

What is the structural formula for 1-ethyl-4-methylbenzene?

A ||||||||||||||||||||||||||||||||||||||||||||||||||||||||||||||||||||||||||||||||||||||||||||||||||||||||||||||||||||||

B ||||||||||||||||||||||||||||||||||||||||||||||||||||||||||||||||||||||||||||||||||||||||||||||||||||||||||||||||||||||

C ||||||||||||||||||||||||||||||||||||||||||||||||||||||||||||||||||||||||||||||||||||||||||||||||||||||||||||||||||||||

A ||||||||||||||||||||||||||||||||||||||||||||||||||||||||||||||||||||||||||||||||||||||||||||||||||||||||||||||||||||||||||||||

You are incorrect. You may have selected this answer hurriedly. Look at the formula again:

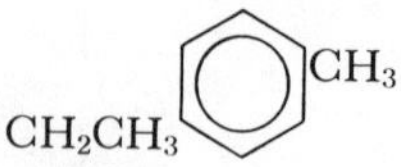

$$CH_2CH_3 \quad \bigcirc \quad CH_3$$

Do you see anything wrong? Look at the ethyl group carefully. Its structural formula would be

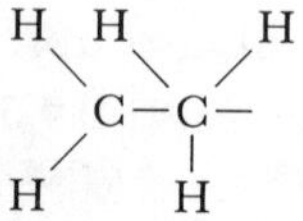

$$\begin{array}{ccc} H & H & H \\ & | & | \\ & C & - C - \\ & | & | \\ & H & H \end{array}$$

That is wrong, isn't it? Examine all formulas thoroughly from now on. Turn to page 89.

B ||||||||||||||||||||||||||||||||||||||||||||||||||||||||||||||||||||||||||||||||||||||||||||||||||||||||||||||||||||||||||||||

You are wrong. The formula you have selected for 1-ethyl-4-methylbenzene is

$$\bigcirc \quad CH_2CH_3 \\ CH_3$$

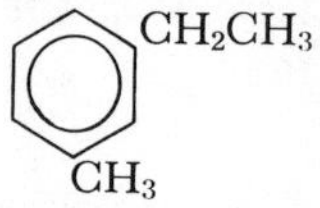

Number the carbon atoms again. The carbon bearing the ethyl group is number 1. The one with the methyl group is number 3. This is the formula for 1-ethyl-3-methylbenzene. Turn back and choose another answer.

C ||||||||||||||||||||||||||||||||||||||||||||||||||||||||||||||||||||||||||||||||||||||||||||||||||||||||||||||||||||||||||||||

You are correct. The structural formula for 1-ethyl-4-methylbenzene is

$$\bigcirc \quad CH_3 \\ CH_3CH_2$$

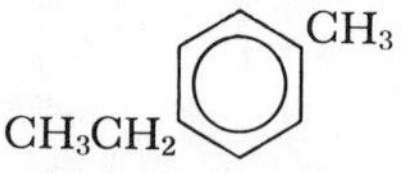

In this particular instance the numbering of the ring can go in either direction. Go on to page 89.

The systematic name for all three dimethylbenzenes is xylene (zī' lēn). The formulas and names of the three xylenes are:

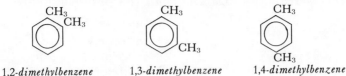

1,2-*dimethylbenzene* 1,3-*dimethylbenzene* 1,4-*dimethylbenzene*

The second system for locating substituents involves prefixes. The prefixes are *ortho-*, *meta-*, and *para-*. They represent the positions of carbon atoms in the ring relative to the carbon atom bearing the first substituent group. In the xylenes the first substituent is a CH_3— group. This diagram shows the prefixes for the other five positions in the benzene ring:

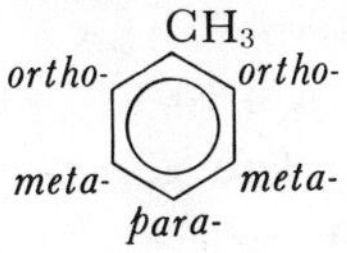

Note: The two *ortho-* positions are adjacent to the first substituent. The two *meta-* positions are separated by one carbon atom from the first substituted carbon atom. The single *para-* position is separated by two carbon atoms from the first.

Abbreviations for the prefixes are *o-*, *m-* and *p-* for *ortho-*, *meta-*, and *para-*, respectively. Neither the words nor their abbreviations are considered in establishing the alphabetical order for listing substituent groups.

What is an approved name for 1,3-dimethylbenzene?

A

ortho-xylene

B

meta-xylene

C

para-xylene

This formula represents a common English word meaning "a seemingly contradictory statement or observation." Can you guess the word? Answer on page 90.

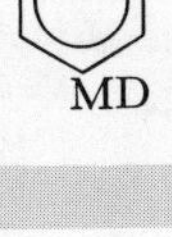

A ‖‖

Incorrect. Here is the diagram from the previous page.

CH₃
ortho- ⬡ *ortho-*
meta-   *meta-*
para-

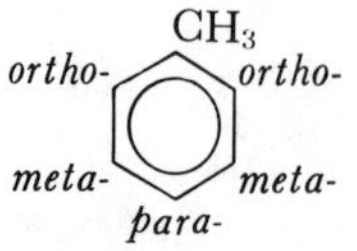

Notice that the two *ortho-* positions are adjacent to the first substituent. *Ortho*-xylene is 1,2-dimethylbenzene. Go back and choose another answer.

B ‖‖

You are right. The common name of 1,3-dimethylbenzene is *meta-*xylene. Here is the diagram from the previous page again.

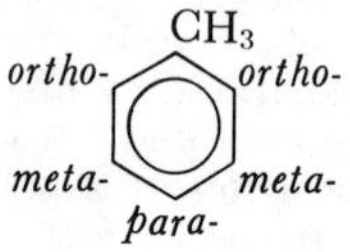

CH₃
ortho- ⬡ *ortho-*
meta-   *meta-*
para-

Remember that the 1,2-combination is *ortho-*, the 1,3-combination is *meta-*, and the 1,4-combination is *para-*. Go on to page 91.

C ‖‖

You are wrong. Here is the diagram from the previous page.

CH₃
ortho- ⬡ *ortho-*
meta-   *meta-*
para-

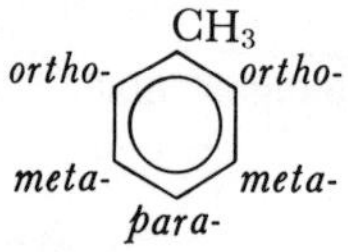

Notice that the *para-* position is separated from the first substituent by two other carbons. *Para*-xylene is 1,4-dimethylbenzene. Turn back and choose another answer.

Answer: *paradox*

Below are names for six hydrocarbon compounds. Each name contains at least one error. Correct the error and write the preferred systematic name. You may find it helpful to write skeleton or structural formulas. Answers are given below each name.

1. 1-ethyl-6-methylbenzene

   1-ethyl-2-methylbenzene

2. 2-methyl-4-propylbenzene

   1-methyl-3-propylbenzene

3. 1-methyl-3-methylbenzene

   1,3-dimethylbenzene (*m*-xylene or *meta*-xylene)

4. Phenylmethane

   toluene or methylbenzene

5. 3,4-dimethylpentene-2

   3,4-dimethyl-2-pentene

6. 4-ethyl-4-methyl-1-butene

   4-methyl-1-hexene

Condensed structural formulas for each of these six compounds are shown on page 92. If you still have difficulty, go back to page 85 and review this section. Otherwise go on to page 93.

1. 1-ethyl-2-methylbenzene

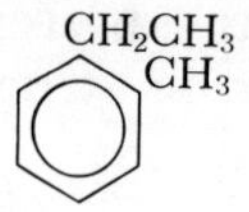

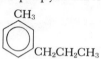

4. toluene or methylbenzene

2. 1-methyl-3-propylbenzene

5. 3, 4-dimethyl-2-pentene

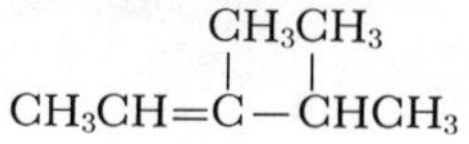

$$CH_3CH=\overset{\overset{\displaystyle CH_3}{|}}{C}-\overset{\overset{\displaystyle CH_3}{|}}{C}HCH_3$$

3. 1, 3-dimethylbenzene

6. 4-methyl-1-hexene

$$CH_2=CHCH_2\overset{\overset{\displaystyle CH_3}{|}}{C}HCH_2CH_3$$

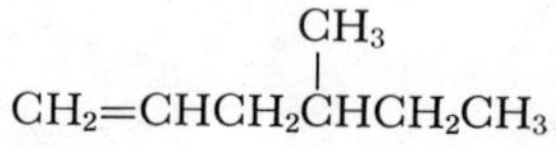

Go on to page 93.

Cyclic Hydrocarbons And Substituted Hydrocarbons / 93

Here are three fused aromatic hydrocarbon ring systems that you may come upon. The basic structures and names are given below:

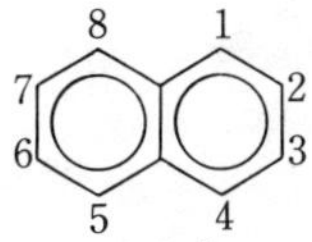

naphthalene
$C_{10}H_8$

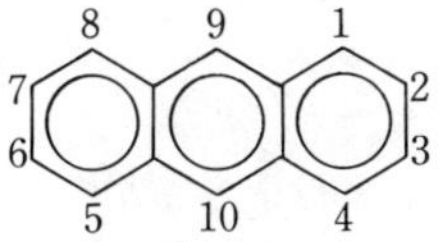

anthracene
$C_{14}H_{10}$

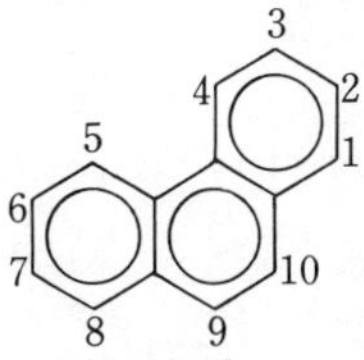

phenanthrene
$C_{14}H_{10}$

Note that anthracene and phenanthrene have the same molecular formula but differ in structure. In interpreting these formulas you should remember that there is a hydrogen atom on each numbered carbon atom. Each numbered carbon atom is a member of only one ring. The numbers indicate these carbon atoms and also the system for designating the location of substituents. For the time being you need not try to remember the numbers.

This completes our discussion of the naming of hydrocarbons. The next part of this program will deal with the names and formulas of organic compounds containing elements other than carbon and hydrogen.

ALKANES

General formula: C_nH_{2n+2} Series name: *-ane*

ALKENES

General formula: C_nH_{2n} Series name: *-ene*

ALKYNES

General formula: C_nH_{2n-2} Series name: *-yne*

ALICYCLIC HYDROCARBONS

Series name: *cyclo-*

AROMATIC HYDROCARBONS

General formula: One benzene   Series name: *-benzene*
                 ring
                 Two or more   Depends on
                 rings   structure

2.3 ALKYL AND ARYL HALIDES (HALOCARBONS)

When fluorine, chlorine, bromine, or iodine replaces one or more of the hydrogen atoms in an aliphatic or aromatic hydrocarbon, the resulting compounds are *alkyl* or *aryl halides*. They are useful in the synthesis of more complex organic compounds.

Alkyl halides are named in the same way as branched hydrocarbons. The prefixes are *fluoro-, chloro-, bromo-,* and *iodo-*. Both the number of substituent groups and the location of each must be given. To illustrate this point, compare the two skeletons shown here:

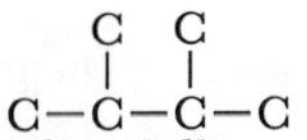

$$\begin{matrix} & C & C & & & & Cl & Cl \\ & | & | & & & & | & | \\ C- & C- & C- & C & & C- & C- & C- & C \end{matrix}$$

2,3-*dimethylbutane* 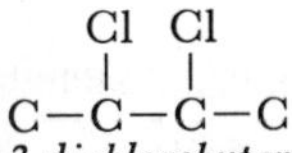   2,3-*dichlorobutane*

One alkyl halide that you know, at least by reputation, has the common name chloroform. Its systematic name is trichloromethane. Which of the following is the formula of chloroform?

A

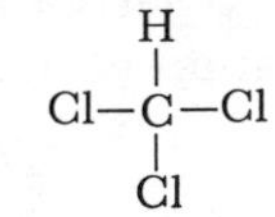

$$\begin{matrix} & H \\ & | \\ Cl- & C- & Cl \\ & | \\ & Cl \end{matrix}$$

B

$$\begin{matrix} & H & H \\ & | & | \\ Cl- & C- & C- & Cl \\ & | & | \\ & H & H \end{matrix}$$

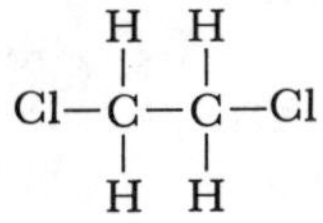

C

$$\begin{matrix} & Cl \\ & | \\ Cl- & C- & Cl \\ & | \\ & Cl \end{matrix}$$

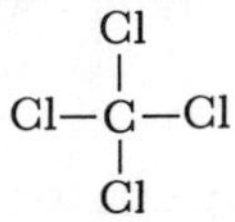

An inhalation anesthetic called halothane is a substituted alkane. It has a muscle-relaxing effect that occurs before a patient is in dangerously deep anesthesia. Its systematic name is 2-bromo-2-chloro-1,1,1-trifluoroethane.

$CF_3CHClBr$
halothane

A ||||||||||||||||||||||||||||||||||||||||||||||||||||||||||||||||||||||||||||||||||||||||||||||||||||||||||||||||||

You are correct. This is the formula for chloroform, or trichloromethane. It has one carbon atom, three chlorine atoms, and one hydrogen atom.

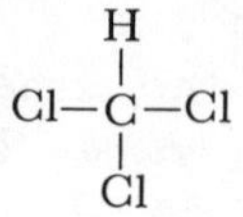

$$\begin{array}{c} H \\ | \\ Cl-C-Cl \\ | \\ Cl \end{array}$$

Go on to page 97.

B ||||||||||||||||||||||||||||||||||||||||||||||||||||||||||||||||||||||||||||||||||||||||||||||||||||||||||||||||||

Incorrect. You made a fundamental error. If the name of the compound is trichloro*methane*, it can contain only one carbon atom. The formula you chose is

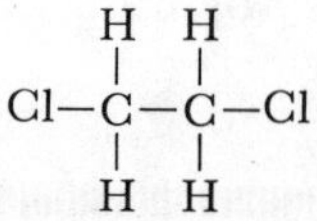

$$\begin{array}{cc} H & H \\ | & | \\ Cl-C-C-Cl \\ | & | \\ H & H \end{array}$$

It has two carbon atoms and is a derivative of ethane. Since there is a chlorine on each carbon, its name is 1,2-dichloroethane. Go back and choose another answer.

C ||||||||||||||||||||||||||||||||||||||||||||||||||||||||||||||||||||||||||||||||||||||||||||||||||||||||||||||||||

You are wrong. Perhaps you need to review the prefixes and their meanings. They are:

di-two	hexa-six
tri-three	hepta-seven
tetra-four	octa-eight
penta-five	nona-nine

The formula you chose shows four chlorine atoms substituted on one carbon atom. This is tetrachloromethane, usually called carbon tetrachloride. Write the formula for trichloromethane here:

Now turn back and see if it appears on page 95.

There are a couple of unsaturated aliphatic halides that are important. One of them has the common name allyl chloride. Its formula is

$$CH_2=CHCH_2Cl$$

What is its systematic name? It is 3-chloropropene, isn't it? Allyl chloride is used as an intermediate in organic synthesis.

Another important unsaturated halide is chloroethylene, or vinyl chloride. Many molecules of chloroethylene can combine with each other to form a polymer known as vinyl resin or vinyl plastic.

$$3x\ CH_2=CHCl \rightarrow [-CH_2CHCl \vdots CH_2CHCl \vdots CH_2CHCl-]x$$

The unsaturated chloride commonly called methallyl chloride has this formula:

$$CH_2=CCH_2Cl$$
$$|$$
$$CH_3$$

What is its correct name?

A ||||||||||||||||||||||||||||||||||||||||||||||||||||||||||||||||||||||||||||||||||||||||||||||||||||||||||||

1-chloro-2-methyl-2-propene

B ||||||||||||||||||||||||||||||||||||||||||||||||||||||||||||||||||||||||||||||||||||||||||||||||||||||||||||

chloromethylpropene

C ||||||||||||||||||||||||||||||||||||||||||||||||||||||||||||||||||||||||||||||||||||||||||||||||||||||||||||

3-chloro-2-methylpropene

The insecticide lindane is 1,2,3,4,5,6-hexachlorocyclohexane, *not* benzene hexachloride.

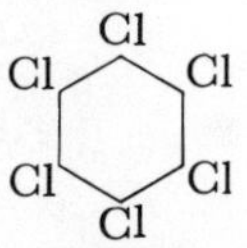

lindane

A ||||||||||||||||||||||||||||||||||||||||||||||||||||||||||||||||||||||||||||||||||||||||||||||||||||||||||||||||||||||||||||||||||||||||||||||||||

Incorrect. Your answer is nearly right. You made one small error. Remember that the carbon chain should be numbered from the end nearest the double bond. Here is the formula again:

$$CH_2=CCH_2Cl$$
$$|$$
$$CH_3$$

It should be named as a derivative of 1-propene. Work out the name again and then turn back to see if there is a corresponding answer.

B ||||||||||||||||||||||||||||||||||||||||||||||||||||||||||||||||||||||||||||||||||||||||||||||||||||||||||||||||||||||||||||||||||||||||||||||||||

You are wrong. The compound represented by the formula

$$CH_2=CCH_2Cl$$
$$|$$
$$CH_3$$

is a derivative of propene. It does have a chlorine and a methyl group as substituents. You did not specify their locations. You must do this in order to have a unique name. Turn back and try again.

C ||||||||||||||||||||||||||||||||||||||||||||||||||||||||||||||||||||||||||||||||||||||||||||||||||||||||||||||||||||||||||||||||||||||||||||||||||

You are correct. The systematic name for methallyl chloride is 3-chloro-2-methylpropene. It is used as a raw material for the production of *Lucite* and *Plexiglas*. Go on to page 99.

The skeletons or names of a few more halocarbons are given below. If you see a skeleton, write the name; if you see a name, write the skeleton. Cover the answers until you have worked out your own.

1.
$$\underset{|}{\overset{Cl}{\underset{|}{C}}}-C-C-\underset{|}{\overset{Cl}{C}}$$

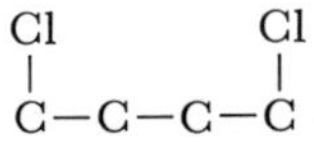

1,4-dichlorobutane

2.
$$C=C-C-C-\overset{Br}{\underset{|}{C}}$$

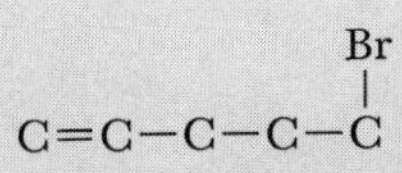

5-bromo-1-pentene, *not* 1-bromo-4-pentene

3. 1-bromo-3-chlorobenzene

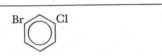

4.

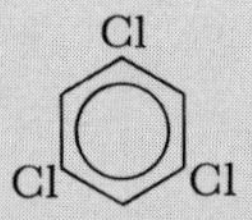

1,3,5-trichlorobenzene

5. 2,4,6-tribromotoluene (2,4,6-tribromo-1-methylbenzene)

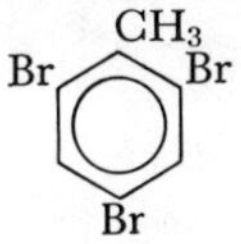

Br⟨ ⟩Br with CH₃ on top and Br on bottom

Go on to page 101.

Another widely used family of halocarbons are the fluorinated hydrocarbons, which are used as refrigerants and propellants in aerosol-spray preparations. They are sold under the trademarked names Freon, Ucon, and Genetron. The generic term for all of them is Halocarbon.

Halocarbon-12, used for aerosol bombs, is dichlorodifluoromethane, CCl_2F_2. Halocarbon-114 is the most widely used refrigerant for household refrigerators. Its structural formula is:

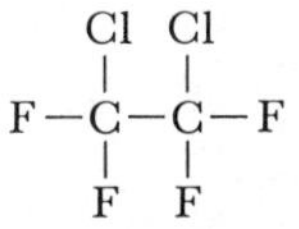

$$\begin{array}{ccc} & Cl & Cl \\ & | & | \\ F- & C- & C-F \\ & | & | \\ & F & F \end{array}$$

What is the preferred systematic name for Halocarbon-114?

A ||||||||||||||||||||||||||||||||||||||||||||||||||||||||||||||||||||||||||||||||||||||||||||||||||||

dichlorotetrafluoroethane

B ||||||||||||||||||||||||||||||||||||||||||||||||||||||||||||||||||||||||||||||||||||||||||||||||||||

1,2-dichloro-1,2-tetrafluoroethane

C ||||||||||||||||||||||||||||||||||||||||||||||||||||||||||||||||||||||||||||||||||||||||||||||||||||

1,2-dichlorotetrafluoroethane

D ||||||||||||||||||||||||||||||||||||||||||||||||||||||||||||||||||||||||||||||||||||||||||||||||||||

Freon-114

Fluoromar, an inhalation anesthetic, is an ether. It is trifluoroethyl vinyl ether. It puts a patient to sleep rapidly—in 30 to 60 seconds—and lets him awake faster with less likelihood of nausea.

$$CF_3CH_2OCH=CH_2$$
trifluoroethyl vinyl ether

A ▌▌

Incorrect. The compound represented by the formula

$$
\begin{array}{ccc}
 & Cl & Cl \\
 & | & | \\
F - & C - & C - F \\
 & | & | \\
 & F & F
\end{array}
$$

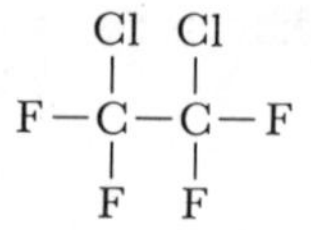

is indeed a dichlorotetrafluoroethane. Isn't this one, too?

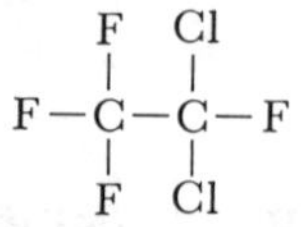

$$
\begin{array}{ccc}
 & F & Cl \\
 & | & | \\
F - & C - & C - F \\
 & | & | \\
 & F & Cl
\end{array}
$$

The preferred systematic name must specify the location of enough halogen atoms to make it a unique name. Turn back and choose another answer.

B ▌▌

You are wrong. The compound represented by the formula

$$
\begin{array}{ccc}
 & Cl & Cl \\
 & | & | \\
F - & C - & C - F \\
 & | & | \\
 & F & F
\end{array}
$$

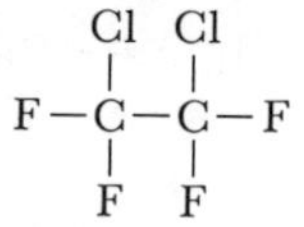

is not 1,2-dichloro-1,2-tetrafluoroethane. The formula and the tetra-prefix both indicate that there are four fluorine atoms, and you have specified the locations of two of them with numbers. Are any needed? Is there more than one way to arrange the four fluorines? Turn back and choose another name.

C ▌▌

Correct. The preferred systematic name for Halocarbon-114 is 1, 2-dichlorotetrafluoroethane. Go on to page 103.

D ▌▌

You are incorrect. Freon-114 is a trademarked name. A refrigerator expert might be able to infer the formula from it, but most chemists would want something more. Turn back and choose a satisfactory chemical name.

Now and then you will see a substituted phenyl group which is itself a substituent. For instance

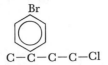

$$C-C-C-C-Cl$$

According to what you have learned so far, this compound should be named as a substituted butane. There is a chlorine on the number one carbon atom, but what about that aryl group on number three? It is a substituted phenyl group. Let's look at it alone.

The free valence, or point of attachment to the butane, is considered to be the number one carbon atom of the ring. The bromine is then in the number 4, or *para*-, position. The name of the group is 4-bromophenyl or *p*-bromophenyl. The compound at the top of the page is therefore 3-(*p*-bromophenyl)-1-chlorobutane. The parentheses are used to show that the entire *p*-bromophenyl group is attached to the number 3 carbon atom of the butane.

How would you name this substituted phenyl group?

A ||||||||||||||||||||||||||||||||||||||||||||||||||||||||||||||||||||||||||||||||||||||||||||||||||||

1,3-dichlorophenyl group

B ||||||||||||||||||||||||||||||||||||||||||||||||||||||||||||||||||||||||||||||||||||||||||||||||||||

2,4-dichlorophenyl group

C ||||||||||||||||||||||||||||||||||||||||||||||||||||||||||||||||||||||||||||||||||||||||||||||||||||

2,4-dichloro-1-phenyl group

D ||||||||||||||||||||||||||||||||||||||||||||||||||||||||||||||||||||||||||||||||||||||||||||||||||||

m-dichlorophenyl group

A ||||||||||||||||||||||||||||||||||||||||||||||||||||||||||||||||||||||||||||||||||||||||||||||||||||||||||

Incorrect. The group represented by this formula

is not a 1,3-dichlorophenyl group. You have forgotten that the carbon with the free valence must be number 1. Keep this in mind when you go back to choose another answer.

B |||||||||||||||||||||||||||||||||||||||||||||||||||||||||||||||||||||||||||||||||||||||||||||||||||||||||||

Right. The preferred name for the aryl group (shown above) is 2,4-dichlorophenyl. Go on to page 105.

C |||||||||||||||||||||||||||||||||||||||||||||||||||||||||||||||||||||||||||||||||||||||||||||||||||||||||||

You are not quite right. If the carbon atom with the free valence is given the number 1, then the chlorine atoms are substituted on the number 2 and number 4 carbon atoms.

The custom, however, is for the carbon atom in the benzene ring with the free valence always to be number 1. For benzene rings, it doesn't have to be specified. Therefore the preferred name is just 2,4-dichlorophenyl. Go on to page 105.

D ||||||||||||||||||||||||||||||||||||||||||||||||||||||||||||||||||||||||||||||||||||||||||||||||||||||||||||

Wrong. Your answer is that the group represented by the formula

is a *m*-dichlorophenyl group. This is confusing. The prefix *meta-*, or *m-*, is used to indicate two substituents on a benzene ring that are separated by one carbon atom. In this group the two chlorines are "meta" to each other, but where are they in relation to the carbon with the free valence? Your name should not leave this to the imagination. Turn back and find a satisfactory answer.

Occasionally you will find compounds that have two or more identical substituents which are themselves substituted groups. Examples of this type are the insecticides DDD and DDT. The formula for DDD is

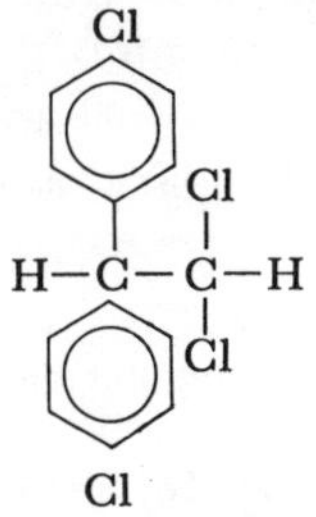

$$\text{Cl}$$

$$H-C-C-H$$

The steps in naming DDD are: (1) Locate the longest carbon chain. It has two carbons and therefore the base name is ethane. (2) Name and locate the substituent groups. There are two p-chlorophenyl groups

$\left(\text{Cl} \bigcirc - \right)$ on one of the carbon atoms. In order to avoid confusion, a

set of multiplicative prefixes has been devised to indicate that an entire group within a parenthesis is to be taken a certain number of times. These prefixes are

Prefix	Multiplying factor
bis-	2
tris-	3
tetrakis-	4
pentakis-	5

Finally, there are two chlorine atoms substituted on the other carbon of the ethane chain. The full name for DDD is 1,1-dichloro-2,2-bis (p-chlorophenyl)ethane. Compare this name carefully with the formula shown above to be sure you understand it.

The formula for DDT is:

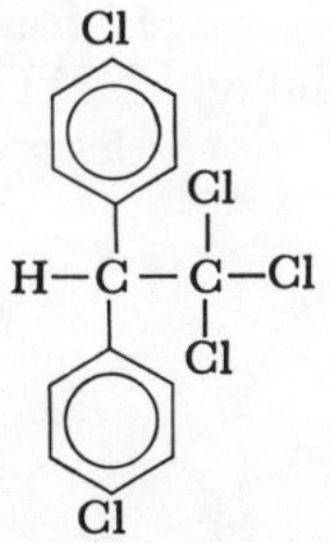

$$\text{Cl}$$

$$H-C-C-Cl$$

Its preferred systematic name is

A

dichlorophenyltrichloroethane

B

2,2-p-chlorophenyl-1,1,1-trichloroethane

C

1,1,1-trichloro-2,2-bis(p-chlorophenyl)ethane

A ||||||||||||||||||||||||||||||||||||||||||||||||||||||||||||||||||||||||||||||||||||||||||||||||||||||||||||||||||||||||||||||||

You are incorrect. By now you should know that substituent groups need to be named *and* located according to their position on the carbon chain that is used for the base name of the compound. You have correctly deduced that DDT is a substituted ethane, but have not named or located the substituents correctly. Turn back and read page 105 again carefully.

B ||||||||||||||||||||||||||||||||||||||||||||||||||||||||||||||||||||||||||||||||||||||||||||||||||||||||||||||||||||||||||||||||

Close but not entirely correct. You have correctly judged that DDT is a substituted ethane. You have, however, missed the point of the present discussion. Your chosen name for DDT is 2,2-*p*-chlorophenyl-1,1, 1-trichloroethane. Here is the formula again:

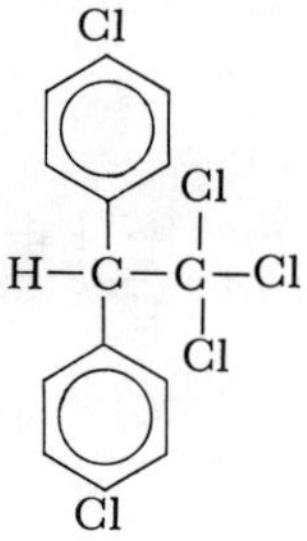

Are there two *p*-chlorophenyl groups on the number 2 carbon? If so, you need to indicate this fact in some way. Go back and read page 105 again. Then choose another answer.

C ||||||||||||||||||||||||||||||||||||||||||||||||||||||||||||||||||||||||||||||||||||||||||||||||||||||||||||||||||||||||||||||||

Correct. The systematic name for DDT is 1,1,1-trichloro-2,2-bis (*p*-chlorophenyl)ethane. Although DDT is certainly shorter, you must agree that the other name is more descriptive. Go on to page 107.

2.4 NITRO COMPOUNDS

One small but mighty group of substituted hydrocarbons is the *nitro* (nī′ trō) *compounds*. They are usually synthesized by treating the hydrocarbon with nitric acid. The end result is that the nitro group, $-NO_2$, replaces one or more hydrogens on the hydrocarbon. The nitroalkanes nitromethane and nitroethane are used as fuel additives in competition automobile racing.

$$
\begin{array}{cc}
\underset{\text{nitromethane}}{\text{H}-\overset{\overset{\displaystyle H}{|}}{\underset{\underset{\displaystyle H}{|}}{\text{C}}}-NO_2} &
\underset{\text{nitroethane}}{\text{H}-\overset{\overset{\displaystyle H}{|}}{\underset{\underset{\displaystyle H}{|}}{\text{C}}}-\overset{\overset{\displaystyle H}{|}}{\underset{\underset{\displaystyle H}{|}}{\text{C}}}-NO_2}
\end{array}
$$

When benzene is treated with nitric acid, one of the products is nitrobenzene. It was once used as a flavoring agent because its odor resembles oil of almonds. Its high toxicity, however, has eliminated this use as well as all others in which it might come in contact with the skin.

Further nitration of benzene yields 1,3,5-trinitrobenzene, a powerful explosive. Which of these is the formula for this compound?

A ||||||||||||||||||||||||||||||||||||||||||||||||||||||||||||||||||||||||||||||||||||||||||||||||||||||||||||||||

B ||||||||||||||||||||||||||||||||||||||||||||||||||||||||||||||||||||||||||||||||||||||||||||||||||||||||||||||||

C ||||||||||||||||||||||||||||||||||||||||||||||||||||||||||||||||||||||||||||||||||||||||||||||||||||||||||||||||

A ||||||||||||||||||||||||||||||||||||||||||||||||||||||||||||||||||||||||||||||||||||||||||||||||||||||||||||||||||||||||||||||||||||||||

You are correct. Since all three substituent groups are alike, the carbon bearing any one of them can be designated as number 1. The others, then, are found to be in the number 3 and number 5 positions. Go on to page 109.

B ||||||||||||||||||||||||||||||||||||||||||||||||||||||||||||||||||||||||||||||||||||||||||||||||||||||||||||||||||||||||||||||||||||||

Wrong. The formula you chose is

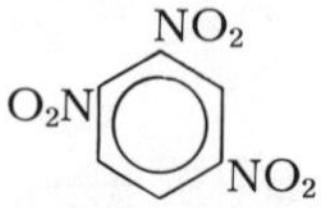

Since two of the nitro- groups are on adjacent carbons, it should be apparent that the compound cannot be 1,3,5-trinitrobenzene. How would the compound represented by this formula be named. There are several ways to number the carbons in the ring. Some are shown here.

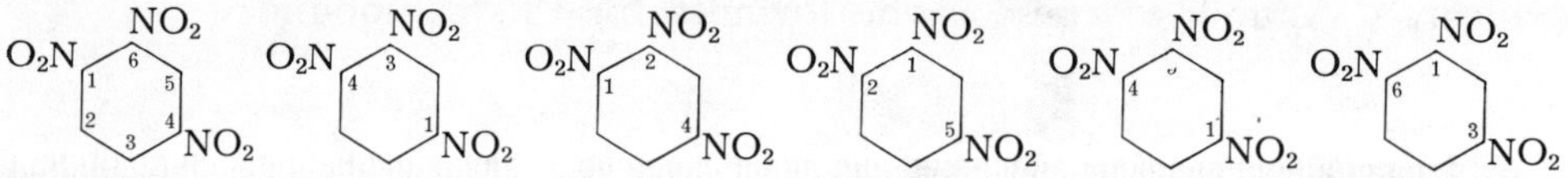

Which is correct? The one with the lowest combination of numbers, or 1,2,4-trinitrobenzene. With these principles in mind, turn back and choose another answer.

C ||||||||||||||||||||||||||||||||||||||||||||||||||||||||||||||||||||||||||||||||||||||||||||||||||||||||||||||||||||||||||||||||||||||

You are incorrect. The formula you chose is

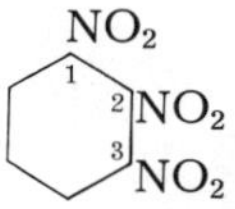

Since the three nitro- groups are on adjacent carbon atoms, the simplest (and correct) name for this compound is 1,2,3-trinitrobenzene. Turn back and choose another answer.

As it happens, 1,3,5-trinitrobenzene is difficult to prepare. A more easily made explosive, though slightly less powerful, is known as TNT. It is still the most important of the military explosives. TNT melts at 81° C., but does not explode until it reaches 280° C. Consequently, it can be melted and poured into shells while liquid.

The formula for TNT is

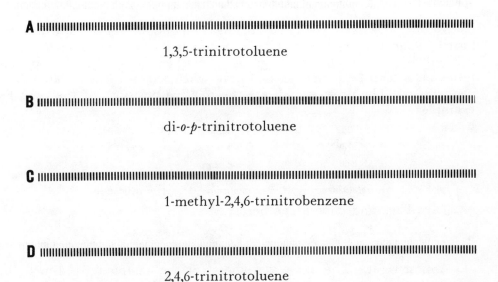

What is the systematic name for TNT?

A ||||||||||||||||||||||||||||||||||||||||||||||||||||||||||||||||||||||||||||||||||||||||||||||||||||||||||||||||||||||||||||||

1,3,5-trinitrotoluene

B ||||||||||||||||||||||||||||||||||||||||||||||||||||||||||||||||||||||||||||||||||||||||||||||||||||||||||||||||||||||||||||||

di-*o*-*p*-trinitrotoluene

C ||||||||||||||||||||||||||||||||||||||||||||||||||||||||||||||||||||||||||||||||||||||||||||||||||||||||||||||||||||||||||||||

1-methyl-2,4,6-trinitrobenzene

D ||||||||||||||||||||||||||||||||||||||||||||||||||||||||||||||||||||||||||||||||||||||||||||||||||||||||||||||||||||||||||||||

2,4,6-trinitrotoluene

A ||||||||||||||||||||||||||||||||||||||||||||||||||||||||||||||||||||||||||||||||||||||||||||||||||||||||||||

Incorrect. The name you chose is 1,3,5-trinitrotoluene.

CH₃
O₂N⟨ring⟩NO₂
NO₂

It correctly names the substituent groups but does not locate them properly. Even though the methyl group is included in the base name toluene, it must still be considered to be in the number 1 position. With this in mind, determine the proper numbers for the positions of the three nitro- groups. Turn back and choose another answer.

B ||||||||||||||||||||||||||||||||||||||||||||||||||||||||||||||||||||||||||||||||||||||||||||||||||||||||||

Wrong. The name you chose for the compound is di-*o*-*p*-trinitrotoluene. Part of your answer is correct. The compound is a trinitrotoluene. Your method of locating the nitro- groups, however, is wrong. The prefixes *ortho-*, *meta-*, and *para-* can be used only when there are only *two* substituent groups. The prefixes indicate the relative positions of the two. For example

CH₃ ⟨ring⟩NO₂   CH₃⟨ring⟩ NO₂   CH₃⟨ring⟩ NO₂

o-nitrotoluene   *m-nitrotoluene*   *p-nitrotoluene*

Turn back and choose another answer.

C |||||||||||||||||||||||||||||||||||||||||||||||||||||||||||||||||||||||||||||||||||||||||||||||||||||||||

Almost right. The name you chose for the compound is 1-methyl-2, 4, 6-trinitrobenzene. This name completely describes the compound:

CH₃
O₂N⟨ring⟩NO₂
NO₂

Toluene, CH₃⟨ring⟩ is a common compound, and its name is accepted as part

of our system. How would you name the compound as a substituted toluene? When you have your answer, turn back and find it on page 109.

D ||||||||||||||||||||||||||||||||||||||||||||||||||||||||||||||||||||||||||||||||||||||||||||||||||||||||

You are correct. TNT is properly named 2,4,6-trinitrotoluene. Here is its formula again:

CH₃
O₂N⟨ring⟩NO₂
NO₂

Notice that the nitro group on the left-hand side of the formula is written O₂N rather than NO₂. This shows that the bond is between carbon and nitrogen. Go on to page 111.

Summary: Nomenclature of Hydrocarbons and Substituted Hydrocarbons

Unsaturated hydrocarbons containing one carbon-carbon double bond are known as *alkenes*. Their general formula is C_nH_{2n}. The name of each alkene is formed by changing the *-ane* ending of the alkane with the same number of carbon atoms to *-ene*. The location of the double bond must be specified in alkenes which have four or more carbon atoms. To do this, number the carbon atoms consecutively from the end of the chain nearest the double bond and indicate the double bond by giving the lower number of the two carbon atoms joined by the double bond. For instance

$$\underset{5\quad 4\quad 3\quad 2\quad 1}{C-C-C=C-C} \qquad \textit{2-pentene}$$

Compounds that contain two or more double bonds are known as dienes, trienes, and so forth. The location of each double bond must be specified by a number. Other substituent groups are named and located in the same manner as with alkanes.

Alkynes are hydrocarbons that contain a carbon-carbon triple bond. The general formula is C_nH_{2n-2} and the names are derived by replacing the *-ane* ending of the parent alkane with the suffix *-yne*. Substituted alkynes are named in a manner similar to the alkenes.

Homocyclic compounds, which include the cyclic hydrocarbons, may be divided into two groups: alicyclic and aromatic. The *alicyclic* compounds are named in the same way as the aliphatic hydrocarbons except that the prefix *cyclo-* is placed at the beginning of the name.

Hydrocarbons containing unsaturated ring systems such as benzene and naphthalene are known as *aromatic* hydrocarbons. The molecular formula of benzene is C_6H_6. Its structural formula is usually written as

 or

It must be remembered that each of the carbon atoms is bonded to one hydrogen atom and that all of the carbon atoms have the same chemical reactivity. The phenyl group is formed by the removal of one hydrogen atom from benzene. Its structural formula is

Mono-substituted benzenes are named by combining the name of the substituent group with the word benzene

ethylbenzene

Di-substituted benzenes can be named by numbering the carbons in the ring consecutively beginning with the carbon atom bearing one of the substituent groups. The position of each substituent is specified by a number. A special notation may be used when the substituents are identical or when the first substituent can be included in the base name.

For example

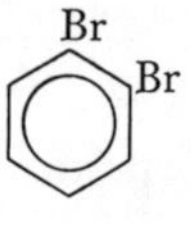

o-dibromobenzene 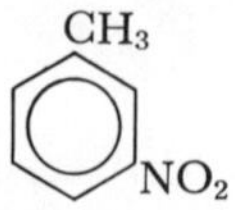   *m-nitrotoluene*    *p-dichlorobenzene*

Removal of one hydrogen atom from the terminal carbon atom of a hydrocarbon leads to a radical or group. Radicals derived from alkanes are named by replacing the *-ane* ending with *-yl*; those from alkenes by changing *-e* to *-yl*; from alkynes by changing *-e* to *-yl*. For instance

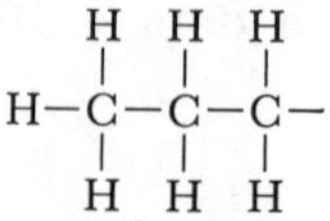

propyl group 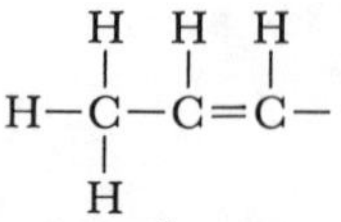   *1-propenyl group* 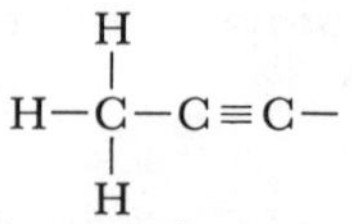   *1-propynyl group*

Halocarbons are named in the same way as hydrocarbons, using the prefixes *fluoro-, chloro-, bromo-,* and *iodo-* to indicate the substituent halogen atoms.

Nitro compounds contain the -NO$_2$ group. Its location is specified in a manner identical to any other substituent.

For those compounds in which there are identical substituent groups that contain substituents themselves, the prefixes bis-, tris-, tetrakis-, pentakis-, and so forth, are used as multiplicative prefixes. The group which is to be multiplied is enclosed in parentheses.

All these rules and conventions are illustrated by this hypothetical compound. Study its name carefully to be sure that you understand it.

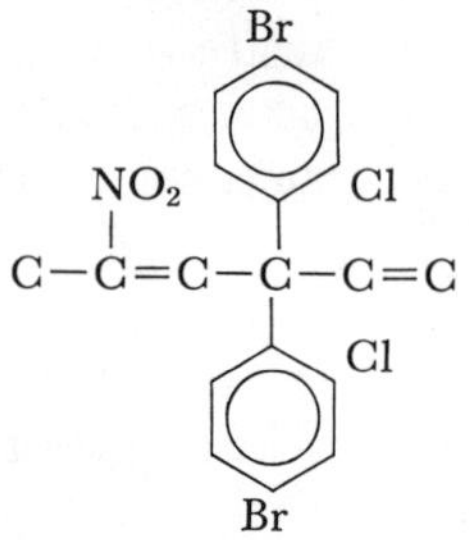

3,3-bis(4-bromo-2-chlorophenyl)-5-nitro-1,4-hexadiene

Turn to page 114 for a brief series of quiz questions.

ALKANES

General formula: C_nH_{2n+2} Series name: *-ane*

ALKENES

General formula: C_nH_{2n} Series name: *-ene*

ALKYNES

General formula: C_nH_{2n-2} Series name: *-yne*

ALICYCLIC HYDROCARBONS

Series name: *cyclo-*

AROMATIC HYDROCARBONS

General formula: benzene ring   Series name: *-benzene*
  Two or more rings   Depends on structure

HALOCARBONS

General formula: RX   Series name: *chloro-,*
  R = Alkyl or aryl group, X = F,   *bromo-, fluoro-, iodo-*
  Cl, Br, I

NITRO COMPOUNDS

General formula: RNO_2 Series name: *nitro-*
  $-NO_2$ = nitro group

This quiz consists of four questions. You should be able to answer all four correctly. If you make a mistake return to the page indicated for review. As usual, you should cover the answers until you have worked out your own.

1. The plastic Teflon is a polymer of tetrafluoroethylene. What is the structural formula of the monomer?

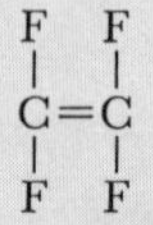

$$\underset{\underset{F}{|}}{\overset{\overset{F}{|}}{C}} = \underset{\underset{F}{|}}{\overset{\overset{F}{|}}{C}}$$

Review pages 95 and 97 if you made an error.

2. Neoprene rubber is a polymer of this compound. Its common name is chloroprene. What is its systematic name?

$$H-\underset{\underset{H}{|}}{C}=\underset{\underset{H}{|}}{C}-\underset{\overset{\overset{Cl}{|}}{}}{C}=\underset{\underset{H}{|}}{C}-H$$

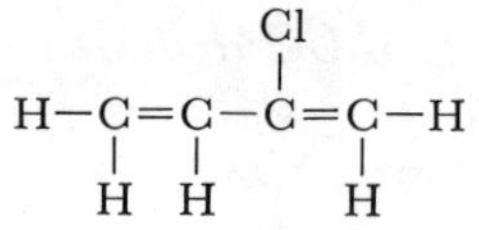

2-chloro-1,3-butadiene

Review page 67 if you were wrong.

3. What is the molecular formula of diphenylmethane?

Molecular formula: $C_{13}H_{12}$
Structural formula:

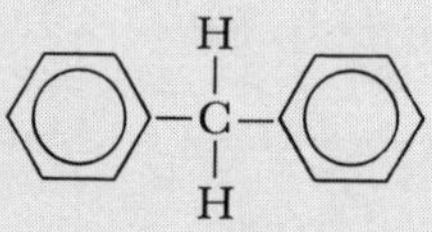

Review pages 85 and 87 if necessary.

4. Chloropicrin (tear gas) has this formula: CCl_3NO_2 What is its systematic name?

trichloronitromethane

Review pages 95 and 107 if necessary.

3
Functional Groups

Atoms or groups that change the chemical properties of hydrocarbons when they appear as substituents are called *functional groups* or *characteristic groups*. Most of the homologous series of organic compounds have characteristic functional groups. The number of these functional groups is small compared to the vast number of organic compounds. Emphasis on the functional group of each series simplifies the naming of the compounds as well as the study of their chemistry. The remainder of this chapter will present the nomenclature of a dozen or so families with different functional groups.

3.1 ALIPHATIC ALCOHOLS (ALKANOLS)

These compounds have the monovalent hydroxy radical, -OH, as their functional group. Both the name and formula of the functional group are important. The simplest member of the family is methanol. Its structural formula is

$$
\begin{array}{c}
H \\
| \\
H-C-OH \\
| \\
H
\end{array}
$$
methanol

Alkanols are given their systematic names by changing the final *-e* of the parent alkane to *-ol*. In the United States, however, the simple, unsubstituted alkanols from ethanol to dodecanol are usually called by their common names. For example

$$
\begin{array}{c}
H \; H \\
| \; | \\
H-C-C-OH \\
| \; | \\
H \; H
\end{array}
\qquad
\begin{array}{c}
H \; H \; H \\
| \; | \; | \\
H-C-C-C-OH \\
| \; | \; | \\
H \; H \; H
\end{array}
\qquad
\begin{array}{c}
H \; H \; H \; H \\
| \; | \; | \; | \\
H-C-C-C-C-OH \\
| \; | \; | \; | \\
H \; H \; H \; H
\end{array}
$$
ethyl alcohol   *propyl alcohol*   *butyl alcohol*

The contrasting name "methanol" is preferred over "methyl alcohol" in order to emphasize that the compound is poisonous.

What is the systematic name of the alkanol containing two carbon atoms?

A ||||||||||||||||||||||||||||||||||||||||||||||||||||||||||||||||||||||||||||||||||||||||||||||||||||||||||

ethanol

B ||||||||||||||||||||||||||||||||||||||||||||||||||||||||||||||||||||||||||||||||||||||||||||||||||||||||||

methylmethanol

C ||||||||||||||||||||||||||||||||||||||||||||||||||||||||||||||||||||||||||||||||||||||||||||||||||||||||||

hydroxyethane

A ‖‖

You are right. The alkanol containing two carbon atoms is ethanol. It structural formula is

$$\begin{array}{ccc} & H & H \\ & | & | \\ H- & C- & C-OH \\ & | & | \\ & H & H \end{array}$$

To name any alkanol, merely change the final -e of the name of the hydrocarbon to -ol. Go on to page 117.

B ‖‖

You are wrong. The systematic name of the alkanol containing two carbon atoms is not methylmethanol. Although that name does describe the compound, the correct name is derived from the name of the hydrocarbon with two carbon atoms, just as the alkanol itself is derived from that hydrocarbon. Here are the formulas

$$\begin{array}{ccc} H & H \\ | & | \\ H-C- & C-H \\ | & | \\ H & H \\ \textit{ethane} \end{array} \qquad \begin{array}{ccc} H & H \\ | & | \\ H-C- & C-OH \\ | & | \\ H & H \\ ? \end{array}$$

Turn back and choose another answer.

C ‖‖

Incorrect. Although the name hydroxyethane does describe the alkanol containing two carbon atoms, it is not right. The functional group of the alcohols is the hydroxy group, -OH, but it is not part of their names. Here are the structural formulas of ethane and the alkanol derived from it. Turn back and read page 115 carefully before choosing another answer.

$$\begin{array}{ccc} H & H \\ | & | \\ H-C- & C-H \\ | & | \\ H & H \\ \textit{ethane} \end{array} \qquad \begin{array}{ccc} H & H \\ | & | \\ H-C- & C-OH \\ | & | \\ H & H \\ ? \end{array}$$

Because of its almost universal use, we shall refer to the family of compounds whose functional group is -OH as alcohols. You should remember, however, that the term alcohol is not a systematic name.

Structural isomerism becomes possible as soon as there are three carbon atoms in the molecule. The formulas of the two isomers of propanol are

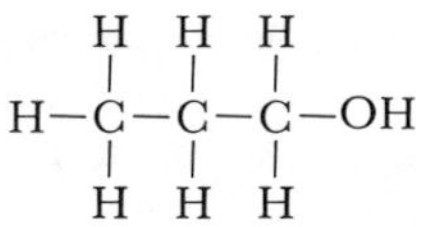

$$
\begin{array}{ccc}
\text{H} & \text{H} & \text{H} \\
| & | & | \\
\text{H}-\text{C}-\text{C}-\text{C}-\text{OH} \\
| & | & | \\
\text{H} & \text{H} & \text{H}
\end{array}
\qquad \text{and} \qquad
\begin{array}{ccc}
\text{H} & \text{H} & \text{H} \\
| & | & | \\
\text{H}-\text{C}-\text{C}-\text{C}-\text{H} \\
| & | & | \\
\text{H} & \text{OH} & \text{H}
\end{array}
$$

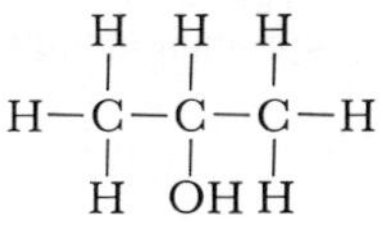

The difference in structure is more apparent if the carbon skeleton and functional group only are shown

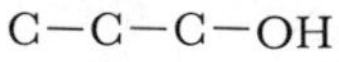

$$
\text{C}-\text{C}-\text{C}-\text{OH} \qquad \text{and} \qquad
\begin{array}{c}
\text{C}-\text{C}-\text{C} \\
| \\
\text{OH}
\end{array}
$$

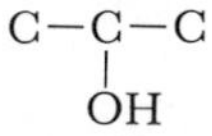

The difference between the two is in the location of the functional group. Once again, the solution to the difficulty lies in numbering the carbon atoms. After the longest continuous chain is found, it is numbered as usual beginning at the end nearest the hydroxy group. Then the location of the hydroxy group is specified. The alkanols shown above are 1-propanol and 2-propanol. The common names of the two compounds, used in *Chemical Abstracts*, are propyl alcohol and isopropyl alcohol. Isopropyl alcohol is used as rubbing alcohol.

Which of these skeletons represents 3-hexanol?

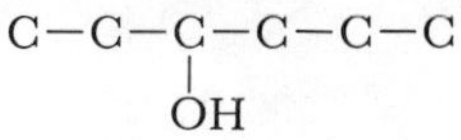

$$
\begin{array}{c}
\text{C}-\text{C}-\text{C}-\text{C}-\text{C}-\text{C} \\
| \\
\text{OH} \\
A
\end{array}
\qquad\qquad
\begin{array}{c}
\text{C}-\text{C}-\text{C}-\text{C}-\text{C}-\text{C} \\
| \\
\text{OH} \\
B
\end{array}
$$

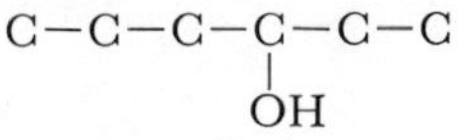

A ||||||||||||||||||||||||||||||||||||||||||||||||||||||||||||||||||||||||||||||||||||||||||||||||||||||||||||||||||||||||||||

Both *A* and *B*

B ||||||||||||||||||||||||||||||||||||||||||||||||||||||||||||||||||||||||||||||||||||||||||||||||||||||||||||||||||||||||||||

Only *A*

C ||||||||||||||||||||||||||||||||||||||||||||||||||||||||||||||||||||||||||||||||||||||||||||||||||||||||||||||||||||||||||||

Only *B*

A ||||||||||||||||||||||||||||||||||||||||||||||||||||||||||||||||||||||||||||||||||||||||||||||||||||||||||||||||||||||||||||||||||||||||||||||||||||||||||||||||

Right. Both of the skeletons shown represent 3-hexanol. Remember always to number the chain from the end nearest to the functional (-OH) group. Go on to page 119.

B ||||||||||||||||||||||||||||||||||||||||||||||||||||||||||||||||||||||||||||||||||||||||||||||||||||||||||||||||||||||||||||||||||||||||||||||||||||||||||||||||

Incorrect. Your answer is that only this skeleton represents

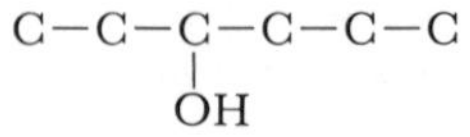

$$C-C-\underset{\underset{OH}{|}}{C}-C-C-C$$

3-hexanol. Consider the other skeleton again for a moment. Here it is.

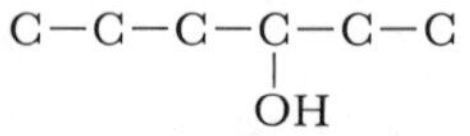

$$C-C-C-\underset{\underset{OH}{|}}{C}-C-C$$

If you number the carbon chain from the right, it's 3-hexanol, too, isn't it? Remember always to number the chain from the end nearest to the functional group. Go on to page 119.

C ||||||||||||||||||||||||||||||||||||||||||||||||||||||||||||||||||||||||||||||||||||||||||||||||||||||||||||||||||||||||||||||||||||||||||||||||||||||||||||||||

Incorrect. Your answer is that only this skeleton represents

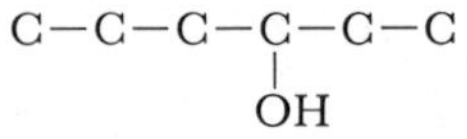

$$C-C-C-\underset{\underset{OH}{|}}{C}-C-C$$

3-hexanol. Consider the other skeleton again for a moment. Here it is.

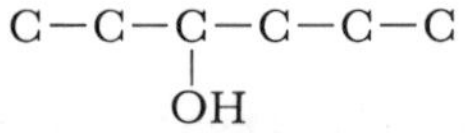

$$C-C-\underset{\underset{OH}{|}}{C}-C-C-C$$

If you number the carbon chain from the left, it's 3-hexanol, too, isn't it? Remember always to number the chain from the end nearest to the functional group. Go on to page 119.

The series of 1-alcohols is often termed the *normal series*. The prefix *n-* is used with the common names. For example, 1-butanol is *n*-butyl alcohol.

When other groups, such as halogen atoms, are substituted on an alcohol, they are named and located in the same way that you have already learned for hydrocarbons. Furthermore, systematic names are always used. One illustration should make the point clear for you. Compare this skeleton and its name.

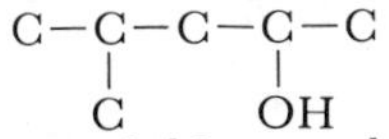

$$C-C-C-C-C$$
$$\quad\ \ \overset{|}{C}\quad\ \overset{|}{OH}$$

4-methyl-2-pentanol

It is tempting to name this compound 2-methyl-4-pentanol, but that is wrong because the lower number (2) should be used to indicate the position of the functional (-OH) group.

What is the skeleton of 2-methyl-2-butanol?

A

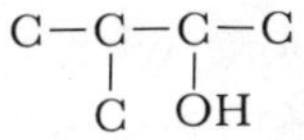

$$C-C-C-C$$
$$\quad\ \overset{|}{C}\quad\overset{|}{OH}$$

B

$$\overset{\displaystyle C}{\overset{|}{C-C-\overset{|}{C}-C}}$$
$$\qquad\ \ \overset{|}{OH}$$

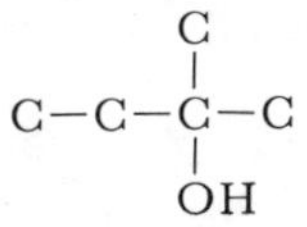

C

$$\overset{\displaystyle C}{\overset{|}{C-\overset{|}{C}-C}}$$
$$\qquad\overset{|}{OH}$$

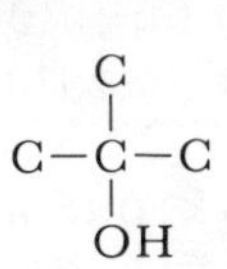

What difference can a single atom make? Ethanol, C_2H_5OH, is a colorless, nearly odorless liquid with a pleasant taste. Substitute a sulfur atom for the oxygen and you have ethyl mercaptan, C_2H_5SH, a liquid with an extremely disagreeable odor.

A ||||||||||||||||||||||||||||||||||||||||||||||||||||||||||||||||||||||||||||||||||||||||||||||||||||||||||||||||||||||||||||||||||||||||

Wrong. Your answer is that the formula of 2-methyl-2-butanol is

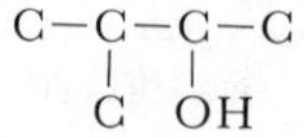

$$C-C-C-C$$
$$\quad\ \ |\quad\ |$$
$$\quad\ \ C\quad OH$$

This could be right only if you numbered the chain from one end to locate the methyl group and from the other to locate the hydroxy group. That's not fair. Always number the chain from the end nearest a functional group. With this in mind work out another skeleton and turn back to page 119.

B ||||||||||||||||||||||||||||||||||||||||||||||||||||||||||||||||||||||||||||||||||||||||||||||||||||||||||||||||||||||||||||||||||||||||

You are right. The skeleton for 2-methyl-2-butanol is

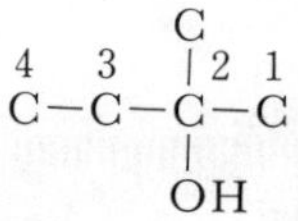

$$\qquad\qquad C$$
$$4\quad 3\quad |2\ \ 1$$
$$C-C-C-C$$
$$\qquad\ \ |$$
$$\qquad\ \ OH$$

It has a chain of four carbons with a methyl group and an hydroxy group on the second carbon from the end. Go on to page 121.

C ||||||||||||||||||||||||||||||||||||||||||||||||||||||||||||||||||||||||||||||||||||||||||||||||||||||||||||||||||||||||||||||||||||||||

Incorrect. The skeleton you have chosen to represent 2-methyl-2-butanol is

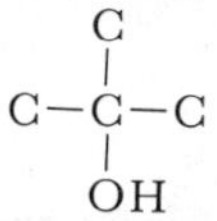

$$\qquad\ \ C$$
$$\qquad\ \ |$$
$$C-C-C$$
$$\qquad\ \ |$$
$$\qquad\ \ OH$$

Although it contains four carbon atoms, it is not a butanol. The longest continuous carbon chain has three carbon atoms. It represents 2-methyl-2-propanol. (On page 123 you will learn that its common name is *tert*-butyl alcohol.) Work out another answer and turn back to page 119.

Since the important structural feature of alcohols is the hydroxy group, the entire series of aliphatic alcohols is often represented by the general formula ROH. R- represents an alkyl radical, substituted or unsubstituted. For instance, consider these formulas for ethanol

Molecular formula: C_2H_6O

Structural formula:

$$H-\overset{\displaystyle \overset{H}{|}}{\underset{\displaystyle \underset{H}{|}}{C}}-\overset{\displaystyle \overset{H}{|}}{\underset{\displaystyle \underset{H}{|}}{C}}-OH$$

Condensed structural formula: CH_3CH_2OH
Skeleton formula: $C-C-OH$
General formula: ROH, where $R=CH_3CH_2$

If 2-methyl-2-propanol is to be represented as ROH, what is the condensed structural formula of R-?

A ‖‖

$$CH_3CH_2CH_2-$$

B ‖‖

$$\overset{\displaystyle CH_3}{\underset{\displaystyle |}{}}$$
$$CH_3CHCH_2-$$

C ‖‖

$$\overset{\displaystyle CH_3}{\underset{\displaystyle |}{}}$$
$$CH_3-\overset{|}{\underset{|}{C}}-CH_3$$

The principal functional group of Vitamin A, an essential factor in the growth of mammals, is the hydroxy group. Vitamin A is a complex alcohol.

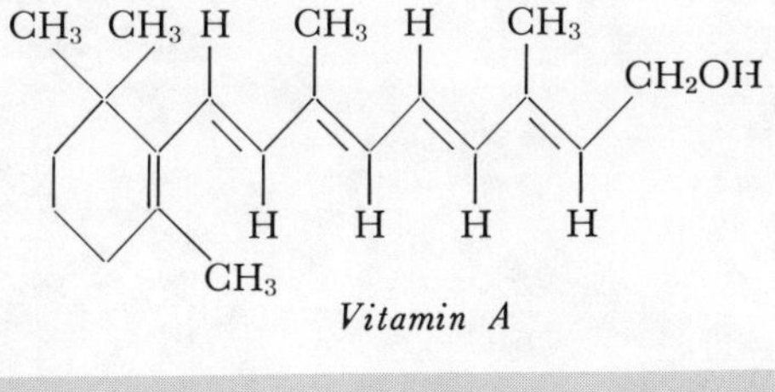

Vitamin A

A

You are wrong. This is not the condensed structural formula for the R- group of 2-methyl-2-propanol.

$$CH_3CH_2CH_2—$$

Suppose that you add the hydroxy group to form the alcohol. Isn't it ordinary propyl alcohol? Why don't you write the formula for 2-methyl-2-propanol and then remove the -OH to find the R- group? Then turn back to page 121 and choose another answer.

B

Incorrect. If an -OH group is added to the R- group you chose, the formula of the alcohol is

$$\begin{array}{c} CH_3 \\ | \\ CH_3CHCH_2OH \end{array}$$

This is the formula for 2-methyl-1-propanol, also called isobutyl alcohol. Make the change that is needed to transform it to 2-methyl-2-propanol. Then remove the -OH to leave the R- group. Now turn back to page 121 and choose another answer.

C

Right. If the -OH group is added, you have the complete formula for 2-methyl-2-propanol (*tert*-butyl alcohol).

$$\begin{array}{c} CH_3 \\ | \\ CH_3CCH_3 \\ | \\ OH \end{array}$$

2-methyl-2-propanol

Go on to page 123.

Aliphatic alcohols are often classified as primary, secondary, or tertiary. This classification is based on the number of carbon atoms joined to the carbon atom bearing the hydroxy group. This table illustrates the idea for some alcohols composed of four carbon atoms each.

Class of Alcohol	No. of C's joined to -OH carbon	Carbon Skeleton	Systematic name; Chemical Abstracts name
Primary	1	C—C—C—C—OH	1-butanol; butyl alcohol

Secondary	2	C—C—C—C
		     |
		    OH
			2-butanol; *sec*-butyl alcohol

Tertiary	3	C
		|
		C—C—C
		  |
		  OH
			2-methyl-2-propanol; *tert*-butyl alcohol

You can see that the name for all alcohols containing four carbon atoms is butyl alcohol: *sec*-butyl and *tert*-butyl are the names for the secondary and tertiary alcohols containing four carbon atoms. The systematic name for *tert*-butyl alcohol is 2-methyl-2-propanol.

The only exception to the definitions illustrated above is the simplest primary alcohol, methanol (CH_3OH). On the opposite side of this page are several skeleton formulas for alcohols. Classify each one as primary, secondary, or tertiary and write both the systematic name and acceptable common name if there is one. The correct answers are below each skeleton. Keep them covered until you are sure of your own answer.

1.

$$C-C-C-OH$$

Primary;   1-propanol (propyl alcohol)

2.

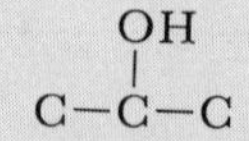

$$\overset{\displaystyle OH}{\underset{\displaystyle |}{C-C-C}}$$

Secondary; 2-propanol (isopropyl alcohol)

3.

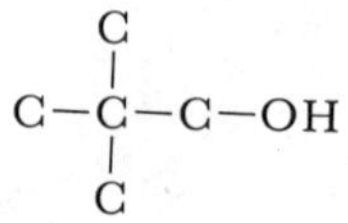

$$\overset{\displaystyle C}{\underset{\displaystyle |}{\underset{\displaystyle C}{C-C-C-OH}}}$$

Primary;   2,2-dimethyl-1-propanol

4.

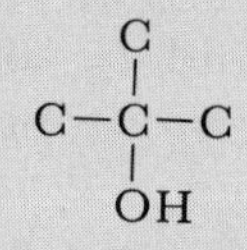

$$\overset{\displaystyle C}{\underset{\displaystyle |}{\underset{\displaystyle OH}{C-C-C}}}$$

Tertiary;   2-methyl-2-propanol (*tert*-butyl alcohol)

5.

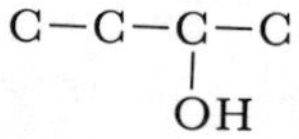

$$\underset{\displaystyle OH}{\underset{\displaystyle |}{C-C-C-C}}$$

Secondary;   2-butanol (*sec*-butyl alcohol)

Go on to page 125.

Procaine, widely used as a local anesthetic, is the hydrochloride of the ester of a substituted alcohol:

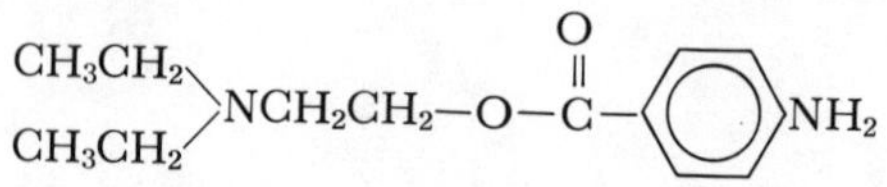

$$CH_3CH_2\!\!\diagdown\!\!N CH_2 CH_2-O-\overset{\displaystyle O}{\overset{\displaystyle \|}{C}}-\langle\bigcirc\rangle NH_2$$
$$CH_3CH_2\!\!\diagup$$

2-(diethylamino)ethyl p-aminobenzoate

There are some aliphatic alcohols that have two or three hydroxy groups. They are named by adding the suffixes -*diol* and -*triol* to the name of the parent hydrocarbon. The location of the hydroxy groups is specified by numbers in the usual way. Study these examples.

Condensed structural formula	Carbon skeleton	Systematic name; Name used by Chemical Abstracts
CH₂OHCH₂OH or HOCH₂CH₂OH	HO—C—C—OH	1,2-ethanediol; ethylene glycol
CH₃CHOHCH₂OH	C—C—C—OH | OH	1,2-propanediol; propylene glycol
CH₂OH | CHOH | CH₂OH	C—OH | C—OH | C—OH	1,2,3-propanetriol; glycerol or glycerine

The hydroxy groups in diols and triols are classified as primary, secondary, or tertiary in the same manner as the monohydroxy alcohols. As you can see by looking at its skeleton, glycerine has two primary and one secondary hydroxy groups.

The insect repellent marketed as "6-12" is named 2-ethyl-1,3-hexanediol. Which of these is the carbon skeleton of "6-12"?

A
$$\begin{array}{c} \text{OH} \\ | \\ \text{C–C–C–C–OH} \\ | \\ \text{C} \\ | \\ \text{C} \end{array}$$

B
$$\begin{array}{c} \text{OH} \\ | \\ \text{C–C–C–C–C–C–OH} \\ | \\ \text{C} \\ | \\ \text{C} \end{array}$$

C
$$\begin{array}{c} \text{OH} \\ | \\ \text{C–C–C–C–C–C–OH} \\ | \\ \text{C} \\ | \\ \text{C} \end{array}$$

A sweet-tasting substance found in the nuts of some trees is an alcohol. It is D-quercitol, or "acorn sugar." Its systematic name is 1,2,3,4,5-cyclohexanepentol.

$$\begin{array}{c} \text{OH} \\ \text{HO} \end{array} \bigcirc \begin{array}{c} \text{OH} \\ \text{OH} \\ \text{OH} \end{array}$$

A |||||||||||||||||||||||||||||||||||||||||||||||||||||||||||||||||||||||||||||||||||||||||||||||||||||||

Wrong. "6-12" is 2-ethyl-1,3-hexanediol. In order for it to be a derivative of hexane, there must be a continuous carbon chain of six atoms. The skeleton you chose has only six

$$
\begin{array}{ccccc}
 & & & \text{OH} & \\
 & & & | & \\
\overset{4}{C}-\overset{3}{C}-\overset{2}{C}-\overset{1}{C}-\text{OH} \\
 & & | \\
 & & C \\
 & & | \\
 & & C
\end{array}
$$

altogether. It represents 2-ethyl-1,3-butanediol. Turn back and choose another answer.

B |||||||||||||||||||||||||||||||||||||||||||||||||||||||||||||||||||||||||||||||||||||||||||||||||||||||

You are correct. The skeleton of "6-12" is

$$
\begin{array}{ccccccc}
 & & & & & \text{OH} & \\
 & & & & & | & \\
\overset{6}{C}-\overset{5}{C}-\overset{4}{C}-\overset{3}{C}-\overset{2}{C}-\overset{1}{C}-\text{OH} \\
 & & & & | \\
 & & & & C \\
 & & & & | \\
 & & & & C
\end{array}
$$

2-ethyl-1,3-hexanediol

One of the hydroxy groups is primary and the other is secondary. If you look closely, you can see that there is a continuous carbon chain that is seven carbon atoms long. Why isn't the compound named as a derivative of heptane? Simply because the seven-carbon chain does not include both of the functional groups. Go on to page 127.

C |||||||||||||||||||||||||||||||||||||||||||||||||||||||||||||||||||||||||||||||||||||||||||||||||||||||

You are incorrect. The skeleton you chose has all the atoms necessary to be 2-methyl-1,3-hexanediol, but they are not arranged properly. Here is the skeleton you picked.

$$
\begin{array}{ccccccc}
 & & & & \text{OH} & \\
 & & & & | & \\
\overset{6}{C}-\overset{5}{C}-\overset{4}{C}-\overset{3}{C}-\overset{2}{C}-\overset{1}{C}-\text{OH} \\
 & & & & | \\
 & & & & C \\
 & & & & | \\
 & & & & C
\end{array}
$$

Can you see that it represents 2-ethyl-1,2-hexanediol? Turn back and select another answer.

3.2 AROMATIC HYDROXY COMPOUNDS

Although hydroxy groups that are united directly to a benzene or other aromatic ring system react quite differently from the hydroxy groups in aliphatic alcohols, their names are conveniently discussed at this point.

The simplest aromatic hydroxy compound is *phenol* (fē′ nōl). Aqueous solutions of phenol are used as a disinfectant under the name carbolic acid. Derivatives are named as substituted phenols. A few examples are

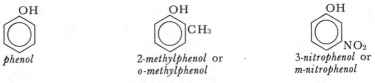

phenol

2-*methylphenol* or
o-*methylphenol*

3-*nitrophenol* or
m-*nitrophenol*

The common name for the three methylphenols is cresol.

Picric acid, a bitter-tasting compound which at times has been used both as a yellow dye and as a military explosive, has this structural formula

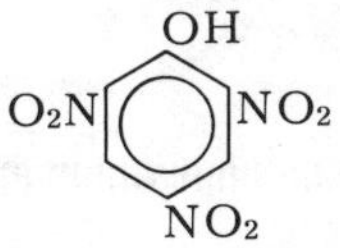

$$O_2N \quad \bigcirc \quad NO_2$$
OH

NO$_2$

What is its systematic name?

A

1-hydroxy-2,4,6-trinitrobenzene

B

trinitrophenol

C

2,4,6-trinitrophenol

A |||||||||||||||||||||||||||||||||||||||||||||||||||||||||||||||||||||||||||||||||||||||||||||||||||||||||||||||||||||||

If phenol were not an accepted systematic name, your answer would be right. Phenol, however, is a proper name and its derivatives are named as substituted phenols. It should be no trick for you to turn back and choose the correct answer.

B |||||||||||||||||||||||||||||||||||||||||||||||||||||||||||||||||||||||||||||||||||||||||||||||||||||||||||||||||||||||

You are wrong. Picric acid is indeed a trinitrophenol. There are, however, several separate and distinct trinitrophenols. They are distinguished by the use of numbers. Here is the formula of picric acid with numbers added.

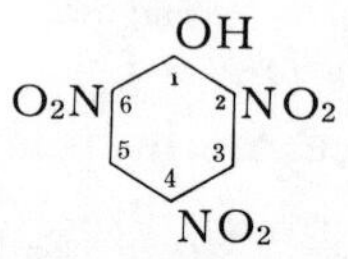

$$O_2N \underset{\underset{NO_2}{\overset{5 \quad 3}{\underset{4}{}}}}{\overset{OH}{\overset{1}{\underset{6 \quad 2}{}}}} NO_2$$

When you have decided on another answer, turn back to page 127 and see if it is there.

C |||||||||||||||||||||||||||||||||||||||||||||||||||||||||||||||||||||||||||||||||||||||||||||||||||||||||||||||||||||||

You are correct. The systematic name for picric acid is 2,4,6-trinitrophenol.

Go on to page 129.

Alcohols and phenols themselves can form radicals when the hydrogen atom is removed from the hydroxy group. Remember that these radicals are *not* compounds. They have a free valence. For the first four members of the aliphatic alcohols, the names of the radicals are formed by dropping the *-anol* portion and replacing it with *-oxy*. For the others, *-oxy* is added to the name of the alkyl group. Phenol forms the phenoxy radical or group. A few examples are the best illustration.

Alcohol		*Radical*	
$CH_3(CH_2)_3OH$	1-butanol	$CH_3(CH_2)_3O-$	butoxy
$CH_3(CH_2)_4OH$	1-pentanol	$CH_3(CH_2)_4O-$	pentyloxy
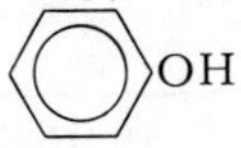 ⬡OH	phenol	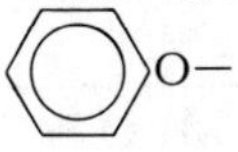 ⬡O—	phenoxy

As a very complex example of the use of the principles you have learned, compare the structure and systematic name of this compound.

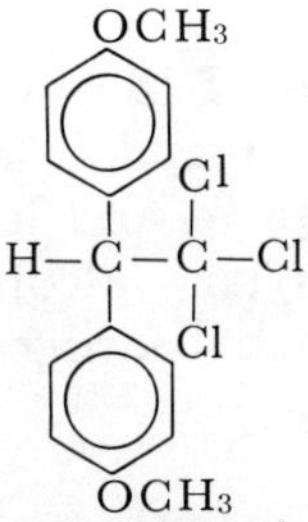

1,1,1-trichloro-2,2-bis(p-methoxyphenyl)ethane

This substance is sold under the name *methoxychlor*. It is an insecticide reported to be as effective as DDT but less toxic. DDT is 1,1,1-trichloro-2, 2-bis(*p*-chlorophenyl)ethane. If you want some practice, write the formula of DDT. You can check your formula against the one on page 105.

Summary: Nomenclature of Alcohols and Phenols

A functional group is a particular structure that imparts special chemical properties to a compound. An example of a functional group is the hydroxy group, -OH, which characterizes the alcohols and phenols. The general formula for aliphatic alcohols is ROH where R- represents an alkyl radical. Alkanols are named by replacing the -e ending of the name of the alkane by -ol. Two-word names such as "propyl alcohol" are used by *Chemical Abstracts* for the first twelve members of the alkanol series. These facts are illustrated by the following table.

Molecular formula:	C_2H_6O	Condensed structural formula:	CH_3CH_2OH
Systematic name:	ethanol	*Chemical Abstracts* name:	ethyl alcohol
General formula:	ROH	Radical:	CH_3CH_2O-

When necessary, the location of the hydroxy group is indicated by a number. The carbon chain is numbered from the end nearest the hydroxy group. Other substituents are named and located as in hydrocarbons.

Primary, secondary, and tertiary alcohols have one, two, or three carbon atoms united to the carbon bearing the hydroxy group as shown in these skeletons

$$\underset{primary}{C-C-C-OH} \qquad \underset{secondary}{C-\overset{\overset{OH}{|}}{C}-C} \qquad \underset{tertiary}{C-\overset{\overset{C}{|}}{\underset{\underset{C}{|}}{C}}-OH}$$

Alcohols with two or more hydroxy groups are named by locating the hydroxy groups with numbers and adding the suffixes -*diol*, -*triol*, and so forth, to the name of the alkane. The common name for the series of diols is glycos.

Hydroxybenzene, ⬡OH, is named phenol.

ALIPHATIC ALCOHOLS (ALKANOLS)

Functional group: -OH   Functional group name: *hydroxy*
General formula: ROH   Series name: -*ol*

PHENOLS

Functional group: -OH   Functional group name: *hydroxy*

General formula: ⬡OH Series name: -*ol*

Here are four questions to test your mastery of the naming of alcohols and phenols. As usual the correct answer follows each question. Cover the answers until you have worked out your own.

1. Write the carbon skeleton for 3-ethyl-4-methyl-2-hexanol.

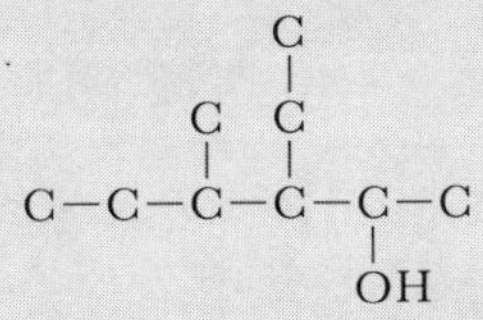

$$
\begin{array}{c}
\quad\quad\quad\quad C \\
\quad\quad\quad\quad | \\
\quad\quad C \quad C \\
\quad\quad | \quad | \\
C-C-C-C-C-C \\
\quad\quad\quad\quad | \\
\quad\quad\quad\quad OH
\end{array}
$$

2. Classify 3-methyl-2-butanol as primary, secondary, or tertiary.

$$
\begin{array}{c}
\quad\quad C \\
\quad\quad | \\
C-C-C-C \\
\quad\quad\quad | \\
\quad\quad\quad OH
\end{array}
$$

Secondary

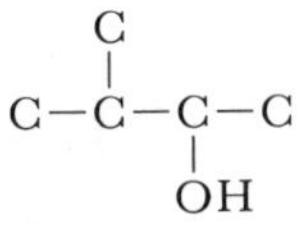

3. Give the structural formula for *p*-bromophenoxy radical

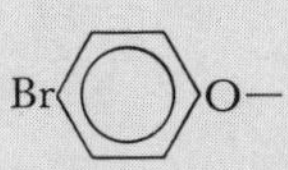

Br⟨◯⟩O—   (Be sure to indicate the free valence!)

4. The systematic name for ethylene glycol is 1,2-ethanediol. Write its complete structural formula and classify each hydroxy group as primary, secondary, or tertiary.

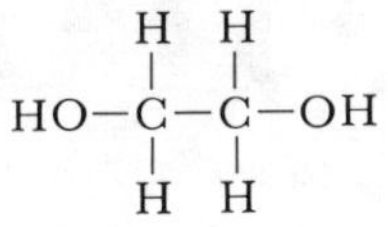

$$
\begin{array}{c}
\quad\; H \; H \\
\quad\; | \;\; | \\
HO-C-C-OH \\
\quad\; | \;\; | \\
\quad\; H \; H
\end{array}
$$
Both hydroxy groups are primary.

If you answered all four questions correctly, go on to page 133.
If you made errors, return to page 115 for review.

3.3 ALDEHYDES AND KETONES

The functional group which identifies aldehydes (ăl′ dĕ hīdz) and ketones (kē′ tōnz) is the *carbonyl* (kär′ bŏ nĭl) group, $-\overset{\overset{\displaystyle O}{\|}}{C}-$. When it occurs at the *end* of a chain of carbon atoms, the compound is an aldehyde. If the carbonyl group appears *within* the carbon atom chain, the compound is a ketone.

Since the carbonyl group in aldehydes always occurs at the end of a carbon atom chain, the general structural formula for the series is $R-\overset{\overset{\displaystyle O}{\|}}{C}-H$. When written on one line as a condensed structural formula, the aldehydes are represented by RCHO. The simplest aldehyde contains only one carbon atom. Its structural formula is $H-\overset{\overset{\displaystyle O}{\|}}{C}-H$. (You should note that in this one instance the R- in the general formula is merely H and not an alkyl radical.)

The IUPAC system names aldehydes by dropping the -*e* and adding -*al* to the name of the hydrocarbon with the longest chain containing the carbonyl group. Thus $H-\overset{\overset{\displaystyle O}{\|}}{C}-H$ is methanal. You are probably familiar with its common name, formaldehyde. In aqueous solutions it is used as a fungicide.

Another aldehyde, acetaldehyde, is an important chemical in organic synthesis. Its systematic name is ethanal. What is its structural formula?

A

$$H-\overset{\overset{\displaystyle H}{|}}{\underset{\underset{\displaystyle H}{|}}{C}}-\overset{\overset{\displaystyle H}{|}}{\underset{\underset{\displaystyle H}{|}}{C}}-\overset{\overset{\displaystyle O}{\|}}{C}-H$$

B

$$H-\overset{\overset{\displaystyle H}{|}}{\underset{\underset{\displaystyle H}{|}}{C}}-\overset{\overset{\displaystyle O}{\|}}{C}-H$$

C

$$H-\overset{\overset{\displaystyle H}{|}}{\underset{\underset{\displaystyle H}{|}}{C}}-\overset{\overset{\displaystyle O}{\|}}{C}-\overset{\overset{\displaystyle H}{|}}{\underset{\underset{\displaystyle H}{|}}{C}}-H$$

A ▌▌▌

Incorrect. You were asked to write the structural formula for ethanal. You should recognize that it is a derivative of ethane and therefore should have two carbon atoms. The formula you chose is

$$
\begin{array}{c}
\quad\ \text{H}\quad\ \text{H}\quad\ \text{O} \\
\quad\ |\quad\ |\quad\ \| \\
\text{H}-\text{C}-\text{C}-\text{C}-\text{H} \\
\quad\ |\quad\ | \\
\quad\ \text{H}\quad\ \text{H}
\end{array}
$$

It has three carbon atoms and is the formula for propanal. Turn back and choose another answer.

B ▌▌▌

You are right. The structural formula for the aldehyde ethanal is

$$
\begin{array}{c}
\quad\ \text{H}\quad\ \text{O} \\
\quad\ |\quad\ \| \\
\text{H}-\text{C}-\text{C}-\text{H} \\
\quad\ | \\
\quad\ \text{H}
\end{array}
$$

Go on to page 135.

C ▌▌▌

You are wrong on two counts. The structural formula you chose for ethanal is

$$
\begin{array}{c}
\quad\ \text{H}\quad\ \text{O}\quad\ \text{H} \\
\quad\ |\quad\ \|\quad\ | \\
\text{H}-\text{C}-\text{C}-\text{C}-\text{H} \\
\quad\ |\qquad\ | \\
\quad\ \text{H}\qquad\ \text{H}
\end{array}
$$

First of all, this formula has too many carbon atoms. Ethanal, a derivative of ethane, has only two. Second, the compound shown above is not an aldehyde. It is a ketone. Remember that the carbonyl group ($-\overset{\displaystyle \text{O}}{\overset{\|}{\text{C}}}-$) in aldehydes must be on the end of the carbon chain. Turn back to page 133 and choose another answer.

The common names of aldehydes are derived from the names of the acids that have the same number of carbon atoms. For example, the acid with one carbon atom is formic acid. The common name of methanal is formaldehyde. Acetaldehyde is the common name for ethanal since acetic acid has two carbon atoms.

Inasmuch as the carbonyl group of an aldehyde is always at the end of the carbon chain, it is never necessary to specify its position. For instance

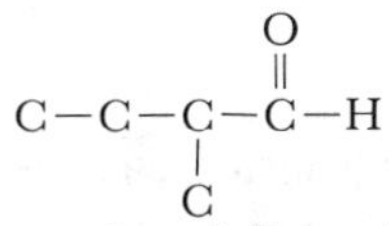

$$
\begin{array}{c}
\quad\quad\quad\quad O \\
\quad\quad\quad\quad \| \\
C-C-C-C-H \\
\quad\quad | \\
\quad\quad C \\
\end{array}
$$

2-methylbutanal

The condensed structural formula for 2-methylbutanal is $CH_3CH_2CH(CH_3)CHO$. The carbon of the carbonyl group is always the number one carbon atom.

Which of these formulas is a representation of 3-chloropentanal?

A

$CH_3CH_2CHClCH_2CHO$

B

$C_5H_{10}OCl$

C

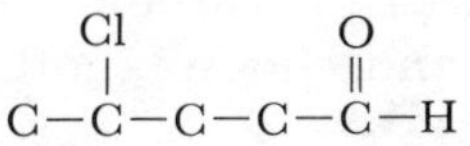

$$
\begin{array}{c}
Cl\quad\quad\quad\quad O \\
|\quad\quad\quad\quad \| \\
C-C-C-C-C-H \\
\end{array}
$$

Two aldehydes which occur in nature are tetradecanal and citronellal (3,7-dimethyl-6-octenal).

$CH_3(CH_2)_{12}CHO$

tetradecanal

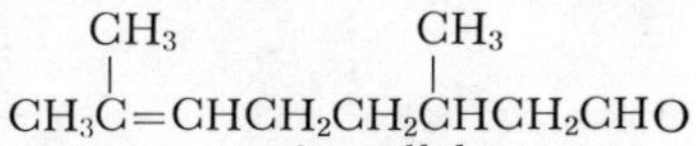

$$
\begin{array}{cc}
CH_3 & CH_3 \\
| & | \\
CH_3C=CHCH_2CH_2CHCH_2CHO \\
\end{array}
$$

citronellal

The luminous bacterium *Achrobacter fischeri* uses tetradecanal in its light-production process. Ants use citronellal as part of their chemical alarm system.

A ||||||||||||||||||||||||||||||||||||||||||||||||||||||||||||||||||||||||||||||||||||||||||||||||||||||||||||||

You are right. The condensed and skeleton formulas for 3-chloro-pentanal are

$$CH_3CH_2CHClCH_2CHO$$

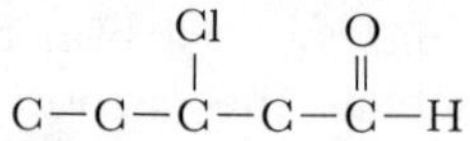

$$
\begin{array}{ccccc}
 & \overset{\displaystyle Cl}{|} & & \overset{\displaystyle O}{\|} & \\
C-C-C-C-C-H
\end{array}
$$

The carbon of the carbonyl group is always number 1. Go on to page 137.

B ||||||||||||||||||||||||||||||||||||||||||||||||||||||||||||||||||||||||||||||||||||||||||||||||||||||||||||||

You are incorrect. $C_5H_{10}OCl$ is not the molecular formula for 3-chloropentanal. Perhaps you will see your mistake if you make a structural formula by adding the requisite hydrogens to this skeleton formula.

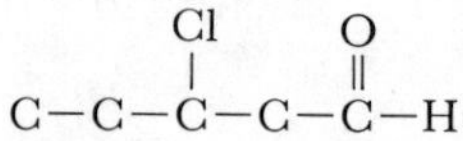

$$
\begin{array}{ccccc}
 & \overset{\displaystyle Cl}{|} & & \overset{\displaystyle O}{\|} & \\
C-C-C-C-C-H
\end{array}
$$

Now turn back and pick another answer.

C ||||||||||||||||||||||||||||||||||||||||||||||||||||||||||||||||||||||||||||||||||||||||||||||||||||||||||||||

You are wrong. This is not the skeleton formula for 3-chloropentanal.

$$
\begin{array}{ccccc}
 & \overset{\displaystyle Cl}{|} & & \overset{\displaystyle O}{\|} & \\
\underset{5}{C}-\underset{4}{C}-\underset{3}{C}-\underset{2}{C}-\underset{1}{C}-H
\end{array}
$$

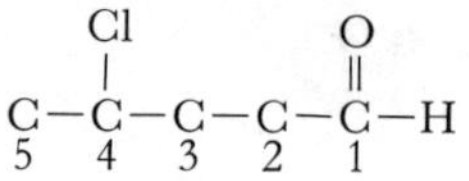

As you can see, the carbonyl carbon is number 1 and the chlorine atom is substituted on the number 4 carbon. This is the skeleton for 4-chloropentanal. Turn back and choose another answer.

$$\overset{\overset{\textstyle O}{\|}}{}$$

It is not possible for the —C—H group of aldehydes to be part of an aromatic ring system. Consequently, from a structural viewpoint, aromatic aldehydes are really substituted aliphatic aldehydes. The simplest and most common aromatic aldehyde has the formula

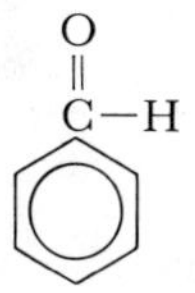

Name: *benzaldehyde*
Molecular formula: C_7H_6O

One important derivative of benzaldehyde is vanillin. It is the principal odorous constituent of vanilla beans. Its formula and systematic name are shown here.

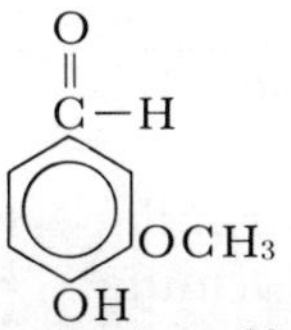

4-hydroxy-3-methoxybenzaldehyde

On the reverse of this page you will find three questions about aldehydes. After you have answered them, we will go on to the section on ketones.

The aldehyde known as ethylvanillin is said to have a finer and more intense flavor and odor than vanillin. Its formula and systematic name are shown here.

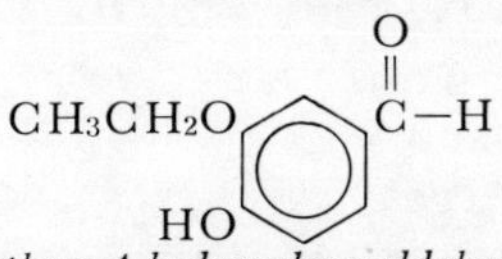

3-ethoxy-4-hydroxybenzaldehyde

1. The name 1-propanal is redundant. Why?

_____

The position of the carbonyl group does not have to be specified by a number in the names of aldehydes. The carbonyl group is always the number 1 carbon atom.

2. Write the carbon skeleton for 3,4-dimethylpentanal.

_____

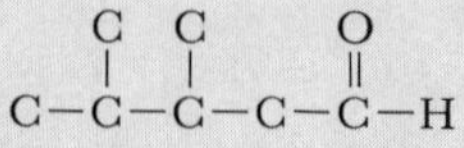

$$
\begin{array}{ccc}
\text{C} & \text{C} & \text{O} \\
| & | & \| \\
\text{C} - \text{C} - \text{C} - \text{C} - \text{C} - \text{H} & &
\end{array}
$$
3,4-dimethylpentanal

3. Write the general structural formula and the one-line condensed general formula for aldehydes.

_____

$$
\qquad\qquad\qquad\qquad\qquad\qquad \begin{array}{c} \text{O} \\ \| \end{array}
$$
General structural formula: $R - C - H$
Condensed general formula: RCHO (*not* RCOH.)

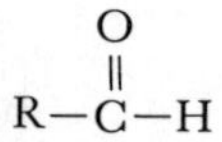

Depending on the state of your self-confidence, either go on to page 139 or turn back to page 133.

Ketones have the same functional group as aldehydes: the carbonyl

group, $-\overset{\overset{\displaystyle O}{\|}}{C}-$. The difference is that it is not at the end of the carbon

chain in ketones. The general formula for ketones is $R-\overset{\overset{\displaystyle O}{\|}}{C}-R'$.   The
condensed structural formula is RCOR'. If R- and R'- are identical, the
ketone is symmetrical. If R- and R'- represent two different alkyl groups,
the compound is a mixed ketone.

The IUPAC system names for ketones are found by numbering the
carbon chain from the end nearest the carbonyl group, indicating its
number, and changing the *-e* on the alkane to *-one*. For example

$$CH_3CH_2CH_2\overset{\overset{\displaystyle O}{\|}}{C}CH_3$$
2-pentanone

Substituent groups are named as before. For instance

$$CH_3\overset{\overset{\displaystyle Cl}{|}}{C}HCH_2\overset{\overset{\displaystyle O}{\|}}{C}CH_3$$
4-chloro-2-pentanone

What is the name of this ketone?

$$CH_3CH_2\overset{\overset{\displaystyle O}{\|}}{C}CH_2CH_2Br$$

A ||||||||||||||||||||||||||||||||||||||||||||||||||||||||||||||||||||||||||||||||||||||||||||||||||||||||||||||

5-bromo-3-pentanone

B ||||||||||||||||||||||||||||||||||||||||||||||||||||||||||||||||||||||||||||||||||||||||||||||||||||||||||||||

1-bromo-3-butanone

C ||||||||||||||||||||||||||||||||||||||||||||||||||||||||||||||||||||||||||||||||||||||||||||||||||||||||||||||

1-bromo-3-pentanone

One of the substances used as an antidote for cyanide
poisoning is a ketone.

$$CH_3CH_2\overset{\overset{\displaystyle O}{\|}}{C}\langle\bigcirc\rangle NH_2$$

p-aminopropiophenone, or
ethyl p-aminophenyl ketone

A ||||||||||||||||||||||||||||||||||||||||||||||||||||||||||||||||||||||||||||||||||||||||||||||||||||||||||||||||||

Incorrect. You named the compound shown by this formula

$$CH_3CH_2\overset{\overset{\displaystyle O}{\|}}{C}CH_2CH_2Br$$

as 5-bromo-3-pentanone. Although this name does describe the compound, there is another name that uses smaller numbers. Bear in mind that whenever you have a choice, you should always number the carbon chain from the end nearer to any substituent groups. Try again.

B ||||||||||||||||||||||||||||||||||||||||||||||||||||||||||||||||||||||||||||||||||||||||||||||||||||||||||||||||||||||||

Count the number of carbon atoms in this formula again.

$$CH_3CH_2\overset{\overset{\displaystyle O}{\|}}{C}CH_2CH_2Br$$

There are five, aren't there? The carbonyl group is the functional group, but it is also in the carbon chain and should be included when you count to determine the base name. The formula represents a pentanone. When you have decided on the complete name, turn back and choose another answer.

C |||||||||||||||||||||||||||||||||||||||||||||||||||||||||||||||||||||||||||||||||||||||||||||||||||||||||||||||||||

Right. Go on to page 141.

The less complex ketones are often named by naming the radicals united to the carbonyl group followed by the word ketone. If the ketone is symmetrical, only one radical needs to be named. You are probably familiar with the odor and uses of acetone. Its formula is $CH_3\overset{\overset{\textstyle O}{\|}}{C}CH_3$. Its systematic name is propanone, of course. In this instance no number is needed since the only carbon that can be the carbonyl group is number two. If either of the others were, the compound would be propanal, not propanone. Acetone is also called (incorrectly) dimethyl ketone.

Methyl ethyl ketone is a widely used organic solvent with a trade designation of MEK. Its structural formula and name are

$$CH_3\overset{\overset{\textstyle O}{\|}}{C}CH_2CH_3$$
butanone

Another widely used solvent is MIPK (methyl isopropyl ketone). Its preferred name is 3-methylbutanone. Which of the following is the carbon skeleton of MIPK?

A ||||||||||||||||||||||||||||||||||||||||||||||||||||||||||||||||||||||||||||||||||||||||||||||||||||||||||||||||||||||

$$\underset{\overset{\displaystyle |}{C}}{C-\overset{\overset{\textstyle O}{\|}}{C}-\overset{\overset{\textstyle C}{|}}{C}}$$

B ||||||||||||||||||||||||||||||||||||||||||||||||||||||||||||||||||||||||||||||||||||||||||||||||||||||||||||||||||||||

$$\underset{\overset{\displaystyle |}{C}}{C-\overset{\overset{\textstyle O}{\|}}{C}-C-C}$$

C ||||||||||||||||||||||||||||||||||||||||||||||||||||||||||||||||||||||||||||||||||||||||||||||||||||||||||||||||||||||

$$C-C-C-\overset{\overset{\textstyle O}{\|}}{C}-C$$

Civetone is a cyclic ketone which finds use as a perfume ingredient. It is obtained from the scent glands of the civet cat.

$$\begin{array}{c} H \\ \diagdown \\ C-(CH_2)_7 \\ \| \qquad\qquad \diagdown \\ \qquad\qquad\quad C{=}O \\ C-(CH_2)_7 \diagup \\ \diagup \\ H \end{array}$$

civetone

A ‖‖‖

You are correct. The skeleton formula of 3-methylbutanone is

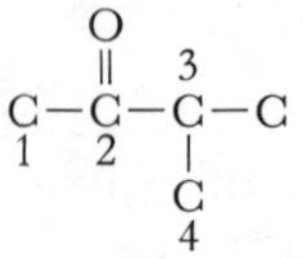

$$
\begin{array}{c}
\quad\quad\ \overset{\displaystyle O}{\underset{\displaystyle \parallel}{}}\ \ \ 3 \\
C-C-C-C \\
1\ \ 2\ \ \ \ |\\
\quad\quad\quad C \\
\quad\quad\quad 4
\end{array}
$$

The carbon chain is numbered from the end nearer to the carbonyl group. Go on to page 143.

B ‖‖‖

You are incorrect. Perhaps you were confused by the way the skeleton was written. Remember that any bends in the carbon chain are not significant. So the skeleton you chose could also be written in a straight line.

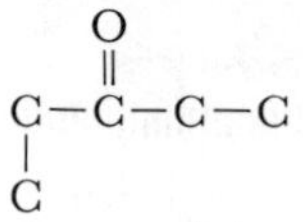

$$
\begin{array}{cc}
\overset{\displaystyle O}{\underset{\displaystyle \parallel}{}} & \overset{\displaystyle O}{\underset{\displaystyle \parallel}{}} \\
C-C-C-C & C-C-C-C-C \\
\ \ |\\
\ \ C \\
\textit{your choice} & \textit{same skeleton}
\end{array}
$$

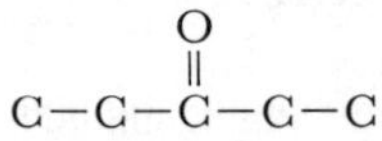

Both represent 3-pentanone, don't they? Turn back and choose another answer.

C ‖‖

Wrong. The skeleton you chose for 3-methylbutanone is

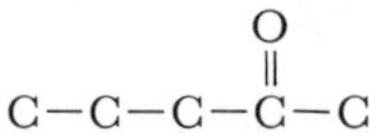

$$
\begin{array}{c}
\quad\quad\quad\ \overset{\displaystyle O}{\underset{\displaystyle \parallel}{}} \\
C-C-C-C-C
\end{array}
$$

Since all of the carbon atoms are contained in a single continuous chain, this is not a substituted ketone. It is plain old ordinary 2-pentanone, Read page 141 again carefully before you select another answer.

Two fairly common ketones are acetophenone and benzophenone. They are both used as intermediates in organic synthesis and to some extent in perfumery. Their formulas are

$$
\begin{array}{cc}
\underset{\substack{\text{methyl phenyl ketone} \\ \text{(acetophenone)}}}{CH_3C-\hexagon} & \underset{\substack{\text{phenyl ketone} \\ \text{(benzophenone)}}}{\hexagon-C-\hexagon}
\end{array}
$$

Note that the first is a mixed alkyl-aryl ketone while the second is an aryl (aromatic) ketone.

Summary: Nomenclature of Aldehydes and Ketones

Aldehydes are named by changing the *-e* ending of the parent hydrocarbon to *-al*. Since the carbonyl group is always at the end of the carbon chain, its position need not be specified by a number. When substituent groups require numbering, the carbonyl group is always numbered 1.

Ketones are named by changing the *-e* ending of the parent hydrocarbon to *-one*. The position of the $-\overset{\text{O}}{\overset{\|}{C}}-$ functional group is indicated by a number. The carbon chain is numbered from the end nearer the carbonyl group. Simple ketones are often given common names merely by naming the radicals attached to the $-\overset{\text{O}}{\overset{\|}{C}}-$ group.

ALCOHOLS

Functional group: -OH   Functional group name: *hydroxy*
General formula: ROH   Series name: *-ol*

PHENOLS

Functional group: -OH   Functional group name: *hydroxy*
General formula: $\hexagon$OH   Series name: *-ol*

ALDEHYDES AND KETONES

Functional group: $-\overset{\text{O}}{\overset{\|}{C}}-$ Functional group name: *carbonyl*
General formulas: RCHO (aldehydes)   Series names: *-al*
RCOR′ (ketones)   *-one*

There are three questions about aldehydes and ketones on the next page. Cover each answer in turn until you have made your own.

1. $CH_2ClCHClCOCH_3$ Is the name 3,4-dichlorobutanone correct?

Yes. The full structural formula is

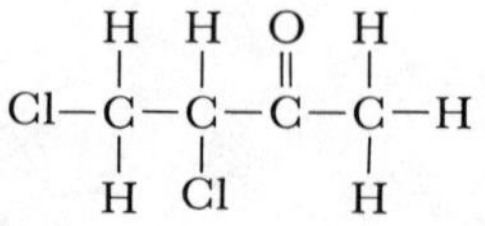

$$
\begin{array}{c}
\text{H}\ \ \text{H}\ \ \text{O}\ \ \text{H}\\
\vert\ \ \ \vert\ \ \ \Vert\ \ \ \vert\\
\text{Cl}-\text{C}-\text{C}-\text{C}-\text{C}-\text{H}\\
\vert\ \ \ \vert\ \ \ \ \ \ \ \vert\\
\text{H}\ \ \text{Cl}\ \ \ \ \ \text{H}
\end{array}
$$

2. Are these two compounds isomers?

CH_3COCH_3 CH_3CH_2CHO
propanone   *propanal*

Yes. Both have the molecular formula C_3H_6O.

3. Is this compound an aldehyde, ketone, or something else?

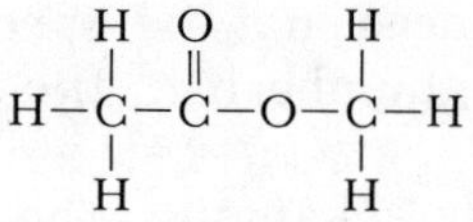

$$
\begin{array}{c}
\text{H}\ \ \text{O}\ \ \ \ \ \text{H}\\
\vert\ \ \ \Vert\ \ \ \ \ \ \vert\\
\text{H}-\text{C}-\text{C}-\text{O}-\text{C}-\text{H}\\
\vert\ \ \ \ \ \ \ \ \ \ \ \ \ \vert\\
\text{H}\ \ \ \ \ \ \ \ \ \ \text{H}
\end{array}
$$

Something else. It is a type of compound called an ester. The general formula is

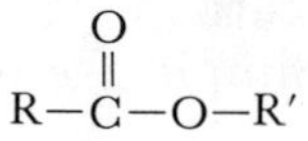

$$
\begin{array}{c}
\ \ \ \ \text{O}\\
\ \ \ \ \Vert\\
\text{R}-\text{C}-\text{O}-\text{R}'
\end{array}
$$

You'll see more of them later in this chapter.

Go on to page 145 if you feel ready. If not, return to page 133 for review.

3.4 CARBOXYLIC ACIDS

The carboxylic (kär bŏk sĭl′ ĭk) acids are one of several classes of organic acids. Since many of them were discovered through the hydrolysis of fats, some are called the fatty acids. Their functional group is

the carboxy (kär bŏk′ sē) group, $-\overset{\overset{\textstyle O}{\|}}{C}-OH$. Their general formula is

$R-\overset{\overset{\textstyle O}{\|}}{C}-OH$, condensed into one line as RCO_2H.

The unsubstituted carboxylic acids are slightly dissociated in water as illustrated by this equation

$$R-\overset{\overset{\textstyle O}{\|}}{C}-OH \quad = \quad R-\overset{\overset{\textstyle O}{\|}}{C}-O^- \quad + \quad H^+$$

carboxylic acid   *carboxylate ion*   *hydrogen ion*

Salts are formed when the carboxylic acids are neutralized by strong bases:

$$R-\overset{\overset{\textstyle O}{\|}}{C}-OH \ + \ NaOH \ = \ R-\overset{\overset{\textstyle O}{\|}}{C}-O^-Na^+ \ + \ H_2O$$

The systematic names of the acids are formed by dropping the *-e* from the name of the parent alkane and adding the suffix *-oic* followed by the word *acid*. All carbon atoms in the longest chain including the carboxy group are counted. The simplest of the series has the formula

$H-\overset{\overset{\textstyle O}{\|}}{C}-OH$, and takes the name methanoic acid.

What is the formula of ethanoic acid?

A ||||||||||||||||||||||||||||||||||||||||||||||||||||||||||||||||||||||||||||||||||||||||||||||||||||||||||||||||||||||

$$H-\overset{\overset{\textstyle H}{|}}{\underset{\underset{\textstyle H}{|}}{C}}-\overset{\overset{\textstyle O}{\|}}{C}-OH$$

B ||||||||||||||||||||||||||||||||||||||||||||||||||||||||||||||||||||||||||||||||||||||||||||||||||||||||||||||||||||||

$$H-\overset{\overset{\textstyle O}{\|}}{C}-\overset{\overset{\textstyle H}{|}}{\underset{\underset{\textstyle H}{|}}{C}}-OH$$

C ||||||||||||||||||||||||||||||||||||||||||||||||||||||||||||||||||||||||||||||||||||||||||||||||||||||||||||||||||||||

$$H-\overset{\overset{\textstyle H}{|}}{\underset{\underset{\textstyle H}{|}}{C}}-\overset{\overset{\textstyle H}{|}}{\underset{\underset{\textstyle H}{|}}{C}}-\overset{\overset{\textstyle O}{\|}}{C}-OH$$

A ‖‖

Correct. The formula for ethanoic acid is

$$
\begin{array}{cc}
\text{H} & \text{O} \\
| & \| \\
\text{H}-\text{C}-\text{C}-\text{OH} \\
| \\
\text{H}
\end{array}
$$

Its common name is acetic acid. Note again that the carbon atom in the carboxy group is counted as a member of the chain. Go on to page 147.

B ‖‖

Incorrect. The formula you chose contains the right number of carbon atoms, but not the correct functional group. The functional group

$$
\begin{array}{c}
\text{O} \\
\|
\end{array}
$$

of the carboxylic acids is —C—OH. It is called a carboxy group and is a carbonyl group with an hydroxy group attached to it. In your choice, shown again here

$$
\begin{array}{cc}
\text{O} & \text{H} \\
\| & | \\
\text{H}-\text{C}-\text{C}-\text{OH} \\
| \\
\text{H}
\end{array}
$$

the hydroxy group is not attached to the carbonyl group. The compound is not a carboxylic acid, but an hydroxy aldehyde. Turn back to page 145 and choose another answer.

C ‖‖

Wrong. The formula you chose for ethanoic acid is

$$
\begin{array}{ccc}
\text{H} & \text{H} & \text{O} \\
| & | & \| \\
\text{H}-\text{C}-\text{C}-\text{C}-\text{OH} \\
| & | \\
\text{H} & \text{H}
\end{array}
$$

$$
\begin{array}{c}
\text{O} \\
\|
\end{array}
$$

It is an acid, all right, because it has the —C—OH group. Count the carbon atoms. There are three in a continuous chain; therefore, it is propanoic acid. The carboxy group in a carboxylic acid is counted as a member of the carbon chain, just as the functional group is for aldehydes and ketones. Turn back and pick another answer.

The names of the carboxylate ions which result from dissociation of the acids are formed by dropping -*oic* from the name of the acid and adding the suffix -*oate*, followed by the word *ion*. The dissociation of ethanoic acid is an example

$$\underset{\textit{ethanoic acid}}{CH_3\overset{\overset{O}{\parallel}}{C}-OH} \quad = \quad \underset{\textit{ethanoate ion}}{CH_3\overset{\overset{O}{\parallel}}{C}-O^-} \quad + \quad \underset{\textit{hydrogen ion}}{H^+}$$

Most of the carboxylic acids were isolated from natural products before their structural similarities were understood. Consequently, all of the lower acids are usually known by common names. This table shows the origins of some of the names.

No. of Carbon Atoms	Acceptable common names	Origin of common names	Systematic names
1	formic acid	L. *formica*, ant	methanoic acid
2	acetic acid	L. *acetum*, vinegar	ethanoic acid
3	propionic acid	Gr. *proto*, first *pion*, fat	propanoic acid
4	butyric acid	L. *butyrum*, butter	butanoic acid
5	valeric acid	valerian root	pentanoic acid

Memorize the systematic names and the first two common names. You will learn the rest as you encounter them.

What is the systematic name of this carboxylate ion?

$$CH_3CH_2\overset{\overset{O}{\parallel}}{C}-O^-$$

A |||||||||||||||||||||||||||||||||||||||||||||||||||||||||||||||||||||||||

ethanoate ion

B |||||||||||||||||||||||||||||||||||||||||||||||||||||||||||||||||||||||||

propionate ion

C |||||||||||||||||||||||||||||||||||||||||||||||||||||||||||||||||||||||||

propanoate ion

A ||||||||||||||||||||||||||||||||||||||||||||||||||||||||||||||||||||||||||||||||||||||||||||||||||||||||||||||||||||||||||||||||||||||||||||||||||||

You are incorrect. This carboxylate ion is not the ethanoate ion

$$CH_3CH_2\overset{\displaystyle O}{\overset{\displaystyle \|}{C}}-O^-$$

The "ethan" portion of the name indicates two carbon atoms in the chain. The formula above has three. Turn back to page 147 and select another answer.

B ||||||||||||||||||||||||||||||||||||||||||||||||||||||||||||||||||||||||||||||||||||||||||||||||||||||||||||||||||||||||||||||||||||||||||||||||||||

If you were looking for a common name, you would be right. This is the formula for the propionate ion

$$CH_3CH_2\overset{\displaystyle O}{\overset{\displaystyle \|}{C}}-O^-$$

You were asked to give the systematic name. You should have no difficulty after reading the table on page 147 again.

C ||||||||||||||||||||||||||||||||||||||||||||||||||||||||||||||||||||||||||||||||||||||||||||||||||||||||||||||||||||||||||||||||||||||||||||||||||||

You are right. The formula represents the propanoate ion.

$$CH_3CH_2\overset{\displaystyle O}{\overset{\displaystyle \|}{C}}-O^-$$

It is identical to propanoic acid with the hydrogen of the carboxy group removed. Go on to page 149.

The method of locating substituent groups and unsaturation in carboxylic acids is to number the carbon chain in the usual fashion beginning with the carboxy group as number 1.

The skeleton of lactic acid, the acid formed when milk turns sour, is shown here.

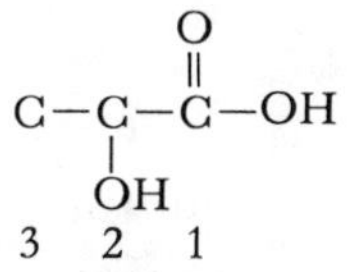

$$\underset{3\quad2\quad1}{\overset{\displaystyle\text{O}}{\underset{\overset{|}{\text{OH}}}{\text{C}-\text{C}-\overset{\|}{\text{C}}-\text{OH}}}}$$

2-hydroxypropanoic acid
(lactic acid)

What is the preferred name of the acid with this skeleton?

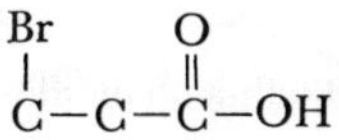

$$\overset{\text{Br}\qquad\text{O}}{\underset{}{\text{C}-\overset{|}{\text{C}}-\overset{\|}{\text{C}}-\text{OH}}}$$

A ||||||||||||||||||||||||||||||||||||||||||||||||||||||||||||||||||||||||||||||||||||||||||||||||||||||

2-bromopropanoic acid

B ||||||||||||||||||||||||||||||||||||||||||||||||||||||||||||||||||||||||||||||||||||||||||||||||||||||

3-bromopropanoic acid

C ||||||||||||||||||||||||||||||||||||||||||||||||||||||||||||||||||||||||||||||||||||||||||||||||||||||

3-bromopropionic acid

A ||||||||||||||||||||||||||||||||||||||||||||||||||||||||||||||||||||||||||||||||||||||||||||||||||||||||||||||

You are incorrect. This skeleton does not represent 2-bromopropanoic acid

$$\begin{array}{ccc} Br & & O \\ | & & || \\ \underset{3}{C}-\underset{2}{C}-\underset{1}{C}-OH \end{array}$$

Numbers have been added so you can see that the carboxy group is always number 1. Study the skeleton before you turn back to choose another answer.

B ||||||||||||||||||||||||||||||||||||||||||||||||||||||||||||||||||||||||||||||||||||||||||||||||||||||||||||||

You are right. The skeleton represents 3-bromopropanoic acid. Go on to page 151.

C ||||||||||||||||||||||||||||||||||||||||||||||||||||||||||||||||||||||||||||||||||||||||||||||||||||||||||||||

If you had been asked to give a common name, you'd be right. 3-bromopropionic acid, however, is not the systematic name. Propionic acid is the common name for propanoic acid.

$$\begin{array}{c} O \\ || \\ C-C-C-OH \end{array}$$
propanoic acid

3-bromopropionic acid is 3-bromopropanoic acid. Be careful to distinguish between systematic and common names. Go on to page 151.

You are familiar with at least two oxides of carbon: carbon monoxide, CO, and carbon dioxide, CO_2. The former is the poisonous product of incomplete combustion, and the latter is a product of human respiration. Have you ever heard of the oxide of carbon with the formula $C_{12}O_9$?

It is the tri-anhydride of benzenehexacarboxylic acid (mellitic acid) and is called mellitic anhydride. It can be prepared by heating mellitic acid, itself prepared by oxidizing wood charcoal with fuming nitric acid or by treating graphite with potassium permanganate.

mellitic acid

mellitic anhydride

Unsaturation in carboxylic acids is indicated by changing the *-anoic* ending of the basic name to *-enoic* (*cf.* alkenes) and prefixing the lower number of the two carbon atoms joined by the double bond. For instance

$$CH_3CH_2CH{=}CHCH_2CO_2H$$
3-hexenoic acid

If an acid has two or more double bonds, the ending of the name is changed to *-dienoic, -trienoic,* and so on.

Among the higher carboxylic acids, (*i.e.,* those with larger numbers of carbon atoms) only the ones with an even number of carbon atoms in the chain have common names because they are the ones that are found in natural fats. The most widely distributed fatty acid has the common name oleic acid. Its systematic name is 9-octadecenoic acid and its skeleton is

$$\overset{\displaystyle O}{\overset{\displaystyle \|}{C-C-C-C-C-C-C-C-C=C-C-C-C-C-C-C-C-C-OH}}$$
9-octadecenoic acid (oleic acid)

The most important unsaturated fatty acids have 18 carbon atoms, with one of their double bonds placed in the middle of the chain as in oleic acid. If other carbon-carbon double bonds are present, they lie farther from the carboxy group.

A typical sample of butter contains 4 to 5 per cent linoleic acid. Its skeleton is

$$\overset{\displaystyle O}{\overset{\displaystyle \|}{C-C-C-C-C-C=C-C-C=C-C-C-C-C-C-C-C-C-OH}}$$

What is its systematic name?

A ||||||||||||||||||||||||||||||||||||||||||||||||||||||||||||||||||||||||||||||||||||||||||||||||||||||||

9,12-octadecadienoic acid

B ||||||||||||||||||||||||||||||||||||||||||||||||||||||||||||||||||||||||||||||||||||||||||||||||||||||||

9,12-octadecenoic acid

C ||||||||||||||||||||||||||||||||||||||||||||||||||||||||||||||||||||||||||||||||||||||||||||||||||||||||

9,12-heptadecadienoic acid

A ||||||||||||||||||||||||||||||||||||||||||||||||||||||||||||||||||||||||||||||||||||||||||||||||||||||||||||||||||||||||||||||||

You are right. The systematic name of linoleic acid is 9,12-octa-decadienoic acid. Just for review, analyze the parts of the name and what they indicate:

-oic acid	carboxylic acid with $-\overset{\displaystyle O}{\overset{\displaystyle \|}{C}}-OH$
-dien-	two double bonds
-octadeca-	18 carbon atoms
9,12-	double bonds in 9-10 and 12-13 positions

Go on to page 153.

B ||||||||||||||||||||||||||||||||||||||||||||||||||||||||||||||||||||||||||||||||||||||||||||||||||||||||||||||||||||||||||||||||

Incorrect. You chose 9,12-octadecenoic acid as the systematic name for linoleic acid. The basic name is all right and you have the correct numbers, but you left out the signal that indicates the presence of two double bonds. Read page 151 again to learn what it is. Then pick another answer.

C ||||||||||||||||||||||||||||||||||||||||||||||||||||||||||||||||||||||||||||||||||||||||||||||||||||||||||||||||||||||||||||||||

You are incorrect. The systematic name for linoleic acid is not 9, 12-heptadecadienoic acid. Your mistake was a simple one that you can avoid by remembering that all of the naturally occurring fatty acids have an *even* number of carbon atoms. Turn back, count again, and choose another answer.

The most abundant fatty acid is palmitic acid. Its systematic name is hexadecanoic acid. What is its molecular formula?

A ||||||||||||||||||||||||||||||||||||||||||||||||||||||||||||||||||||||||||||||||||||||||||||||||||||||||||||||||||||||||||||||

$C_{16}H_{33}O$

B ||||||||||||||||||||||||||||||||||||||||||||||||||||||||||||||||||||||||||||||||||||||||||||||||||||||||||||||||||||||||||||||

$C_{16}H_{32}O_2$

C ||||||||||||||||||||||||||||||||||||||||||||||||||||||||||||||||||||||||||||||||||||||||||||||||||||||||||||||||||||||||||||||

$C_{16}H_{33}O_2$

A new class of broad-spectrum antibiotics, the cephalo-sporins, was announced in 1964. One member is Cephalothin, a chemical modification of cephalosporin C, which is produced by the *Cephalosporium* fungus. The compound is represented by this formula:

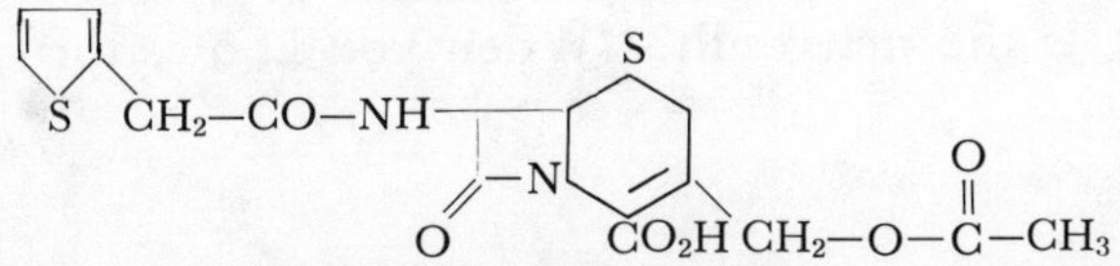

It is indexed by *Chemical Abstracts* as 3-methoxycarbonyl-methyl-8-oxo-7-[2-thenylacetamido]-5-thia-1-azabicyclo[4.2.0]-oct-2-ene-2-carboxylic acid. Fortunately for physicians, we also have generic names such as Cephalothin.

A ||||||||||||||||||||||||||||||||||||||||||||||||||||||||||||||||||||||||||||||||||||||||||||||||||||||||||||||||||||||

Incorrect. You chose the molecular formula $C_{16}H_{33}O$ to represent palmitic or hexadecanoic acid. Since a carboxylic acid has the carboxy group,

$$-\overset{\overset{\displaystyle O}{\|}}{C}-OH,$$

as its functional group, the molecular formula must contain at least two oxygen atoms. Perhaps it will help you to write a skeleton or structural formula before turning back to choose another answer.

B ||||||||||||||||||||||||||||||||||||||||||||||||||||||||||||||||||||||||||||||||||||||||||||||||||||||||||||||||||||||

You are correct. The molecular formula of hexadecanoic acid is $C_{16}H_{32}O_2$. Its structural formula is

$$H-\overset{\overset{\displaystyle H}{|}}{\underset{\underset{\displaystyle H}{|}}{C}}-\overset{\overset{\displaystyle H}{|}}{\underset{\underset{\displaystyle H}{|}}{C}}-\overset{\overset{\displaystyle H}{|}}{\underset{\underset{\displaystyle H}{|}}{C}}-\overset{\overset{\displaystyle H}{|}}{\underset{\underset{\displaystyle H}{|}}{C}}-\overset{\overset{\displaystyle H}{|}}{\underset{\underset{\displaystyle H}{|}}{C}}-\overset{\overset{\displaystyle H}{|}}{\underset{\underset{\displaystyle H}{|}}{C}}-\overset{\overset{\displaystyle H}{|}}{\underset{\underset{\displaystyle H}{|}}{C}}-\overset{\overset{\displaystyle H}{|}}{\underset{\underset{\displaystyle H}{|}}{C}}-\overset{\overset{\displaystyle H}{|}}{\underset{\underset{\displaystyle H}{|}}{C}}-\overset{\overset{\displaystyle H}{|}}{\underset{\underset{\displaystyle H}{|}}{C}}-\overset{\overset{\displaystyle H}{|}}{\underset{\underset{\displaystyle H}{|}}{C}}-\overset{\overset{\displaystyle H}{|}}{\underset{\underset{\displaystyle H}{|}}{C}}-\overset{\overset{\displaystyle H}{|}}{\underset{\underset{\displaystyle H}{|}}{C}}-\overset{\overset{\displaystyle H}{|}}{\underset{\underset{\displaystyle H}{|}}{C}}-\overset{\overset{\displaystyle H}{|}}{\underset{\underset{\displaystyle H}{|}}{C}}-\overset{\overset{\displaystyle O}{\|}}{C}-OH$$

Go on to page 155.

C ||||||||||||||||||||||||||||||||||||||||||||||||||||||||||||||||||||||||||||||||||||||||||||||||||||||||||||||||||||||||||||

You are incorrect. The molecular formula for hexadecanoic, or palmitic, acid is not $C_{16}H_{33}O_2$. Would you like to know an easy way to find the right formula? First, take the saturated hydrocarbon with 16 carbon atoms. Using the general formula that you have already learned (C_nH_{2n+2}), you can write its molecular formula as $C_{16}H_{34}$. Now look at the terminal carbon atom. It changes from a methyl group to a carboxy group.

$$-\overset{\overset{\displaystyle H}{|}}{\underset{\underset{\displaystyle H}{|}}{C}}-H \qquad\qquad -\overset{\overset{\displaystyle O}{\|}}{C}-OH$$

methyl group   *carboxy group*

Two oxygen atoms are added and the number of hydrogen atoms decreases by two. What is the net result? When you know, turn back and select another answer.

As you might imagine, the composition of a natural fat like butter varies somewhat. Here are the amounts of different fatty acids obtained by hydrolysis of a typical sample of butter.

Systematic name	Common name	Per cent
butanoic	butyric	3—4
hexanoic	caproic	1—2
octanoic	caprylic	1
decanoic	capric	2—3
dodecanoic	lauric	2—3
tetradecanoic	myristic	7—9
hexadecanoic	palmitic	23—26
octadecanoic	stearic	10—13
9-hexadecenoic	palmitoleic	5
9-octadecenoic	oleic	30—40
9,12-octadecadienoic	linoleic	4—5

On the next page are some practice problems on naming carboxylic acids. Cover each answer until you have decided on your own.

1. Name and give the structural formula for the functional group of the carboxylic acids.

Carboxy group; $-\overset{\overset{\text{O}}{\|}}{\text{C}}-\text{OH}$

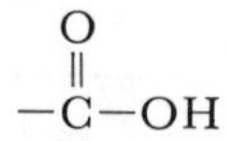

2. What is the systematic name of this acid?

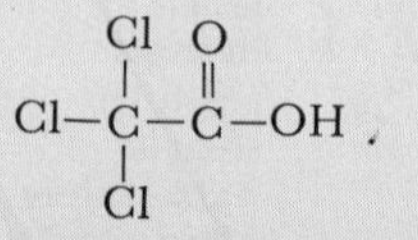

$$\text{Cl}-\overset{\overset{\text{Cl}}{|}}{\underset{\underset{\text{Cl}}{|}}{\text{C}}}-\overset{\overset{\text{O}}{\|}}{\text{C}}-\text{OH} \; ,$$

Trichloroethanoic acid (not 2,2,2-trichloroethanoic acid. Numbers are not needed since there is no other place for the three Cl's.)

3. The insecticide 1080 is the sodium salt of fluoroethanoic acid. What is its structural formula?

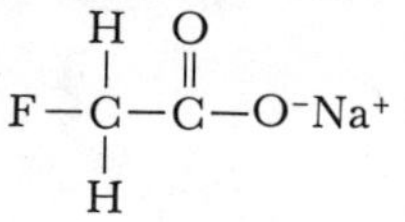

$$\text{F}-\overset{\overset{\text{H}}{|}}{\underset{\underset{\text{H}}{|}}{\text{C}}}-\overset{\overset{\text{O}}{\|}}{\text{C}}-\text{O}^-\text{Na}^+$$

4. Write as many kinds of formula as you can for 4-bromo-2-butenoic acid.

Molecular: $C_4H_5O_2Br$ Structural: $\text{Br}-\overset{\overset{\text{H}}{|}}{\underset{\underset{\text{H}}{|}}{\text{C}}}-\overset{\overset{\text{H}}{|}}{\text{C}}=\overset{\overset{\text{H}}{|}}{\text{C}}-\overset{\overset{\text{O}}{\|}}{\text{C}}-\text{OH}$

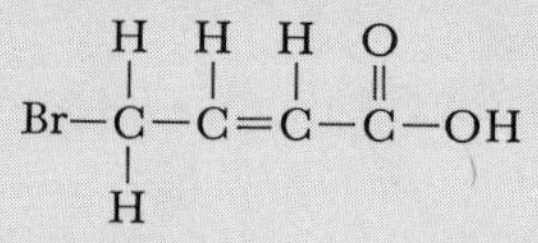

Condensed: $CH_2BrCH{=}CHCO_2H$ Skeleton: $\text{Br}-\text{C}-\text{C}=\text{C}-\overset{\overset{\text{O}}{\|}}{\text{C}}-\text{OH}$

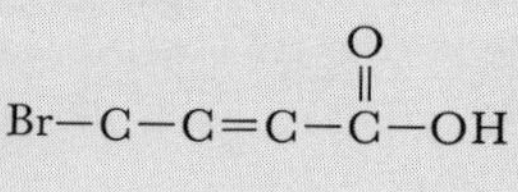

Go on to page 157 if you feel sure of yourself. If not, go back to page 145 for review.

Several of the important carboxylic acids have two carboxy groups. They are known as dicarboxylic acids. Their common names are in general use. The first four dicarboxylic acids are shown in this table. *Chemical Abstracts* uses the common names for both the unsubstituted and substituted acids.

Fomula	Common name*	Systematic name
HO_2CCO_2H	oxalic acid	1,2-ethanedioic acid
$HO_2CCH_2CO_2H$	malonic acid	1,3-propanedioic acid
$HO_2C(CH_2)_2CO_2H$	succinic acid	1,4-butanedioic acid
$HO_2C(CH_2)_3CO_2H$	glutaric acid	1,5-pentanedioic acid

Malic acid, the common name for a constituent of many fruit juices, has the formula

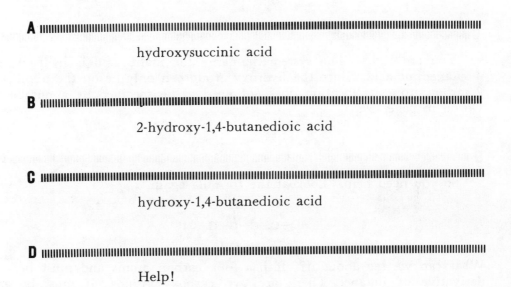

What is its name according to the system?

A ‖‖

hydroxysuccinic acid

B ‖‖

2-hydroxy-1,4-butanedioic acid

C ‖‖

hydroxy-1,4-butanedioic acid

D ‖‖

Help!

*The common names for the next five members of the series are adipic, pimelic, suberic, azelaic, and sebacic. *Chemical Abstracts* uses these names for the unsubstituted acids only. One mnemonic for the names is "Oh, My, Such Good Apple Pie; Sweet As Sugar."

A |||||||||||||||||||||||||||||||||||||||||||||||||||||||||||||||||||||||||||||||||||||||||||||||||||||||||||||||||||||

You seem to be confused over the difference between systematic names and common names. Succinic acid is the common name for 1, 4-butanedioic acid. Even though malic acid is hydroxysuccinic acid, that is not its preferred systematic name. Turn back and select another answer.

B |||||||||||||||||||||||||||||||||||||||||||||||||||||||||||||||||||||||||||||||||||||||||||||||||||||||||||||||||||||

Your answer is that the preferred name for malic acid is 2-hydroxy-1, 4-butanedioic acid. Here is its formula again.

$$\underset{\displaystyle \underset{H}{\overset{\displaystyle \overset{O}{\|}}{C}}}{HO-C} $$

HO—C—C—C—C—OH with O, H, H, O above and H, OH below

Is there any way that the hydroxy group could be on a carbon other than number 2? No, there isn't. Consequently, the name for malic acid is just hydroxy-1,4-butanedioic acid. Go on to page 159.

C |||||||||||||||||||||||||||||||||||||||||||||||||||||||||||||||||||||||||||||||||||||||||||||||||||||||||||||||||||||

You are right. The systematic name for malic acid is hydroxy-1, 4-butanedioic acid. Since the hydroxy group can only be on the number 2 carbon atom, its location does not need to be specified by a number. Go on to page 159.

D |||||||||||||||||||||||||||||||||||||||||||||||||||||||||||||||||||||||||||||||||||||||||||||||||||||||||||||||||||||

So you need help. Look at the formula again.

HO—C—C—C—C—OH with O, H, H, O above and H, OH below

What can we see about it? It has four carbon atoms and must be a derivative of butane. There are two carboxy groups. It must be a butanedioic acid. Finally, there is an hydroxy (—OH) group on one of the other carbon atoms. Put all of these facts together and you should be able to give the correct name. Read page 157 again and select another answer.

You should remember that there are no aromatic aldehydes in which the carbonyl group is part of the ring system. The same holds true for aromatic carboxylic acids. The simplest aromatic acid is benzoic acid. Its structural formula is

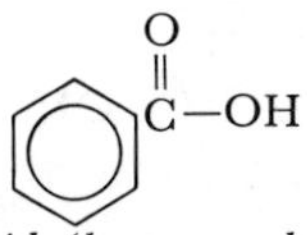

benzoic acid (benzenecarboxylic acid)

Aromatic carboxylic acids with two or more carboxy groups are named as dicarboxylic, tricarboxylic, etc., acids. The three benzenedicarboxylic acids are important in commerce. They are shown here.

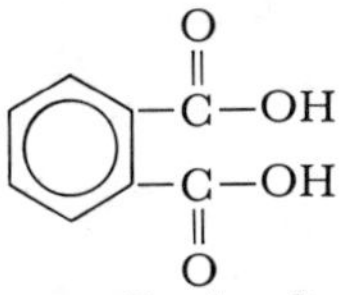

o-benzenedicarboxylic acid
(phthalic acid)

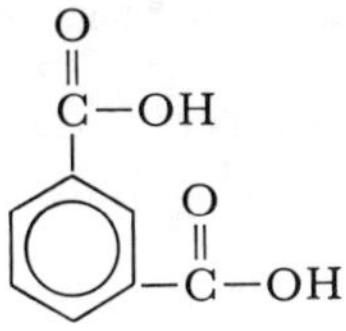

m-benzenedicarboxylic acid
(isophthalic acid)

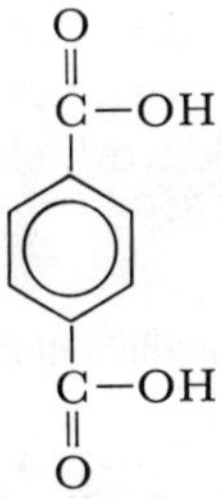

p-benzenedicarboxylic acid
(terephthalic acid)

Terephthalic acid is a component of the textile polymer Dacron (Terylene).

Salicylic acid, an analgesic related to aspirin, is *o*-hydroxybenzoic acid. Which of these is its formula?

A

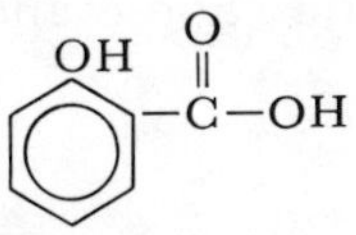

B

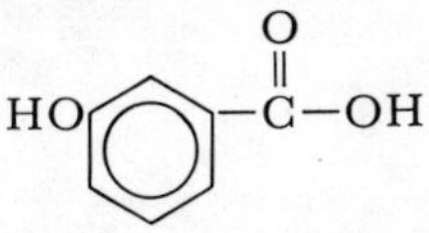

C

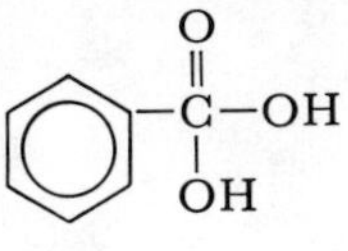

A ||||||||||||||||||||||||||||||||||||||||||||||||||||||||||||||||||||||||||||||||||||||||||||||||||||||||||||||||||||||||||

You are correct. The structural formula for salicylic acid, or *o*-hydroxybenzoic acid, is

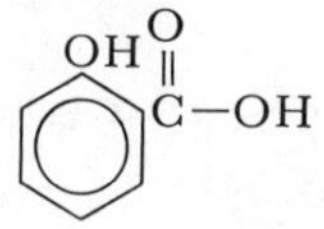

The carbons to which the two substituent groups are attached are adjacent, or *ortho-*, to each other. Go on to page 161.

B ||||||||||||||||||||||||||||||||||||||||||||||||||||||||||||||||||||||||||||||||||||||||||||||||||||||||||||||||||||||||||

You are incorrect. You have selected this structural formula to represent *o*-hydroxybenzoic acid.

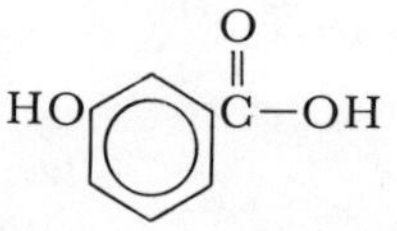

The two carbons which bear substituent groups are not adjacent, are they? They are *meta-* to each other. This is the formula for *meta*-hydroxybenzoic acid. Turn back and choose another answer.

C ||||||||||||||||||||||||||||||||||||||||||||||||||||||||||||||||||||||||||||||||||||||||||||||||||||||||||||||||||||||||||

You have pulled a real boner. You picked this formula for *o*-hydroxybenzoic acid.

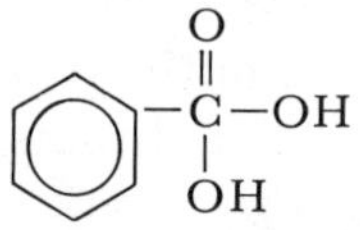

What's wrong with it? First, count the covalent bonds on the carbon atom in the carboxy group. There are five and that's one too many. Read page 159 again before you choose another answer.

Under certain conditions, two molecules of a monobasic carboxylic acid will lose a single molecule of water to form an anhydride. This equation shows the formation of ethanoic anhydride.

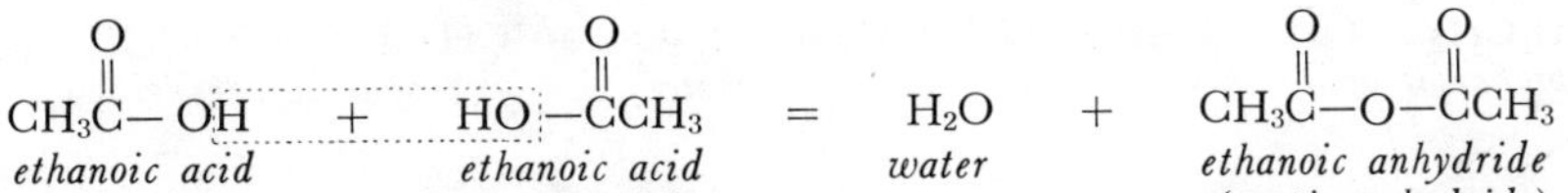

$$\underset{\substack{\textit{ethanoic acid}\\(\textit{acetic acid})}}{CH_3\overset{\overset{O}{\|}}{C}- OH} \quad + \quad \underset{\substack{\textit{ethanoic acid}\\(\textit{acetic acid})}}{HO -\overset{\overset{O}{\|}}{C}CH_3} \quad = \quad \underset{\textit{water}}{H_2O} \quad + \quad \underset{\substack{\textit{ethanoic anhydride}\\(\textit{acetic anhydride})}}{CH_3\overset{\overset{O}{\|}}{C}-O-\overset{\overset{O}{\|}}{C}CH_3}$$

Anhydrides are named merely by using the word *anhydride* in place of the word *acid*.

Occasionally, an anhydride will be formed from molecules of two different acids. For example

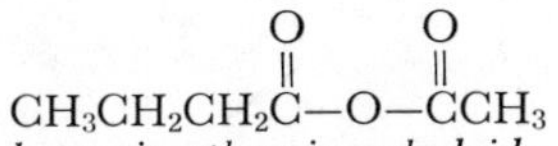

$$\underset{\textit{butanoic ethanoic anhydride}}{CH_3CH_2CH_2\overset{\overset{O}{\|}}{C}-O-\overset{\overset{O}{\|}}{C}CH_3}$$

Several dibasic acids form their anhydrides by losing a molecule of water from one molecule of the acid. This equation shows the formation of phthalic anhydride.

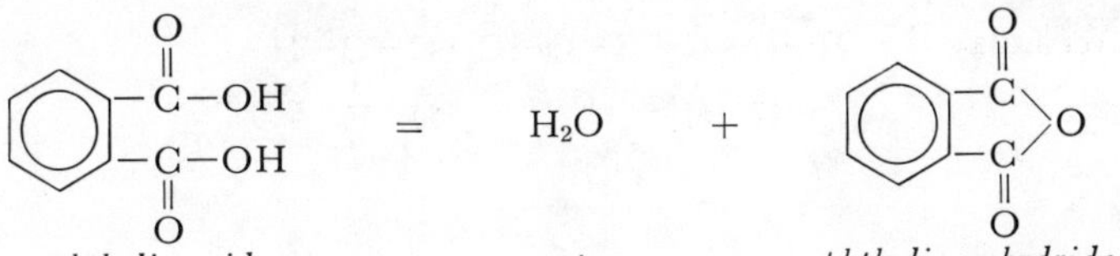

phthalic acid   =   *water*   +   *phthalic anhydride*

Below, write as many formulas as you can for propanoic anhydride. When you have finished, turn to the next page to check your answers.

Formulas for propanoic anhydride:

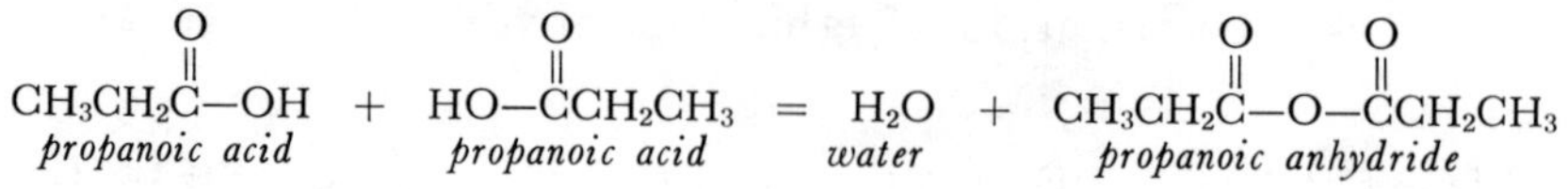

$$\underset{\textit{propanoic acid}}{CH_3CH_2\overset{\displaystyle O}{\overset{\|}{C}}{-}OH} \ + \ \underset{\textit{propanoic acid}}{HO{-}\overset{\displaystyle O}{\overset{\|}{C}}CH_2CH_3} \ = \ \underset{\textit{water}}{H_2O} \ + \ \underset{\textit{propanoic anhydride}}{CH_3CH_2\overset{\displaystyle O}{\overset{\|}{C}}{-}O{-}\overset{\displaystyle O}{\overset{\|}{C}}CH_2CH_3}$$

Condensed formula: $CH_3CH_2\overset{\displaystyle O}{\overset{\|}{C}}{-}O{-}\overset{\displaystyle O}{\overset{\|}{C}}CH_2CH_3$

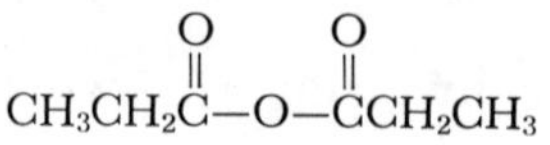

Alternate condensed formula: $(CH_3CH_2CO)_2O$

Molecular formula: $C_6H_{10}O_3$

Skeleton: $C{-}C{-}\overset{\displaystyle O}{\overset{\|}{C}}{-}O{-}\overset{\displaystyle O}{\overset{\|}{C}}{-}C{-}C$

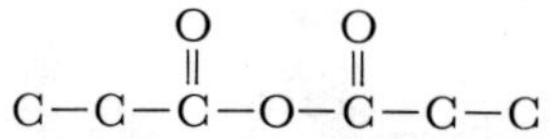

Structural formula:

$$H{-}\overset{\displaystyle H}{\underset{\displaystyle H}{\overset{|}{\underset{|}{C}}}}{-}\overset{\displaystyle H}{\underset{\displaystyle H}{\overset{|}{\underset{|}{C}}}}{-}\overset{\displaystyle O}{\overset{\|}{C}}{-}O{-}\overset{\displaystyle O}{\overset{\|}{C}}{-}\overset{\displaystyle H}{\underset{\displaystyle H}{\overset{|}{\underset{|}{C}}}}{-}\overset{\displaystyle H}{\underset{\displaystyle H}{\overset{|}{\underset{|}{C}}}}{-}H$$

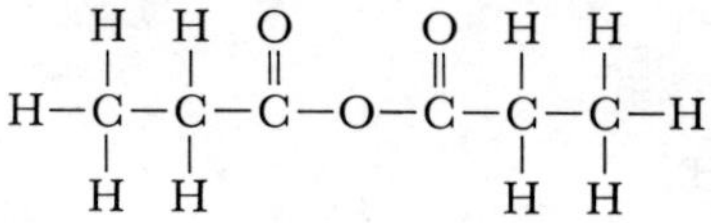

Turn to page 163.

In general, carboxylic acids do not react rapidly with other organic compounds. Chemists have found that the reactivity is enhanced if the -OH group of the acid is replaced by a halogen, usually chlorine. The family are named the acyl (alkanoyl) halides and their general formula is:

$$\underset{\text{R}-\overset{\displaystyle\text{O}}{\overset{\|}{\text{C}}}-\text{X}}{}\qquad\underset{\textit{acetic acid}}{\text{CH}_3\overset{\displaystyle\text{O}}{\overset{\|}{\text{C}}}-\text{OH}}\qquad\underset{\textit{acetyl chloride}}{\text{CH}_3\overset{\displaystyle\text{O}}{\overset{\|}{\text{C}}}-\text{Cl}}$$

Because the compounds were in widespread use before the adoption of the IUPAC system, the names of the first five acyl radicals are based on the common names of the acids. This table shows the names and formulas of the acids and acyl radicals.

Acid	Name	Acyl radical	Name
$\text{H}-\overset{\text{O}}{\overset{\|}{\text{C}}}-\text{OH}$	formic acid	$\text{H}-\overset{\text{O}}{\overset{\|}{\text{C}}}-$	formyl
$\text{CH}_3\overset{\text{O}}{\overset{\|}{\text{C}}}-\text{OH}$	acetic acid	$\text{CH}_3\overset{\text{O}}{\overset{\|}{\text{C}}}-$	acetyl
$\text{CH}_3\text{CH}_2\overset{\text{O}}{\overset{\|}{\text{C}}}-\text{OH}$	propionic acid	$\text{CH}_3\text{CH}_2\overset{\text{O}}{\overset{\|}{\text{C}}}-$	propionyl
$\text{CH}_3\text{CH}_2\text{CH}_2\overset{\text{O}}{\overset{\|}{\text{C}}}-\text{OH}$	butyric acid	$\text{CH}_3\text{CH}_2\text{CH}_2\overset{\text{O}}{\overset{\|}{\text{C}}}-$	butyryl
$\text{CH}_3\text{CH}_2\text{CH}_2\text{CH}_2\overset{\text{O}}{\overset{\|}{\text{C}}}-\text{OH}$	valeric acid	$\text{CH}_3\text{CH}_2\text{CH}_2\text{CH}_2\overset{\text{O}}{\overset{\|}{\text{C}}}-$	valeryl

When an acyl halide contains six or more carbon atoms, the name is derived by dropping the *-ic acid* ending from the systematic name and replacing it with *-yl chloride* (or other halogen). For instance

$$\underset{\textit{hexanoyl bromide}}{\text{CH}_3\text{CH}_2\text{CH}_2\text{CH}_2\text{CH}_2\overset{\displaystyle\text{O}}{\overset{\|}{\text{C}}}-\text{Br}}$$

Which of these is the formula for benzoyl chloride?

A

B

C

A ||||||||||||||||||||||||||||||||||||||||||||||||||||||||||||||||||||||||||||||||||||||||||||||||||||||||||||||||||||||||||||||||||||

Your are wrong. You chose this formula for benzoyl chloride.

$$\underset{\textit{o-chlorobenzoic acid}}{\overset{\overset{\displaystyle O}{\|}}{\text{C—OH}}}$$

This formula does not represent an acyl halide. Acyl halides have the

general formula R—$\overset{\overset{\displaystyle O}{\|}}{\text{C}}$—X. The formula above is for a carboxylic acid since the chlorine atom is substituted on the ring and not the carboxy group. Turn back for another answer.

B ||||||||||||||||||||||||||||||||||||||||||||||||||||||||||||||||||||||||||||||||||||||||||||||||||||||||||||||||||||||||||||||||||

Incorrect. The formula you chose does not represent an acyl chloride.

The acyl chlorides have the general formula R—$\overset{\overset{\displaystyle O}{\|}}{\text{C}}$—Cl. A chlorine atom is substituted for the -OH group in a carboxylic acid. The correct answer to this question is the formula for the acyl chloride derived from benzoic acid.

$$\underset{\textit{benzoic acid}}{\overset{\overset{\displaystyle O}{\|}}{\text{C—OH}}}$$

Turn back and select another answer.

C ||||||||||||||||||||||||||||||||||||||||||||||||||||||||||||||||||||||||||||||||||||||||||||||||||||||||||||||||||||||||||||||||

You are correct. Benzoyl chloride is the acyl chloride derived from benzoic acid.

$$\underset{\textit{benzoic acid}}{\overset{\overset{\displaystyle O}{\|}}{\text{C—OH}}} \qquad\qquad \underset{\textit{benzoyl chloride}}{\overset{\overset{\displaystyle O}{\|}}{\text{C—Cl}}}$$

Go on to page 165.

3.5 ESTERS

When hydroxy compounds (alcohols and phenols) react with acids, the product is an ester. For the present only esters of carboxylic acids and alkanols will be considered. A typical reaction is represented by the equation

$$\underset{acid}{CH_3\overset{\overset{O}{\|}}{C}{-}OH} \;+\; \underset{alcohol}{HOCH_3} \;=\; \underset{ester}{CH_3\overset{\overset{O}{\|}}{C}{-}O{-}CH_3} \;+\; \underset{water}{H_2O}$$

The esters are named as if they were alkyl salts of the organic acids. This method stems from the early belief that esterification was analogous to neutralization.

You must be very careful to distinguish between the portion of the ester molecule derived from the acid and the portion derived from the alcohol. It is easy if you remember that the alkyl group from the alcohol is joined to the carbonyl group through an oxygen atom. The general structural formula illustrates this point.

$$R{-}\overset{\overset{O}{\|}}{C}{-}O{-}R' \qquad\qquad \begin{array}{l} R{-} = \text{alkyl group from acid} \\ R'{-} = \text{alkyl group from alcohol} \end{array}$$

Consider this structural formula of an ester:

$$CH_3\overset{\overset{O}{\|}}{C}{-}O{-}\overset{\overset{\displaystyle CH_3}{|}}{\underset{\underset{\displaystyle CH_3}{|}}{CH}}$$

From which of these alcohols is the ester derived?

A |||||||||||||||||||||||||||||||||||||||||||||||||||||||||||||||||||||||||||||||||||||||||||||||||||||||||||||||||||||||||||

ethanol

B |||||||||||||||||||||||||||||||||||||||||||||||||||||||||||||||||||||||||||||||||||||||||||||||||||||||||||||||||||||||||||

1-propanol

C |||||||||||||||||||||||||||||||||||||||||||||||||||||||||||||||||||||||||||||||||||||||||||||||||||||||||||||||||||||||||||

2-propanol

A |||||||||||||||||||||||||||||||||||||||||||||||||||||||||||||||||||||||||||||||||||||||||||||||||||||||||||||||||||||||||||||

You are wrong. Ethanol is not the alcohol which reacts to form this ester.

$$CH_3\overset{\overset{\displaystyle O}{\|}}{C}-O-\overset{\overset{\displaystyle CH_3}{|}}{\underset{\underset{\displaystyle CH_3}{|}}{CH}}$$

Remember that the alcohol portion of the ester is linked to the carbonyl group *through* the oxygen atom. In this example the R'— group for the alcohol is

$$-\overset{\overset{\displaystyle CH_3}{|}}{\underset{\underset{\displaystyle CH_3}{|}}{CH}}$$

What is the alcohol with the same R- group? Turn back to page 165 and choose it as your answer.

B |||||||||||||||||||||||||||||||||||||||||||||||||||||||||||||||||||||||||||||||||||||||||||||||||||||||||||||||||||||||||||||

Incorrect. This ester is not derived from 1-propanol.

$$CH_3\overset{\overset{\displaystyle O}{\|}}{C}-O-\overset{\overset{\displaystyle CH_3}{|}}{\underset{\underset{\displaystyle CH_3}{|}}{CH}}$$

You know that the alcohol portion of the ester is linked to the carbonyl group through the oxygen atom. In this example the R— group for the alcohol is

$$-\overset{\overset{\displaystyle CH_3}{|}}{\underset{\underset{\displaystyle CH_3}{|}}{CH}}$$

If the alcohol were 1-propanol, the R— group would be $CH_3CH_2CH_2-$, wouldn't it? The difference is in the position of the free valence. Turn back to page 165 and pick another answer.

C |||||||||||||||||||||||||||||||||||||||||||||||||||||||||||||||||||||||||||||||||||||||||||||||||||||||||||||||||||||||||||||

You are right. This ester is derived from 2-propanol and ethanoic acid.

$$CH_3\overset{\overset{\displaystyle O}{\|}}{C}-O-\overset{\overset{\displaystyle CH_3}{|}}{\underset{\underset{\displaystyle CH_3}{|}}{CH}}$$

Go on to page 167.

Esters are named by stating the alkyl radical of the alcohol as the first word. The second word is formed by dropping the -*ic* ending of the name of the acid and replacing it with -*ate*. The procedure applies to both the systematic and common names of the alcohols and acids.

Through the use of alcohols that have been isotopically enriched with $^{18}_{8}O$, it has been proved that the molecule of water is split out as shown here

$$CH_3\overset{O}{\overset{\|}{C}}-\boxed{OH \ + \ H}OCH_3 \ = \ CH_3\overset{O}{\overset{\|}{C}}-O-CH_3 \ + \ H_2O$$
$$\textit{ethanoic acid} \qquad \textit{methanol} \qquad \textit{methyl ethanoate} \qquad \textit{water}$$

On the next page are four questions concerning simple carboxylic esters. After you answer them, we will go on to more complex esters.

Cover the answers until you have made an answer of your own.

1. Name this ester

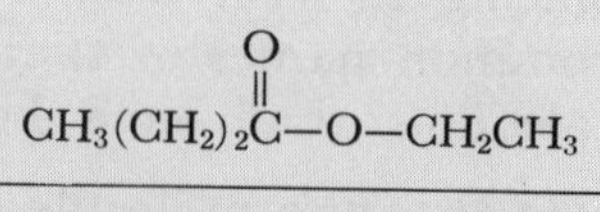

$$CH_3(CH_2)_2\overset{\displaystyle O}{\overset{\displaystyle \|}{C}}-O-CH_2CH_3$$

ethyl butanoate (Acceptable name: ethyl butyrate)

2. Write the structural formula for 2-butyl methanoate (*sec*-butyl methanoate).

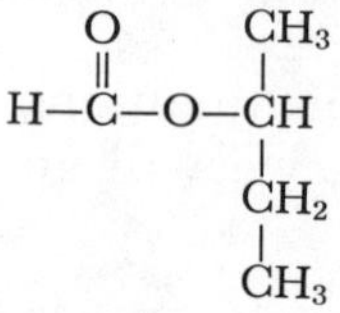

$$H-\overset{\displaystyle O}{\overset{\displaystyle \|}{C}}-O-\overset{\displaystyle CH_3}{\overset{\displaystyle |}{\underset{\displaystyle \underset{\displaystyle CH_3}{\overset{\displaystyle |}{CH_2}}}{\overset{\displaystyle |}{CH}}}}$$

3. What is the parent acid of methyl pentanoate?

pentanoic acid

4. Write structural formulas for methyl benzoate and phenyl methanoate.

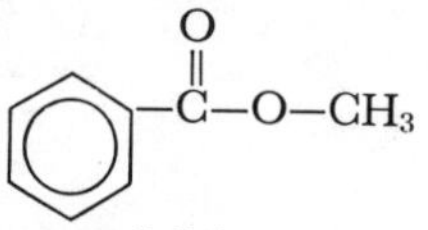

methyl benzoate 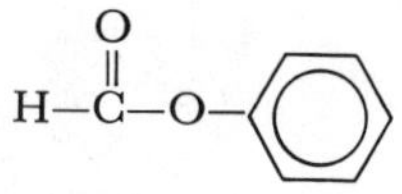   *phenyl methanoate*

Go on to page 169.

Condensed structural formulas of esters written on one line may cause you some difficulty at first. You should have no trouble if you remember that the oxygen of the carbonyl group is always written *after* the carbon to which it is attached. For instance

$$CH_3CH_2COOC(CH_3)_3 \qquad \text{is the same as}$$

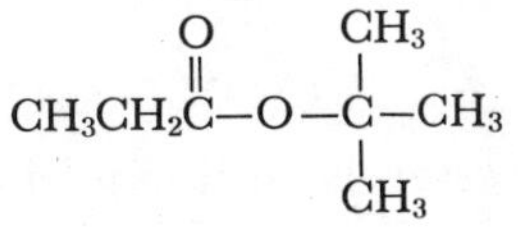

$$\begin{array}{ccc} & O & CH_3 \\ & \| & | \\ CH_3CH_2C & -O-C & -CH_3 \\ & & | \\ & & CH_3 \end{array}$$

tert-butyl propanoate

Consider this condensed formula of an ester:

$$CH_3COO(CH_2)_2CH_3$$

What is its name?

A |||||||||||||||||||||||||||||||||||||||||||||||||||||||||||||||||||||||||||||||||||||||||||||||

methyl butanoate

B |||||||||||||||||||||||||||||||||||||||||||||||||||||||||||||||||||||||||||||||||||||||||||||||

propyl ethanoate

C |||||||||||||||||||||||||||||||||||||||||||||||||||||||||||||||||||||||||||||||||||||||||||||||

I need help.

A ||||||||||||||||||||||||||||||||||||||||||||||||||||||||||||||||||||||||||||||||||||||||||||||||||||||||||||||||||||||||||||||||||||||||

Wrong. Let's write the full structural formula beside the condensed formula

$$CH_3COO(CH_2)_2CH_3 \qquad CH_3-\overset{\overset{\displaystyle O}{\|}}{C}-O-CH_2CH_2CH_3$$

This ester is derived from

$$CH_3\overset{\overset{\displaystyle O}{\|}}{C}-OH \qquad and \qquad CH_3CH_2CH_2OH$$

Now how would you name it? Turn back and choose another answer.

B ||||||||||||||||||||||||||||||||||||||||||||||||||||||||||||||||||||||||||||||||||||||||||||||||||||||||||||||||||||||||||||||||||||||||

Correct. The condensed formula represents propyl ethanoate.

$$CH_3-\overset{\overset{\displaystyle O}{\|}}{C}-O-CH_2CH_2CH_3$$

Go on to page 171.

C ||||||||||||||||||||||||||||||||||||||||||||||||||||||||||||||||||||||||||||||||||||||||||||||||||||||||||||||||||||||||||||||||||||||||

Here is the condensed formula again: $CH_3COO(CH_2)_2CH_3$. Since the oxygen of the carbonyl group is always written after the carbon to which it is attached, the complete structural formula would be

$$CH_3-\overset{\overset{\displaystyle O}{\|}}{C}-O-CH_2CH_2CH_3$$

Now divide it into acid and alcohol portions. The R- group from the acid is CH_3- and the R′− group from the alcohol is $CH_3CH_2CH_2-$. Combine them properly into a name and you have the answer. Turn back to page 169 and see if it is there.

Substituent groups on substituted esters are located by numbering the carbon atoms in both directions from the oxygen atom that bridges the alcohol and acid parts of the ester. As an illustration

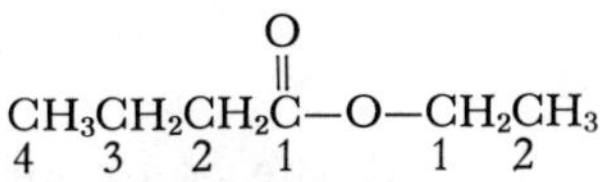

$$\underset{4\quad3\quad2\quad1}{CH_3CH_2CH_2}\overset{O}{\underset{}{\overset{\parallel}{C}}}-O-\underset{1\quad2}{CH_2CH_3}$$

ethyl butanoate

$$\underset{4\quad3\quad2\quad1}{CH_3}\overset{OH}{\underset{}{\overset{|}{C}}}HCH_2\overset{O}{\underset{}{\overset{\parallel}{C}}}-O-\underset{1\quad2}{CH_2CH_2Cl}$$

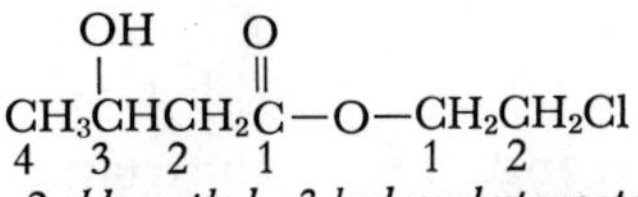

2-chloroethyl   3-hydroxybutanoate

What is the skeleton formula for the ester 3-bromo-1-propyl chloroethanoate?

A

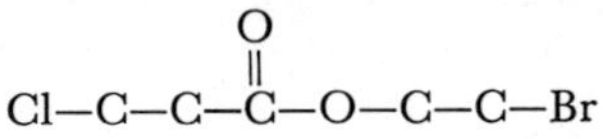

$$Cl-C-C-\overset{O}{\overset{\parallel}{C}}-O-C-C-Br$$

B

$$Cl-C-\overset{O}{\overset{\parallel}{C}}-O-C-C-C-Br$$

C

$$Br-C-C-\overset{O}{\overset{\parallel}{C}}-O-C-C-Cl$$

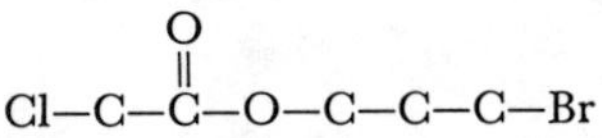

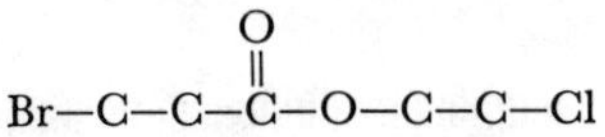

A ||||||||||||||||||||||||||||||||||||||||||||||||||||||||||||||||||||||||||||||||||||||||||||||||||||||||||||||||||||||||||||||||||||||||

You chose this skeleton to represent 3-bromopropyl chloroethanoate.

$$Cl-C-C-\overset{\overset{\displaystyle O}{\|}}{C}-O-C-C-Br$$

You are wrong. From the name we can tell that the compound is the ester of 3-bromopropanol and chloroethanoic acid. Their formulas are

$$BrCH_2CH_2CH_2OH$$

3-bromopropanol

$$Cl-\overset{\overset{\displaystyle H}{|}}{\underset{\underset{\displaystyle H}{|}}{C}}-\overset{\overset{\displaystyle O}{\|}}{C}-OH$$

chloroethanoic acid

Write the formula for the ester and see if it appears as a choice for you on page 171.

B ||||||||||||||||||||||||||||||||||||||||||||||||||||||||||||||||||||||||||||||||||||||||||||||||||||||||||||||||||||||||||||||||||||||||

Right. This is the skeleton for 3-bromopropyl chloroethanoate.

$$Cl-C-\overset{\overset{\displaystyle O}{\|}}{C}-O-C-C-C-Br$$

There is no reason to designate the location of the Cl by a number because it cannot be on the other carbon atom. Continue on to page 173.

C ||||||||||||||||||||||||||||||||||||||||||||||||||||||||||||||||||||||||||||||||||||||||||||||||||||||||||||||||||||||||||||||||||||||||

Incorrect. The skeleton you chose to represent 3-bromopropyl chloroethanoate is

$$Br-C-C-\overset{\overset{\displaystyle O}{\|}}{C}-O-C-C-Cl$$

From the name you should know that the bromine atom is part of the alcohol portion of the molecule and the chlorine is substituted on the acid portion. In the skeleton above they are reversed. (Remember that the alcohol portion is linked to the $-\overset{\overset{\displaystyle O}{\|}}{C}-$ group *through* the oxygen.) Go back, read page 171 again, and pick another answer.

Esters react with strong bases to form the parent alcohol and the salt of the parent acid. This process is called saponification. The saponification of ethyl benzoate can serve as an example.

ethyl benzoate   *sodium benzoate*   *ethanol*

Summary: Nomenclature of Carboxylic Acids, Anhydrides, Acyl Halides, and Esters

The functional group of the carboxylic acids is the carboxy group,

$-C-OH$ or$-CO_2H$. Their systematic names are formed by dropping the *-e* from the name of the parent alkane and adding *-oic* followed by the word acid. The names of the carboxylate anions are formed by dropping the *-ic* from the name of the acid and adding *-ate*. Substituent groups on carboxylic acids are located by numbering the carbon chain beginning with the carboxy carbon as number 1.

Unsaturated carboxylic acids are named by changing the *-anoic* ending of the basic name to *-enoic* or *-ynoic* (*cf.* alkenes and alkynes) and indicating the position of the double or triple bond as in the hydrocarbons. If more than one double bond is present, the ending is *-dienoic*, *-trienoic*, etc.

The systematic names of the dicarboxylic acids are formed by changing the *-oic* ending to *-edioic*. The common names, however, are in general use. (See page 157.)

The simplest aromatic carboxylic acid is benzoic acid.

benzoic acid

Acid anhydrides are formed by the loss of a molecule of water from two carboxy groups. These groups may come from two acid molecules or a single molecule of a dibasic acid such as phthalic acid. The general formula of the acid anhydrides is $R-C-O-C-R$. Simple anhydrides are named by replacing the word acid with anhydride. Mixed anhydrides are named by giving the names of the two acids followed by anhydride as a third word.

Acyl halides result from the replacement of the —OH group of an acid by a halogen. (See page 163.)

Esters result from the reactions between acids and alcohols. Their

$$\overset{\text{O}}{\underset{\|}{}}$$

general formula is R—C—O—R′. The alkyl radical linked through the oxygen (R′-) is the radical from the alcohol and the radical attached to the carbonyl group (R-) is the radical from the acid. Esters are named by stating the radical from the alcohol as the first word and the name of the carboxylate anion as the second word. For instance

$$\overset{\text{O}}{\overset{\|}{\text{CH}_3\text{CH}_2\text{C}}}\text{—O—CH}_3$$
methyl propanoate

ALCOHOLS

Functional group: —OH
General formula: ROH

Functional group name: *hydroxy*
Series Name: *-ol*

PHENOLS

Functional group: —OH

General formula: ⬡—OH

Functional group name: *hydroxy*

ALDEHYDES AND KETONES

Functional group:
$$-\overset{\overset{\displaystyle O}{\|}}{C}-$$

General formulas:
$$R-\overset{\overset{\displaystyle O}{\|}}{C}-H$$
(aldehydes)

$$R-\overset{\overset{\displaystyle O}{\|}}{C}-R' \text{ (ketones)}$$

Functional group name: *carbonyl*

Series names: *-al*

-one

CARBOXYLIC ACIDS

Functional group:
$$-\overset{\overset{\displaystyle O}{\|}}{C}-OH$$

General Formula:
$$R-\overset{\overset{\displaystyle O}{\|}}{C}-OH$$

Functional group name: *carboxy*

Series name: *-oic acid*

ACYL HALIDES

Functional group:
$$-\overset{\overset{\displaystyle O}{\|}}{C}-X$$

General Formula:
$$R-\overset{\overset{\displaystyle O}{\|}}{C}-X$$

Functional group name: *none*

Series name: *-yl* halide or
-oyl halide

ACID ANHYDRIDES

Functional group:
$$-\overset{\overset{\displaystyle O}{\|}}{C}-O-\overset{\overset{\displaystyle O}{\|}}{C}-$$

General formula:
$$R-\overset{\overset{\displaystyle O}{\|}}{C}-O-\overset{\overset{\displaystyle O}{\|}}{C}-R$$

Functional group name: *haloformyl*

Series name: *-ic anhydride*

CARBOXYLIC ACID ESTERS

Functional group:
$$-\overset{\overset{\displaystyle O}{\|}}{C}-O-R'$$

General formula:
$$R-\overset{\overset{\displaystyle O}{\|}}{C}-O-R'$$

Functional group name: *alkoxycarbonyl*

Series name: *-yl .... -oate*

Go on to page 177.

3.6 ETHERS

Simple ethers are organic compounds with the general formula R—O—R'. If R— and R'— represent identical alkyl or aryl groups, the ether is symmetrical. If they are different, the ether is unsymmetrical.

Symmetrical ethers are named by naming the radical and adding ether as a second word. Thus the simplest symmetrical ether is CH_3OCH_3, methyl ether. The substance commonly called ether and used as an anesthetic is ethyl ether, $CH_3CH_2OCH_2CH_3$.

Unsymmetrical ethers are usually named by giving the names of the two radicals in alphabetical order and appending ether as a third word. Thus $CH_3OCH_2CH_3$, an unsymmetrical ether, is ethyl methyl ether. As you will see and hear, many chemists are not too careful to name the radicals in alphabetical order.

What is the name of this ether?

$$CH_3CH_2OCH_2CH_2CH_2CH_3$$

A ‖‖‖

ethyl butyl ether

B ‖‖

butyl ethyl ether

C ‖‖

butylethyl ether

A ||||||||||||||||||||||||||||||||||||||||||||||||||||||||||||||||||||||||||||||||||||||||||||||||||||||||||||||||||||||||||||||||||

The ether with the formula

$$CH_3CH_2OCH_2CH_2CH_2CH_3$$

does have an ethyl group and a butyl group. In the name, however, these groups should be given in alphabetical order. The correct name is butyl ethyl ether. Alphabetical order makes the indexing of names easier. Continue on to page 179.

B ||||||||||||||||||||||||||||||||||||||||||||||||||||||||||||||||||||||||||||||||||||||||||||||||||||||||||||||||||||||||||||||||||

You are right. This is the formula of butyl ethyl ether.

$$CH_3CH_2OCH_2CH_2CH_2CH_3$$

Go on to page 179.

C ||||||||||||||||||||||||||||||||||||||||||||||||||||||||||||||||||||||||||||||||||||||||||||||||||||||||||||||||||||||||||||||||||

Close, but not quite right. Unsymmetrical ethers always have three words in their names. One for each alkyl or aryl radical and then the word ether. In this example the proper name is butyl ethyl ether. Be more careful next time. Turn to page 179.

When an organic molecule contains two or more kinds of functional groups, the principal one is expressed by the ending of the name and the others by prefixes. How is this determined? Chemists are not always consistent in this matter, but *Chemical Abstracts* uses an order of precedence in its indexing. The order does not constitute an attempt to give the relative importance of functions, but only the general usage in selection of the one to be employed for the ending of the name. The complete list can be found in the appendix. An abbreviated order of precedence for the functions disscussed in this book is:

acids, acid halide, amide, aldehyde, ketone, alcohol, phenol, amine, ether, sulfide, sulfoxide, sulfone.

For example

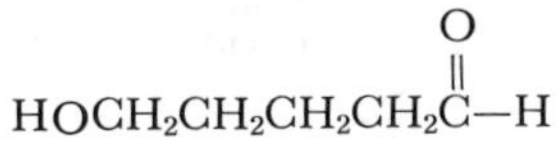

$$\underset{5\text{-}hydroxypentanal}{HOCH_2CH_2CH_2CH_2\overset{\displaystyle O}{\overset{\|}{C}}-H}$$

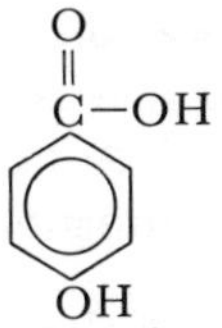

p-hydroxybenzoic acid

How would you name this compound?

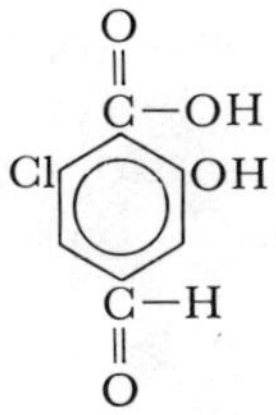

A ‖‖

As an aldehyde

B ‖‖

As a substituted benzene

C ‖‖

As a carboxylic acid

D ‖‖

As a phenol

A ⁣⁣⁣

Incorrect. The compound in question does contain the functional group of the aldehydes, $-\overset{\overset{\textstyle O}{\|}}{C}-H$. In addition, however, it has a carboxy group and a hydroxy group. So it might be named as an aldehyde, acid, or phenol. The correct choice depends on which function comes first in the order of precedence. Go back and choose another answer.

B ⁣⁣⁣

You are wrong. Compounds are named as substituted hydrocarbons only if they do not have a functional group. A quick look at the formula for the compound in question should show you that it has at least one functional group. Turn back and read page 179 again before you choose another answer.

C ⁣⁣⁣

Right. There are three functional groups in the compound: carboxy, hydroxy, and carbonyl. The carboxy group and its acid function lies highest on the order of precedence. Consequently, the compound is properly named as a carboxylic acid. Go on to page 181.

D ⁣⁣⁣

Incorrect. The compound does contain the functional group of the phenols, $-OH$. In addition, however, it has a carboxy group and a carbonyl group. It might be named as an aldehyde, acid, or phenol. The proper choice depends on which function comes first in the order of precedence. Go back and choose another answer.

The ether function is very low on the established order of precedence. So low, in fact, that ethers are sometimes named as substituted hydrocarbons. The group RO— is known as an *alkoxy-* or *aryloxy-* group. As always, base the name on the longest continuous carbon chain. For example

$$OCH_2CH_3$$
$$|$$
$$CH_3CH_2OCH_2CHCH_2OCH_2CH_3$$
$$1,2,3\text{-}triethoxypropane$$

Precedence limits the use of the alkoxy nomenclature to compounds which have other, and more important, functional groups. (See page 185.) Simple ethers should be named as ethers.

The ethers, R—O—R′, are isomeric with the alcohols, ROH. For example, ethanol and methyl ether both have the molecular formula C_2H_6O.

$$CH_3OCH_3 \qquad\qquad CH_3CH_2OH$$
methyl ether   *ethanol*

How many straight-chain ethers are isomeric with 2-pentanol?

A ▌▌▌

2

B ▌▌▌

3

C ▌▌▌

4

D ▌▌▌

Help!

A ||||||||||||||||||||||||||||||||||||||||||||||||||||||||||||||||||||||||||||||||||||||||||||||||||||||||||||||||||||||||||||||||||||||||||||||||||||||||

You are right. There are only two straight-chain ethers that are isomeric with 2-pentanol. They are butyl methyl ether and ethyl propyl ether. Go on to page 183.

B ||||||||||||||||||||||||||||||||||||||||||||||||||||||||||||||||||||||||||||||||||||||||||||||||||||||||||||||||||||||||||||||||||||||||||||||||||||||||

Incorrect. Ethers that are isomeric with 2-pentanol must contain five carbon atoms. If they contain straight-chain radicals only, there is no branching. Check your formulas again to be sure that none is branched and that no two of them are identical but written in reverse order. For example, both of these are ethyl propyl ether.

$$C–C–O–C–C–C \qquad\qquad C–C–C–O–C–C$$

Turn back and choose another answer.

C ||||||||||||||||||||||||||||||||||||||||||||||||||||||||||||||||||||||||||||||||||||||||||||||||||||||||||||||||||||||||||||||||||||||||||||||||||||||||

You say that there are four unsubstituted ethers that are isomeric with 2-pentanol. To be unique, each one must contain five carbon atoms and there can be no branching. Check your formulas again to be sure that none is branched and that no two are identical but written in reverse order. Go back and choose another answer.

D ||||||||||||||||||||||||||||||||||||||||||||||||||||||||||||||||||||||||||||||||||||||||||||||||||||||||||||||||||||||||||||||||||||||||||||||||||||||||

You are asked to determine the number of straight-chain ethers that are isomeric with 2-pentanol. These isomers must contain five carbon atoms. One example is butyl methyl ether.

$$CH_3CH_2CH_2CH_2OCH_3$$

How many others can you find? Turn back and choose another answer.

When necessary, the carbon atoms in the alkyl or aryl groups of ethers can be numbered. Start with 1 for both carbon atoms next to the oxygen atom and go toward the ends. Locate substituent alkyl groups or halogen atoms in the usual way.

$$\underset{2}{Cl}\underset{1}{CH_2}\underset{}{CH_2}\underset{1}{O}\underset{}{CH_2}\underset{2}{CH_2}\underset{3}{CH_3}$$

2-chloroethyl propyl ether

On the next page are the formulas of three ethers. Name them and then check your answer with the correct names given below each formula.

1.

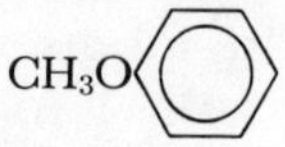

$$CH_3O\bigcirc$$

methyl phenyl ether (Acceptable name: anisole)

2.

$$CH_3CHCH_2OCH_2CH_2CH_2CH_2I$$
$$\underset{CH_3}{|}$$

4-iodobutyl isobutyl ether

3.

$$\underset{\underset{CH_3}{|}}{\overset{\overset{CH_3}{|}}{CH_3CH_2OCH_2CCH_3}}$$

ethyl 2,2-dimethylpropyl ether

Note: When unsubstituted, the $-CH_2\underset{\underset{CH_3}{|}}{\overset{\overset{CH_3}{|}}{C}}-CH_3$ group is called neopentyl.

Thus, an acceptable name is ethyl neopentyl ether.

Go on to page 185.

Alkoxy groups are often present in compounds which contain other functional groups such as the hydroxy group, —OH, carbonyl group,

$$\overset{O}{\underset{\|}{-C-}}, \text{ or carboxy group, } \overset{O}{\underset{\|}{-C}}-OH.$$ In these instances the compounds are named as alkoxy derivatives of the compound of the other function. These three examples should make the point clear.

Compound	Principal functional group	Systematic name
$CH_3OCH_2CH_2CH_2OH$	—OH hydroxy	3–methoxy–1–propanol
$CH_3CH_2CH_2\overset{O}{\underset{\|}{C}}\overset{}{\underset{\|}{C}}HCH_3$ $\quad\quad OCH_3$	$\overset{O}{\underset{\|}{-C-}}$ carbonyl	2–methoxy–3–hexanone
$\overset{O}{\underset{\|}{C}}-OH$ $Br\;\bigcirc\;OCH_3$ $\quad OCH_3$	$\overset{O}{\underset{\|}{-C}}-OH$ carboxy	6–bromo–2,4–dimethoxy-benzoic acid

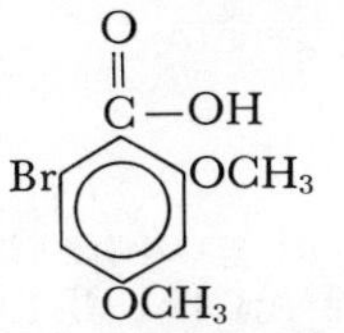

What is the name of this compound?

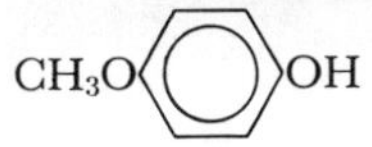

$$CH_3O\bigcirc OH$$

A

p-methoxyphenol

B

p-hydroxyphenyl methyl ether

C

1-hydroxy-4-methoxybenzene

A ||||||||||||||||||||||||||||||||||||||||||||||||||||||||||||||||||||||||||||||||||||||||||||||||||||||||||||||||||||||||||||||||||||

You are right. The principal functional group in this compound is the —OH group and it is properly named as an alkoxy

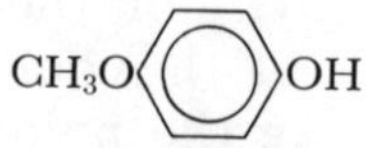

$$CH_3O\text{---}\langle\bigcirc\rangle\text{---}OH$$

derivative of phenol. Go on to page 187.

B ||||||||||||||||||||||||||||||||||||||||||||||||||||||||||||||||||||||||||||||||||||||||||||||||||||||||||||||||||||||||||||||||||||

The name *p*-hydroxyphenyl methyl ether is descriptive of the compound represented by the formula

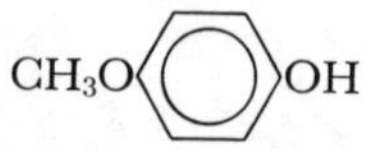

$$CH_3O\text{---}\langle\bigcirc\rangle\text{---}OH$$

There is, however, an order of precedence for functional groups that is used to determine names. The hydroxy group is higher on the list than the ether function. The result is that this compound is not named as an ether. Turn back and choose another answer which indicates the hydroxy group as the main functional group.

C ||||||||||||||||||||||||||||||||||||||||||||||||||||||||||||||||||||||||||||||||||||||||||||||||||||||||||||||||||||||||||||||||||||

You picked 1–hydroxy–4–methoxybenzene as the name for

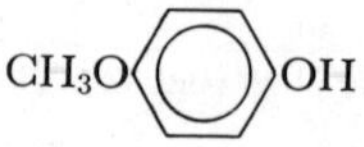

$$CH_3O\text{---}\langle\bigcirc\rangle\text{---}OH$$

This name describes the compound correctly, but since there is an accepted name for hydroxybenzene, it is more properly named *p*-methoxyphenol. Continue on to page 187.

The herbicide 2,4–D has the systematic name 2,4–dichlorophenoxy-ethanoic acid. What is its structural formula?

A

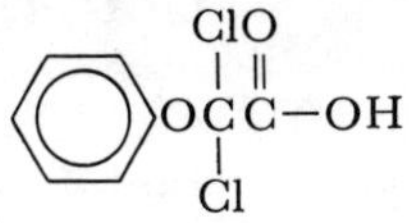

$$\text{C}_6\text{H}_5\text{-O}\overset{\overset{\displaystyle Cl}{|}}{\underset{\underset{\displaystyle Cl}{|}}{C}}\overset{\overset{\displaystyle O}{\|}}{C}\text{-OH}$$

B

$$\text{Cl}_2\text{C}_6\text{H}_3\text{CH}_2\overset{\overset{\displaystyle O}{\|}}{C}\text{-OH}$$

C

$$\text{Cl}_2\text{C}_6\text{H}_3\text{-OCH}_2\overset{\overset{\displaystyle O}{\|}}{C}\text{-OH}$$

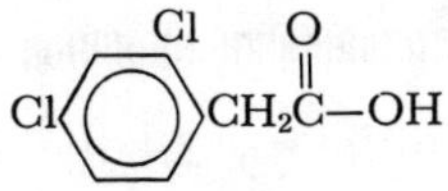

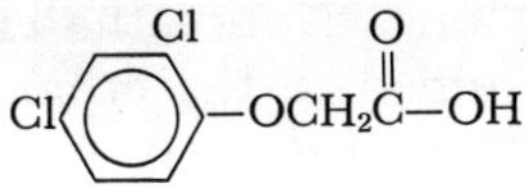

A ||||||||||||||||||||||||||||||||||||||||||||||||||||||||||||||||||||||||||||||||||||||||||||||||||||||||||||||||||||||||||||

Incorrect. The formula you chose for 2,4-dichlorophenoxyethanoic acid is

$$\overset{3\quad 2}{\underset{5\quad 6}{\bigcirc}}\!4 \quad OC\overset{ClO}{\underset{Cl}{C}}C\text{—}OH$$

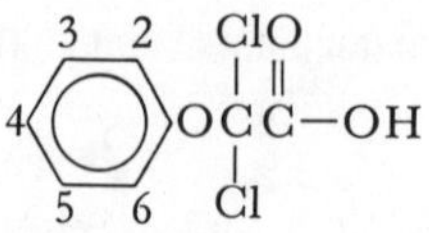

The name indicates that there should be a pair of chlorine atoms substituted on the ring. Where are they? Turn back and choose another answer.

B ||||||||||||||||||||||||||||||||||||||||||||||||||||||||||||||||||||||||||||||||||||||||||||||||||||||||||||||||||||||||||||

Your choice for the formula for 2,4-dichlorophenoxyethanoic acid is

$$Cl\overset{Cl}{\bigcirc}CH_2\overset{O}{\overset{\|}{C}}\text{—}OH$$

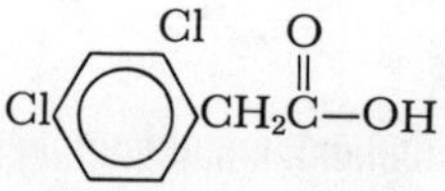

It's OK in all respects but one. Notice the *oxy* in the name. This means that the ring structure is joined to the ethanoic acid through an oxygen atom. Turn back and select another formula for 2,4-D.

C ||||||||||||||||||||||||||||||||||||||||||||||||||||||||||||||||||||||||||||||||||||||||||||||||||||||||||||||||||||||||||||

You are right. The formula for 2,4-dichlorophenoxyethanoic acid is

$$Cl\overset{Cl}{\bigcirc}\text{—}OCH_2\overset{O}{\overset{\|}{C}}\text{—}OH$$

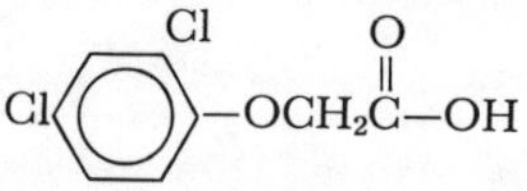

Is it any wonder that it's commonly called 2,4-D? Go on to page 189.

Compounds which have two or more —O— functional groups are called polyethers. If they are not derived from complex ring systems, they are named as ethers if they are symmetrical, or as derivatives of the most central hydrocarbon. Here are two examples.

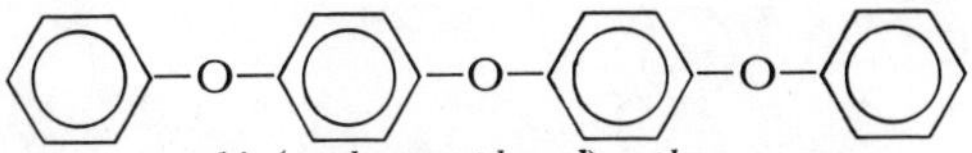

bis(p-phenoxyphenyl) ether

$CH_3CH_2CH_2OCH_2OCH_2CH_2CH_3$

dipropoxymethane

The first of these is symmetrical about the central oxygen atom and is named as an ether. The second is not symmetrical about an oxygen atom. Hence it is named as a derivative of methane.

How would you name this polyether?

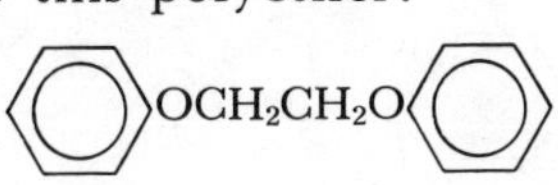

A ‖‖

diphenoxyethane

B ‖‖

bis-phenoxyethane

C ‖‖

1,2-diphenoxyethane

A ||||||||||||||||||||||||||||||||||||||||||||||||||||||||||||||||||||||||||||||||||||||||||||||||||||||||||||||||||||||

The compound represented by the formula is properly named as a derivative of ethane.

$$\langle O \rangle OCH_2C_2HO \langle O \rangle$$

Since there are two phenoxy groups, it is a diphenoxyethane. There are, however, other diphenoxyethanes. For example

$$\langle O \rangle O$$
$$|$$
$$\langle O \rangle O - CHCH_3$$

You must rely on numbers to specify the location of the substituents. Turn back to page 189 and choose another answer.

B ||||||||||||||||||||||||||||||||||||||||||||||||||||||||||||||||||||||||||||||||||||||||||||||||||||||||||||||||||||||

Incorrect. The multiplicative prefixes *bis-*, *tris-*, etc., are used only when there is a substituent which bears substituents itself. For instance, if there were two of these groups substituted on ethane, the designation would be bis(3,5-dinitrophenyl).

$$O_2N$$
$$|$$
$$\langle O \rangle -$$
$$|$$
$$O_2N$$

Two simple phenoxy groups can be indicated by the prefix *di-*. Turn back and choose another answer.

C ||||||||||||||||||||||||||||||||||||||||||||||||||||||||||||||||||||||||||||||||||||||||||||||||||||||||||||||||||||||

You are correct. Since the compound is not symmetrical about a central oxygen atom, it is named as a derivative of ethane.

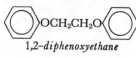

$$\langle O \rangle OCH_2CH_2O \langle O \rangle$$
1,2–diphenoxyethane

Go on to page 191.

Summary: Nomenclature of Ethers

The general formula for the ethers is R—O—R'. Symmetrical ethers have identical alkyl or aryl groups attached to the oxygen and can be named by naming the group and adding ether as a second word. Unsymmetrical ethers can be named by giving the two alkyl or aryl groups in alphabetical order and adding ether as a third word.

The radical RO— is an alkoxy or aryloxy group. Alkoxy and aryloxy group names are used for compounds that have other functional groups besides the ether linkage.

Polyethers are named as ethers if symmetrical or as derivatives of hydrocarbons if not symmetrical.

ALCOHOLS

Functional group: —OH   Functional group name: *hydroxy*
General formula: ROH   Series name: *-ol*

PHENOLS

Functional group: —OH   Functional group name: *hydroxy*

General formula: ⬡—OH   Series name: *-ol*

ALDEHYDES AND KETONES

$$\text{Functional group: } -\overset{\overset{\textstyle O}{\|}}{C}-$$

Functional group name: *carbonyl*

$$\text{General formulas: } R-\overset{\overset{\textstyle O}{\|}}{C}-H \text{ (aldehydes)}$$

Series name: *-al*

$$R-\overset{\overset{\textstyle O}{\|}}{C}-R' \text{ (ketones)}$$

-one

CARBOXYLIC ACIDS

$$\text{Functional group: } -\overset{\overset{\textstyle O}{\|}}{C}-OH$$

Functional group name: *carboxy*

$$\text{General formula: } R-\overset{\overset{\textstyle O}{\|}}{C}-OH$$

Series name: *-oic acid*

ACYL HALIDES

$$\text{Functional group: } -\overset{\overset{\textstyle O}{\|}}{C}-X$$

Functional group name: *haloformyl*

$$\text{General formula: } R-\overset{\overset{\textstyle O}{\|}}{C}-X$$

Series name: *-yl halide* or
-oyl halide

ACID ANHYDRIDES

$$\text{Functional group: } -\overset{\overset{\textstyle O}{\|}}{C}-O-\overset{\overset{\textstyle O}{\|}}{C}-$$

Functional group name: *none*

$$\text{General formula: } R-\overset{\overset{\textstyle O}{\|}}{C}-O-\overset{\overset{\textstyle O}{\|}}{C}-R$$

Series name: *-ic anhydride*

CARBOXYLIC ACID ESTERS

$$\text{Functional Group: } -\overset{\overset{\textstyle O}{\|}}{C}-O-R'$$

Functional group name: *alkoxylcarbonyl*

$$\text{General Formula: } R-\overset{\overset{\textstyle O}{\|}}{C}-O-R'$$

Series name: *-yl .... -oate*

ETHERS

Functional group: —O—   Functional group name: *none*
General Formula: R—O—R'   Series name: *-yl ... -yl ether*

Go on to page 193.

3.7 AMINES

Amines (ă-mēnz') are organic bases that are derived from ammonia, NH_3. One, two, or all three hydrogen atoms of the ammonia may be replaced by alkyl or aryl radicals. These are known as primary, secondary, and tertiary amines, respectively. This table will show you the general formulas and functional groups.

Class of amine	General formula	Functional group	Example
Primary	$R-NH_2$	$-NH_2$	CH_3NH_2 *methylamine*
Secondary	$\begin{smallmatrix}R\\R'\end{smallmatrix}\!\!>\!NH$	$>\!NH$	$(CH_3)_2NH$ *dimethylamine*
Tertiary	$\begin{smallmatrix}R\\R'\\R'\end{smallmatrix}\!\!>\!N$	$>\!N$	$(CH_3)_3N$ *trimethylamine*

Primary amines are named by adding the suffix -amine to the name of the hydrocarbon radical. If it is necessary to number the carbon atoms in order to designate substituents, start numbering with the carbon atom next to the $-NH_2$ group.

What is the name of the amine represented by this formula:

$$ClCH_2CH_2NH_2$$

A ||||||||||||||||||||||||||||||||||||||||||||||||||||||||||||||||||||||||||||||||||||||||||||||||||||||||||||||

chloromethylamine

B ||||||||||||||||||||||||||||||||||||||||||||||||||||||||||||||||||||||||||||||||||||||||||||||||||||||||||||||

chloroethylamine

C ||||||||||||||||||||||||||||||||||||||||||||||||||||||||||||||||||||||||||||||||||||||||||||||||||||||||||||||

2-chloroethylamine

A ||||||||||||||||||||||||||||||||||||||||||||||||||||||||||||||||||||||||||||||||||||||||||||||||||||||||||||||||||||||

Incorrect. You named this compound chloromethylamine.

$$ClCH_2CH_2NH_2$$

As the name implies, chloromethylamine is a derivative of methylamine, CH_3NH_2. The formula above has two carbon atoms and must, therefore, be a derivative of ethylamine. Turn back to page 193 and choose another answer.

B ||||||||||||||||||||||||||||||||||||||||||||||||||||||||||||||||||||||||||||||||||||||||||||||||||||||||||||||||||||||

Your answer is that this formula represents chloroethylamine.

$$ClCH_2CH_2NH_2$$

You are right, but doesn't this formula also represent chloroethylamine?

$$CH_3CHCl\, NH_2$$

You can distinguish between the two by means of numbers. Work out a name for both of these amines. Then go back and pick another answer.

C ||||||||||||||||||||||||||||||||||||||||||||||||||||||||||||||||||||||||||||||||||||||||||||||||||||||||||||||||||||||

Correct. The name for the compound is 2-chloroethylamine.

$$ClCH_2CH_2NH_2$$

The carbon chain is numbered from the $-NH_2$ functional group. Continue to page 195.

Secondary and tertiary amines that have the same alkyl groups are named by using the prefixes *di-* and *tri-* before the name of the radical. When numbers are needed, primes and double primes are used to indicate the second and third groups. As an example consider this formula for the tertiary amine, tripropylamine.

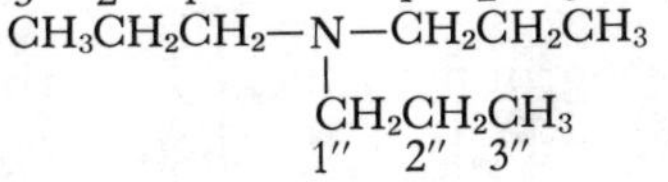

$$\overset{3\quad2\quad1}{CH_3CH_2CH_2}-N-\overset{1'\ 2'\ 3'}{CH_2CH_2CH_3}$$
$$\underset{1''\ 2''\ 3''}{CH_2CH_2CH_3}$$

Following these guidelines, the formula for 2,2',2''-trichlorotriethylamine is

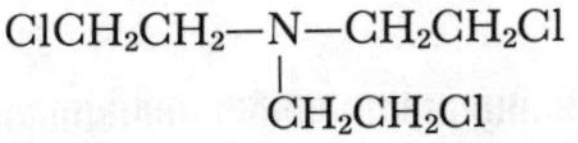

$$ClCH_2CH_2-N-CH_2CH_2Cl$$
$$CH_2CH_2Cl \quad \text{or} \quad (ClCH_2CH_2)_3N$$

Chemical Abstracts calls it tris(2-chloroethyl)amine.

What is the formula for 1,1'-dichlorotriethylamine? (*Chemical Abstracts* would call it bis(2-chloroethyl)ethylamine.)

A ||||||||||||||||||||||||||||||||||||||||||||||||||||||||||||||||||||||||||||||||||||||||||||||||||||||||||||||||||||||||||||

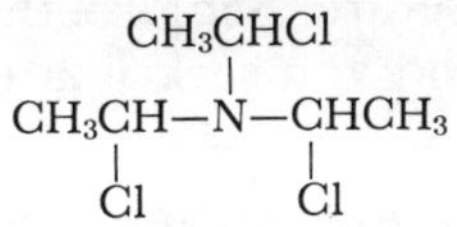

$$CH_3CHCl$$
$$CH_3CH-N-CHCH_3$$
$$Cl \qquad Cl$$

B ||||||||||||||||||||||||||||||||||||||||||||||||||||||||||||||||||||||||||||||||||||||||||||||||||||||||||||||||||||||||||||

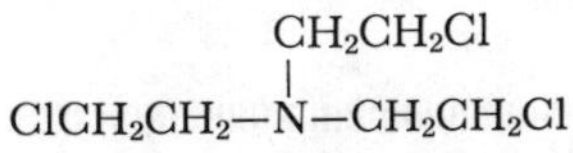

$$CH_2CH_2Cl$$
$$ClCH_2CH_2-N-CH_2CH_2Cl$$

C ||||||||||||||||||||||||||||||||||||||||||||||||||||||||||||||||||||||||||||||||||||||||||||||||||||||||||||||||||||||||||||

$$CH_2CH_3$$
$$CH_3CH-N-CHCH_3$$
$$Cl \qquad Cl$$

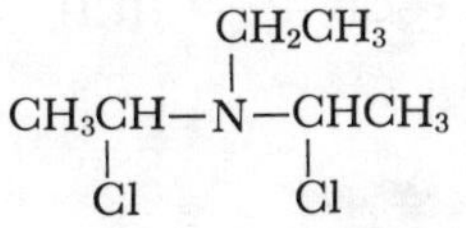

A ||||||||||||||||||||||||||||||||||||||||||||||||||||||||||||||||||||||||||||||||||||||||||||||||||||||||||||||||||||

You chose this formula for 1,1'-dichlorotriethylamine.

$$CH_3CHCl$$
$$|$$
$$CH_3CH-N-CHCH_3$$
$$|\qquad|$$
$$Cl\qquad Cl$$

It appears that all three groups attached to the nitrogen are identical. According to the name, only two of them are to have chlorine atoms substituted on the ethyl groups. Think this over and select another answer.

B ||||||||||||||||||||||||||||||||||||||||||||||||||||||||||||||||||||||||||||||||||||||||||||||||||||||||||||||||||||

You picked this formula to represent 1,1'-dichlorotriethylamine.

$$CH_2CH_2Cl$$
$$|$$
$$ClCH_2CH_2-N-CH_2CH_2Cl$$

All three groups attached to the nitrogen are the same, aren't they? They are $ClCH_2CH_2-$. These are 2-chloroethyl groups. From the name you can see that the compound you seek is a derivative of triethylamine.

$$CH_2CH_3$$
$$|$$
$$CH_3CH_2-N-CH_2CH_3$$

Chlorine atoms are to be substituted on the number 1 and 1' carbons. When you have done this, turn back and choose another answer.

C ||||||||||||||||||||||||||||||||||||||||||||||||||||||||||||||||||||||||||||||||||||||||||||||||||||||||||||||||||||

You are correct. This formula depicts 1,1'-dichlorotriethylamine.

$$CH_2CH_3$$
$$|$$
$$CH_3CH-N-CHCH_3$$
$$|\qquad|$$
$$Cl\qquad Cl$$

Go on to page 197.

Mixed amines (*i.e.*, those in which the alkyl or aryl groups are not identical) are named as nitrogen-substituted derivatives of the primary amine with the largest radical. Substituents on the nitrogen atom are indicated by an italic *N*—. Thus

$$\underset{\text{N-methylpropylamine}}{\overset{\overset{\text{H}}{|}}{CH_3CH_2CH_2NCH_3}}$$

Tertiary amines that have two identical groups can be named as *N,N*- derivatives of primary amines or as *N*- derivatives of secondary amines. For instance

$$CH_3CH_2CH_2CH_2-N\underset{CH_2CH_3}{\overset{CH_2CH_3}{\diagup}}$$

N,N-diethylbutylamine
or
N-butyldiethylamine

How many isomeric amines have the molecular formula C_3H_9N ?

A ||||||||||||||||||||||||||||||||||||||||||||||||||||||||||||||||||||||||||||||||||||||||||||||||||||||

3

B ||||||||||||||||||||||||||||||||||||||||||||||||||||||||||||||||||||||||||||||||||||||||||||||||||||||

4

C ||||||||||||||||||||||||||||||||||||||||||||||||||||||||||||||||||||||||||||||||||||||||||||||||||||||

5

This compound, 2-phenethylamine, is the parent of a large group of medicinally important compounds known as sympathomimetic amines (so called because they mimic the action of the sympathetic nervous system).

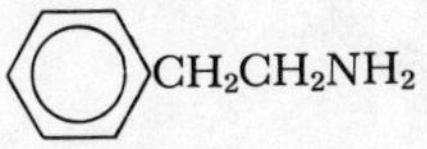

One of its derivatives is adrenaline.

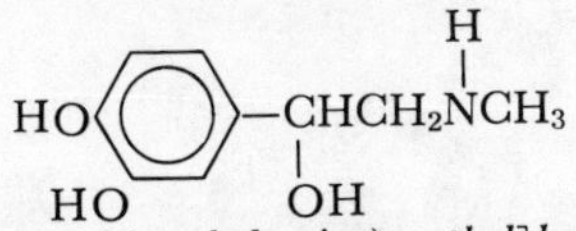

L-3,4-dihydroxy-α-[(methylamino)methyl]benzyl alcohol

Notice that adrenaline. is named as an alcohol rather than an amine because the alcohol function is higher in the order of precedence than the amine function.

A ||||||||||||||||||||||||||||||||||||||||||||||||||||||||||||||||||||||||||||||||||||||||||||||||||||||||||||||||||||||||||||||||||||

You found three isomers with the molecular formula C_3H_9N. That's not enough. Remember that there are three kinds of amines: primary, secondary, and tertiary.

$$R-NH_2 \qquad \begin{matrix} R \\ R' \end{matrix}\!\!\!\!\nearrow\!\!\!\searrow NH \qquad R-\underset{|}{\overset{\overset{R'}{|}}{N}}-R''$$

primary   *secondary*   *tertiary*

There is at least one of each kind with the formula C_3H_9N. Check your formulas again and see if you can find some more isomers. Then turn back and pick another answer.

B ||||||||||||||||||||||||||||||||||||||||||||||||||||||||||||||||||||||||||||||||||||||||||||||||||||||||||||||||||||||||||||||||||||

Right you are. There are four amines with the molecular formula C_3H_9N. Two are primary, one is secondary, and one tertiary. Here are their formulas and names.

$$CH_3CH_2CH_2NH_2 \qquad \underset{|}{\overset{\overset{NH_2}{|}}{CH_3CHCH_3}} \qquad \underset{|}{\overset{\overset{H}{|}}{CH_3CH_2NCH_3}} \qquad \underset{|}{\overset{\overset{CH_3}{|}}{CH_3-N-CH_3}}$$

propylamine   *isopropylamine*   *ethylmethylamine*   *trimethylamine*
(*primary*)   (*primary*)   (*secondary*)   (*tertiary*)

Go on to page 199.

C ||||||||||||||||||||||||||||||||||||||||||||||||||||||||||||||||||||||||||||||||||||||||||||||||||||||||||||||||||||||||||||||||||||

You have found five isomers with the molecular formula C_3H_9N. This is too many. Write skeleton formulas for each one and check carefully to be certain that no two are identical. Watch especially for left-to-right and right-to-left reversals. Then go back and choose another answer.

Aromatic amines may also be primary, secondary, or tertiary. In the last two instances one or two of the hydrocarbon radicals may be aliphatic. The primary amines are properly named as amine derivatives of the aromatic hydrocarbon, but many of them have common names that are customarily used. Aminobenzene, for example, is nearly always referred to as aniline.

NH_2

aminobenzene
(aniline)

Two other aromatic amines with common names are

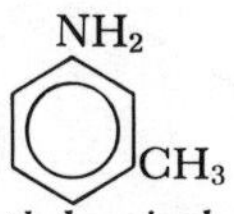

NH_2 CH_3

m-methyl-aminobenzene
(m-toluidine)

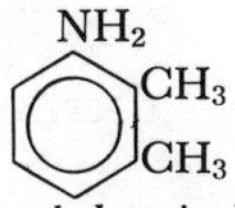

NH_2 CH_3 CH_3

2,3-dimethyl-aminobenzene
(2,3-xylidine)

On the next page are the common and systematic names of a few more aromatic amines. Write their structural formulas. The correct formulas are below each name. Keep them covered until you have written your answer.

Diphenylamine finds use in veterinary medicine as one of the active ingredients in the preventive treatment of screwworm infestation.

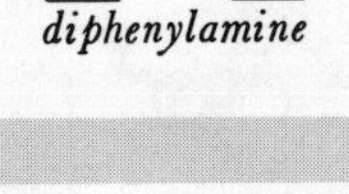

H
|
N

diphenylamine

1. *m*-diaminobenzene (*m*-phenylenediamine)

2. 2-methylaniline (*o*-toluidine)

3. 2,4,6-trinitroaniline (picramide)

4. 2,4,6-trimethylaniline (mesidine)

5. *N,N*-dimethylaniline

$$CH_3NCH_3$$

Go on to page 201.

Many compounds that contain —NH$_2$, —N—, and —N— groups also contain other functional groups. Depending on the order of precedence, they may be named as amino- derivatives of the other function or as amines.

Amino alcohols are an example of this type. Strictly speaking, they should be named alcohols.

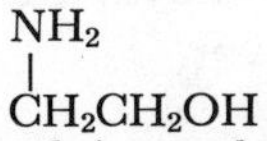

$$\overset{\displaystyle NH_2}{\underset{\displaystyle CH_2CH_2OH}{|}}$$

2-aminoethanol (monoethanolamine)

$$(HOCH_2CH_2)_2NH$$

bis (2-hydroxyethyl) amine (diethanolamine)

Amino acids are important physiological compounds. The α- amino acids result from the hydrolysis of proteins. Two examples are

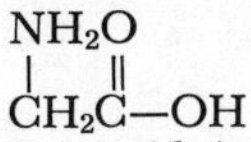

$$\overset{\displaystyle NH_2\,O}{\underset{\displaystyle CH_2C\!-\!OH}{|\quad\|}}$$

aminoethanoic acid (glycine)

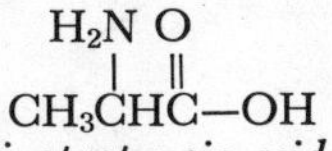

$$\overset{\displaystyle H_2N\ O}{\underset{\displaystyle CH_3CHC\!-\!OH}{|\quad\|}}$$

2-aminopropanoic acid (alanine)

Further discussion of the naming of amino acids will be found later in this chapter.

What is the formula of 1-amino-2-propanol?

A

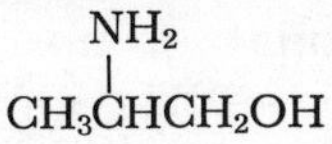

$$\overset{\displaystyle NH_2}{\underset{\displaystyle CH_3CHCH_2OH}{|}}$$

B

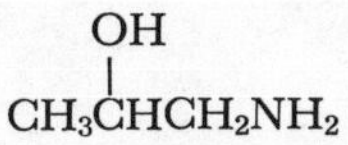

$$\overset{\displaystyle OH}{\underset{\displaystyle CH_3CHCH_2NH_2}{|}}$$

C

$$\overset{\displaystyle O}{\underset{\displaystyle CH_3CCH_2NH_2}{\|}}$$

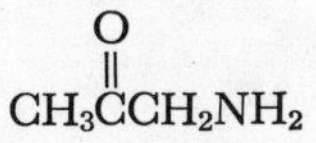

A ||||||||||||||||||||||||||||||||||||||||||||||||||||||||||||||||||||||||||||||||||||||||||||||||||||||||||||||||||||||||||||||||||||||

Incorrect. The formula you chose for 1-amino-2-propanol is

$$\underset{3\quad 2\quad 1}{CH_3\overset{\overset{\displaystyle NH_2}{|}}{C}HCH_2OH}$$

Since the -OH group is attached to the number 1 carbon atom, this formula must represent a derivative of 1-propanol. What is it? 2-amino-1-propanol, of course. Turn back and pick another answer.

B ||||||||||||||||||||||||||||||||||||||||||||||||||||||||||||||||||||||||||||||||||||||||||||||||||||||||||||||||||||||||||||||||||||||

Right. The formula for 1-amino-2-propanol is

$$CH_3\overset{\overset{\displaystyle OH}{|}}{C}HCH_2NH_2$$

Go on to page 203.

C ||||||||||||||||||||||||||||||||||||||||||||||||||||||||||||||||||||||||||||||||||||||||||||||||||||||||||||||||||||||||||||||||||||||

You picked this formula to represent 1-amino-2-propanol.

$$CH_3\overset{\overset{\displaystyle O}{\|}}{C}CH_2NH_2$$

Does it have the right functional groups? According to the name, the compound has an amino group, $-NH_2$, and is an alcohol. The functional group of the alcohols is $-OH$. Your formula doesn't have it. Read page 201 again carefully before you select another answer.

Compounds containing two or more amino groups are named by adding *diamine*, *triamine*, etc., to the name of the parent compound. Many of them have common names as well. Two diamines with very descriptive common names occur among the decomposition products of proteins.

$$H_2N(CH_2)_4NH_2 \qquad 1,4\text{-}butanediamine \;\; (putrescine)$$
$$H_2N(CH_2)_5NH_2 \qquad 1,5\text{-}pentanediamine \;\; (cadaverine)$$

The compound 1,6-hexanediamine is an important intermediate in the synthesis of nylon 66. What is its condensed structural formula?

A ||||||||||||||||||||||||||||||||||||||||||||||||||||||||||||||||||||||||||||||||||||||||||||||||||||||||||||||||

$$H_2N(CH_2)_6NH_2$$

B ||||||||||||||||||||||||||||||||||||||||||||||||||||||||||||||||||||||||||||||||||||||||||||||||||||||||||||||||

$$\overset{\displaystyle H}{\underset{\displaystyle |}{H_2N(CH_2)_3N(CH_2)_2CH_3}}$$

C ||||||||||||||||||||||||||||||||||||||||||||||||||||||||||||||||||||||||||||||||||||||||||||||||||||||||||||||||

$$\overset{\displaystyle NH_2}{\underset{\displaystyle |}{CH_3(CH_2)_4CHNH_2}}$$

A ||||||||||||||||||||||||||||||||||||||||||||||||||||||||||||||||||||||||||||||||||||||||||||||||||||||||||||||||||||||||||||||||||||||

You are correct. The condensed structural formula for 1,6-hexanediamine is

$$H_2N(CH_2)_6NH_2$$

It is also known as hexamethylenediamine. Go on to page 205.

B |||||||||||||||||||||||||||||||||||||||||||||||||||||||||||||||||||||||||||||||||||||||||||||||||||||||||||||||||||||||||||||||||||||| |||

You are incorrect. You picked this formula for 1,6-hexanediamine.

$$\overset{\displaystyle H}{\underset{\displaystyle |}{H_2N(CH_2)_3N(CH_2)_2CH_3}}$$

There are two amino groups in this formula; one primary and one secondary. But there is no continuous chain to form the basis for the name. The compound here would be named as a secondary amine: N-propyl-1,3-propanediamine. Study this name. When you understand it fully, turn back and choose another answer.

C ||||||||||||||||||||||||||||||||||||||||||||||||||||||||||||||||||||||||||||||||||||||||||||||||||||||||||||||||||||||||||||||||||||||

Incorrect. This is the formula you selected to represent 1,6-hexanediamine.

$$\overset{\displaystyle NH_2}{\underset{\displaystyle |}{CH_3(CH_2)_4CHNH_2}}$$

It's a diamine and there is a continuous chain of six carbon atoms. The amino groups, however, are both on the same carbon atom. The name for the compound shown here is 1,1-hexanediamine. Turn back and choose another formula to represent 1,6-hexanediamine.

3.8 AMIDES

Ammonia and amines can react with acids to yield amides (ăm' īdz). The general formulas are illustrated by these equations.

$$\underset{acid}{R-\overset{\overset{\displaystyle O}{\|}}{C}-OH} \quad + \quad \underset{ammonia}{NH_3} \quad \longrightarrow \quad \underset{amide}{R-\overset{\overset{\displaystyle O}{\|}}{C}-NH_2} \quad + \quad H_2O$$

$$\underset{acid}{R-\overset{\overset{\displaystyle O}{\|}}{C}-OH} \quad + \quad \underset{primary\ amine}{R'-NH_2} \quad \longrightarrow \quad \underset{amide}{R-\overset{\overset{\displaystyle O}{\|}}{C}-\overset{\overset{\displaystyle H}{}}{N}-R'} \quad + \quad H_2O$$

$$\underset{acid}{R-\overset{\overset{\displaystyle O}{\|}}{C}-OH} \quad + \quad \underset{secondary\ amine}{R'-\overset{\overset{\displaystyle H}{|}}{N}-R''} \quad \longrightarrow \quad \underset{amide}{R-\overset{\overset{\displaystyle O}{\|}}{C}-N\overset{R'}{\underset{R''}{\diagup\!\!\!\diagdown}}} \quad + \quad H_2O$$

Tertiary amines do not react to produce amides.

There is a similarity between esters and amides in that the imino group, $-\overset{\overset{\displaystyle H}{|}}{N}-$, replaces oxygen as the link between the carbonyl group, $-\overset{\overset{\displaystyle O}{\|}}{C}-$, and an alkyl group.

$$\underset{ester}{R-\overset{\overset{\displaystyle O}{\|}}{C}-O-R'} \qquad\qquad \underset{amide}{R-\overset{\overset{\displaystyle O}{\|}}{C}-\overset{\overset{\displaystyle H}{}}{N}-R'}$$

Simple amides are named by replacing the *-oic acid* in the name of the acid by *amide*. Carbon atoms are numbered in the same way as esters.

$$\underset{\substack{acetamide \text{ or } ethanamide}}{CH_3\overset{\overset{\displaystyle O}{\|}}{C}-NH_2} \qquad\qquad \underset{\substack{2\text{-}chloropropionamide\\ \text{or } 2\text{-}chloropropanamide}}{CH_3\overset{\overset{\displaystyle Cl}{|}}{C}H\overset{\overset{\displaystyle O}{\|}}{C}-NH_2}$$

What is the name of this amide?

$$BrCH_2CH_2CH_2\overset{\overset{\displaystyle O}{\|}}{C}-NH_2$$

A

bromobutyramide

B

4-bromobutylamide

C

4-bromobutyramide

A ||||||||||||||||||||||||||||||||||||||||||||||||||||||||||||||||||||||||||||||||||||||||||||||||||||||||||||||||||||||||||||||||||||||||

Incorrect. You named the compound shown by this formula as bromobutyramide.

$$\underset{\displaystyle BrCH_2CH_2CH_2C-NH_2}{\overset{\displaystyle O}{\overset{\displaystyle \|}{}}}$$

There are two other carbon atoms that can bear the bromine atom. Wouldn't each compound so formed also be bromobutyramide? As usual, the solution is to number the carbon atoms in the chain. When you've added a number to the name, turn back and choose another answer.

B ||||||||||||||||||||||||||||||||||||||||||||||||||||||||||||||||||||||||||||||||||||||||||||||||||||||||||||||||||||||||||||||||||||||||

You are wrong. Look at this formula carefully. What is the functional group?

$$\underset{\displaystyle BrCH_2CH_2CH_2C-NH_2}{\overset{\displaystyle O}{\overset{\displaystyle \|}{}}}$$

Is it a primary amine with the general formula $R-NH_2$, or is it an amide with the general formula $R-\overset{\displaystyle O}{\overset{\displaystyle \|}{C}}-NH_2$? It's an amide. You had better turn back and read page 205 again before selecting another answer.

C ||||||||||||||||||||||||||||||||||||||||||||||||||||||||||||||||||||||||||||||||||||||||||||||||||||||||||||||||||||||||||||||||||||||||

Right you are. The formula shows 4-bromobutyramide.

$$\underset{\displaystyle BrCH_2CH_2CH_2C-NH_2}{\overset{\displaystyle O}{\overset{\displaystyle \|}{}}}$$

Go on to page 207.

Amides that are derived from amines rather than ammonia are named as N- substituted products of the simple amide. For instance

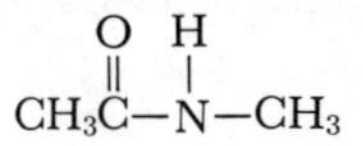

$$\underset{\text{N-methylethanamide}}{CH_3\overset{\overset{O}{\|}}{C}-\overset{\overset{H}{|}}{N}-CH_3}$$

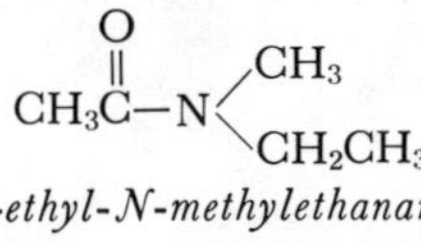

$$\underset{\text{N-ethyl-N-methylethanamide}}{CH_3\overset{\overset{O}{\|}}{C}-N\Big\langle\begin{matrix}CH_3\\CH_2CH_3\end{matrix}}$$

The first is the amide formed from methylamine and ethanoic acid. The second is the amide from ethylmethylamine and ethanoic acid.

The compound acetanilide, used as a pain reliever and an intermediate in organic synthesis, is N-phenylethanamide.

Which of these represents its structural formula?

A ||||||||||||||||||||||||||||||||||||||||||||||||||||||||||||||||||||||||||||||||||||||||||||||||||||||||||||||||||||||||||||||||||

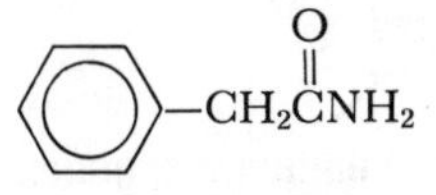

B ||||||||||||||||||||||||||||||||||||||||||||||||||||||||||||||||||||||||||||||||||||||||||||||||||||||||||||||||||||||||||||||||||

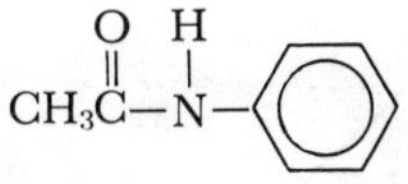

C ||||||||||||||||||||||||||||||||||||||||||||||||||||||||||||||||||||||||||||||||||||||||||||||||||||||||||||||||||||||||||||||||||

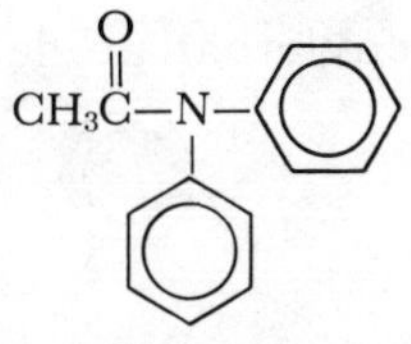

A |||||||||||||||||||||||||||||||||||||||||||||||||||||||||||||||||||||||||||||||||||||||||||||||||||||||||||||||||||||||||||||

Incorrect. This is not the formula for N-phenylethanamide.

$$\bigcirc\!-CH_2\overset{\overset{\displaystyle O}{\|}}{C}-NH_2$$

From the name you can see that acetanilide is a relative of ethanamide, $CH_3\overset{\overset{\displaystyle O}{\|}}{C}-NH_2$. It is the product of the reaction between ethanoic acid and aniline.

$$CH_3\overset{\overset{\displaystyle O}{\|}}{C}-OH \quad + \quad H_2N-\bigcirc \quad \longrightarrow \quad ? \quad + \quad H_2O$$

ethanoic acid   *aniline*   *N-phenylethanamide*

Turn back and choose another answer.

B |||||||||||||||||||||||||||||||||||||||||||||||||||||||||||||||||||||||||||||||||||||||||||||||||||||||||||||||||||||||||||||

You are correct. N-phenylethanamide is the product of the reaction between ethanoic acid and aniline. Go on to page 209.

$$CH_3\overset{\overset{\displaystyle O}{\|}}{C}-OH \quad + \quad H_2N-\bigcirc \quad \longrightarrow \quad CH_3\overset{\overset{\displaystyle O}{\|}}{C}-\overset{\overset{\displaystyle H}{|}}{N}-\bigcirc \quad +H_2O$$

ethanoic acid   *aniline*   *N-phenylethanamide*

C |||||||||||||||||||||||||||||||||||||||||||||||||||||||||||||||||||||||||||||||||||||||||||||||||||||||||||||||||||||||||||||

No. The formula for N-phenylethanamide is not

$$CH_3\overset{\overset{\displaystyle O}{\|}}{C}-N\!\!\begin{array}{c}\bigcirc\\[-2pt]\bigcirc\end{array}$$

This formula shows two phenyl groups attached to the nitrogen. Is there anything in the name to make you think there should be two? If not, the formula must be wrong. Turn back and pick another answer.

Amide linkages are important in both natural and synthetic polymers. The synthetic fiber nylon 66 is formed by the reaction between 1,6-hexanedioic acid and 1,6-hexanediamine. Water is formed as well. The reaction is shown here for only one active functional group on each molecule.

$$HO-\underset{\substack{\| \\ O}}{C}(CH_2)_4\underset{\substack{\| \\ O}}{C}-OH \;+\; H_2N(CH_2)_6NH_2 \;\rightarrow\; HO-\underset{\substack{\| \\ O}}{C}(CH_2)_4\underset{\substack{\| \; | \\ O \;\; H}}{C\,N}(CH_2)_6NH_2 + H_2O$$

1,6-hexanedioic acid   *1,6-hexanediamine*

Notice that both ends of the product molecule have reactive functional groups. Nylon 66, a polymer, is formed when these ends continue to react and form long molecules.

Chains of amino acids that are linked through carboxy and amino groups in similar amide linkages are frequently called peptides. This particular type of amide linkage is known as a peptide linkage or peptide bond. Further examples of peptides will be seen in Chapter 4.

Summary: Nomenclature of Amines and Amides

Amines are organic bases derived from ammonia and can be classified as primary, secondary, or tertiary. This table summarizes the functional groups.

R—NH₂ $\underset{R'}{\overset{R}{\diagdown}}$NH $\underset{R'}{\overset{R}{\diagdown}}$N—R″

primary   *secondary*   *tertiary*

Primary amines are named by adding the suffix *-amine* to the name of the hydrocarbon radical. Secondary and tertiary amines may be named by enumerating the radicals in alphabetical order or as N-substituted derivatives of a primary amine. When numbers are needed to locate substituents, the carbon attached to the nitrogen is always number 1.

Aromatic amines may be primary, secondary, or tertiary. The most common is aminobenzene, or aniline.

aniline

Amino acids contain both an amino group and a carboxy group. Aminoethanoic acid (glycine) is an example. These acids will be discussed in the next section.

Compounds which contain more than one amino group are named by adding *diamine*, *triamine*, etc., to the name of the parent compound.

$$H_2N(CH_2)_4NH_2$$
1,4-butanediamine

Amides result from the reaction between amines or ammonia and carboxylic acids. Ethanamide is an example: $CH_3\overset{\overset{O}{\|}}{C}—NH_2$

The functional group of the amides is $—\overset{\overset{O}{\|}}{C}—N\diagup$ and the general formula

for amides is $R—\overset{\overset{O}{\|}}{C}—N\overset{\diagup R'}{\diagdown R''}$.   R′— and R″— may be hydrogen or aryl or alkyl radicals. Amide linkages are important in biochemistry since they join amino acids to form proteins.

ALCOHOLS

Functional group: —OH
General formula: ROH

Functional group name: *hydroxy*
Series name: *-ol*

PHENOLS

Functional group: —OH
General formula: ⬡—OH

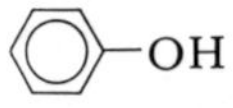

functional group name: *hydroxy*
Series name: *-ol*

ALDEHYDES AND KETONES

Functional group:
$$-\overset{\overset{\text{O}}{\|}}{\text{C}}-$$

General formulas:
$$R-\overset{\overset{\text{O}}{\|}}{\text{C}}-H \text{ (aldehydes)}$$
$$R-\overset{\overset{\text{O}}{\|}}{\text{C}}-R' \text{ (ketones)}$$

Functional group name: *carbonyl*

Series name: *-al*

-one

CARBOXYLIC ACIDS

Functional group:
$$-\overset{\overset{\text{O}}{\|}}{\text{C}}-OH$$

General formula:
$$R-\overset{\overset{\text{O}}{\|}}{\text{C}}-OH$$

Functional group name: *carboxy*

Series name: *-oic acid*

ACYL HALIDES

Functional group:
$$-\overset{\overset{\text{O}}{\|}}{\text{C}}-X$$

General formula:
$$R-\overset{\overset{\text{O}}{\|}}{\text{C}}-X$$

Functional group name: *haloformyl*

Series name: *-yl halide* or
-oyl halide

ACID ANHYDRIDES

Functional group:
$$-\overset{\overset{\text{O}}{\|}}{\text{C}}-O-\overset{\overset{\text{O}}{\|}}{\text{C}}-$$

General formula:
$$R-\overset{\overset{\text{O}}{\|}}{\text{C}}-O-\overset{\overset{\text{O}}{\|}}{\text{C}}-R$$

Functional group name: *none*

Series name: *-ic anhydride*

CARBOXYLIC ACID ESTERS

Functional group:
$$-\overset{\displaystyle O}{\overset{\displaystyle \|}{C}}-O-R'$$

General formula: $R-\overset{\displaystyle O}{\overset{\displaystyle \|}{C}}-O-R'$

Functional group name: *alkoxycarbonyl*

Series name: *-yl* .....*-oate*

ETHERS

Functional group: $-O-$
General formula: $R-O-R'$

Functional group name: *none*
Series name: .... *-yl* .... *-yl ether*

AMINES

Functional groups: $-NH_2$

$$-\overset{\displaystyle H}{\underset{\displaystyle |}{N}}-$$

$$-\overset{\displaystyle |}{\underset{\displaystyle |}{N}}-$$

General formulas: RNH_2 (primary)

$$R-\overset{\displaystyle H}{\underset{\displaystyle |}{N}}-R' \text{ (secondary)}$$

$$R-\overset{\displaystyle R''}{\underset{\displaystyle |}{N}}-R' \text{ (tertiary)}$$

Functional group name: *amino*

Series name: *—amine*

AMIDES

Functional group:
$$-\overset{\displaystyle O}{\overset{\displaystyle \|}{C}}-NH_2$$

General formula: $R-\overset{\displaystyle O}{\overset{\displaystyle \|}{C}}-NH_2$

Functional group name: *carbam*

Series name: *—amide*

Go on to page 213.

3.9 AMINO ACIDS

The importance of amino acids rests largely on the fact that they are the building blocks of animal proteins, the chief components of muscle fibre, skin, nerves, and blood. As you already know, amino acids contain both the amino group and the carboxy group. Hydrolysis of proteins yields mixtures of α-amino acids. An example of an α-amino acid is alanine, or 2-aminopropanoic acid.

$$
\begin{array}{c}
\overset{NH_2}{\underset{|}{}} \quad \overset{O}{\underset{/\!/}{}} \\
CH_3CHC-OH
\end{array}
$$

alanine or *2–aminopropanoic acid*

The amino group is substituted on the carbon atom next to the carboxy group. In the old system of common names, this carbon atom was known as the "alpha" carbon atom. Hence the term α-amino acids. The condensed formula of the α-amino acids is $RCH(NH_2)CO_2H$, and the general structural formula is

$$
\begin{array}{c}
\overset{NH_2}{\underset{|}{}} \quad \overset{O}{\underset{/\!/}{}} \\
R-CH-C-OH
\end{array}
$$

Serine is another amino acid. Its formula is

$$
\begin{array}{c}
\overset{OH}{\underset{|}{}} \overset{NH_2}{\underset{|}{}} \quad \overset{O}{\underset{/\!/}{}} \\
CH_2CHC-OH
\end{array}
$$

What is its preferred systematic name?

A ||||||||||||||||||||||||||||||||||||||||||||||||||||||||||||||||||||||||||||||||||||||||||||||||||||||||||||||

aminohydroxypropanoic acid

B ||||||||||||||||||||||||||||||||||||||||||||||||||||||||||||||||||||||||||||||||||||||||||||||||||||||||||||||

2-amino-3-hydroxypropionic acid

C ||||||||||||||||||||||||||||||||||||||||||||||||||||||||||||||||||||||||||||||||||||||||||||||||||||||||||||||

2-amino-3-hydroxypropanoic acid

A ||||||||||||||||||||||||||||||||||||||||||||||||||||||||||||||||||||||||||||||||||||||||||||||||||||||||||||||||||||||||||

Incorrect. Although the name aminohydroxypropanoic acid does describe the acid represented by this formula, it is not a unique and completely unambiguous name.

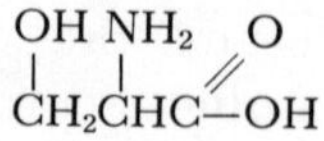

$$\overset{OH}{\underset{|}{C}}\overset{NH_2}{\underset{|}{H_2CHC}}\overset{O}{\overset{\parallel}{C}}-OH$$

By now you should know that whenever there is a possibility of confusion over the location of a substituent group, a number is used to specify its location. Turn back and choose another answer.

B ||||||||||||||||||||||||||||||||||||||||||||||||||||||||||||||||||||||||||||||||||||||||||||||||||||||||||||||||||||||||||

Not quite right. The common name for the carboxylic acid with three carbon atoms in a chain is propionic acid. The systematic name is propanoic acid. Since you were asked for the preferred systematic name of serine, it must be 2-amino-3-hydroxypropanoic acid.

$$\overset{OH}{\underset{|}{C}}\overset{NH_2}{\underset{|}{H_2CHC}}\overset{O}{\overset{\parallel}{C}}-OH$$

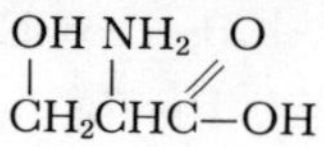

Go on to page 215.

C ||||||||||||||||||||||||||||||||||||||||||||||||||||||||||||||||||||||||||||||||||||||||||||||||||||||||||||||||||||||||||

Correct. The preferred systematic name for serine is 2-amino-3-hydroxypropanoic acid.

$$\overset{OH}{\underset{|}{C}}\overset{NH_2}{\underset{|}{H_2CHC}}\overset{O}{\overset{\parallel}{C}}-OH$$

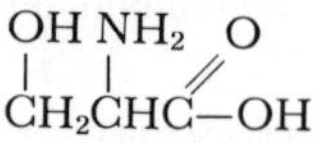

Go on to page 215.

Amino acids are named as acids because of the presence of the carboxy group. Their aqueous solutions may be acidic or basic, however, depending on the relative strength and number of acidic carboxy groups and basic amino groups in the molecule. Most amino acids have equal numbers of amino and carboxy groups and are known as neutral amino acids. A few have more amino groups than carboxy groups and are termed basic amino acids. An example is hydroxylysine.

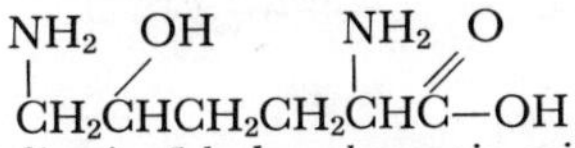

$$\overset{\displaystyle NH_2 \quad OH \qquad NH_2 \quad O}{CH_2CHCH_2CH_2CHC-OH}$$

2,6-diamino-5-hydroxyhexanoic acid
(hydroxylysine)

A few others have more carboxy than amino groups and are known, not surprisingly, as acidic amino acids. Glutamic acid, whose sodium salt is used as a flavor intensifier in foods, is one of them. Glutamic acid is 2-amino-1,5-pentanedioic acid.

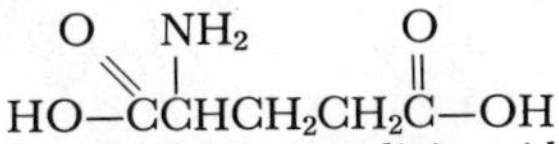

$$\overset{\displaystyle O \quad NH_2 \qquad O}{HO-CCHCH_2CH_2C-OH}$$

2-amino-1,5-pentanedioic acid
(glutamic acid)

The formula for aspartic acid is

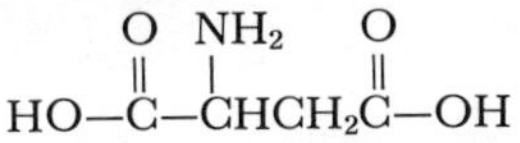

$$\overset{\displaystyle O \quad NH_2 \quad O}{HO-C-CHCH_2C-OH}$$

Is aspartic acid a basic, acidic, or neutral amino acid?

A ||||||||||||||||||||||||||||||||||||||||||||||||||||||||||||||||||||||||||||||||||||||||||||||||||||

acidic

B ||||||||||||||||||||||||||||||||||||||||||||||||||||||||||||||||||||||||||||||||||||||||||||||||||||

basic

C ||||||||||||||||||||||||||||||||||||||||||||||||||||||||||||||||||||||||||||||||||||||||||||||||||||

neutral

A ||||||||||||||||||||||||||||||||||||||||||||||||||||||||||||||||||||||||||||||||||||||||||||||||||||||||||||||||||||||||||||||||||||

You are right. Since aspartic acid has two carboxy groups and one amino group, it is classed as an acidic amino acid.

$$\underset{\substack{\text{2-amino-1,4-butanedioic acid}\\ \text{(aspartic acid)}}}{\overset{\displaystyle \text{O} \quad \text{NH}_2 \quad \text{O}}{\underset{}{\text{HO—CCHCH}_2\text{C—OH}}}}$$

Go on to page 217.

B ||||||||||||||||||||||||||||||||||||||||||||||||||||||||||||||||||||||||||||||||||||||||||||||||||||||||||||||||||||||||||||||||||

Incorrect. This classification of amino acids is based entirely on the relative number of amino and carboxy groups that are present. If they are equal, the acid is termed neutral. If one group or the other predominates, the acid is either acidic or basic. Look at the formula for aspartic acid again carefully before you turn back to choose another answer.

$$\underset{\text{aspartic acid}}{\overset{\displaystyle \text{O} \quad \text{NH}_2 \quad\quad \text{O}}{\text{HO—C—CHCH}_2\text{C—OH}}}$$

C ||||||||||||||||||||||||||||||||||||||||||||||||||||||||||||||||||||||||||||||||||||||||||||||||||||||||||||||||||||||||||||||||||

You are incorrect. Aspartic acid is not classed as a neutral amino acid. This classification of amino acids is based on the relative number of acidic carboxy groups, $\overset{\displaystyle \text{O}}{\text{—C—OH}}$, and basic amino groups, —NH_2. Look at the formula again and then turn back for another answer.

$$\underset{\text{aspartic acid}}{\overset{\displaystyle \text{O} \quad \text{NH}_2 \quad \text{O}}{\text{HO—CCHCH}_2\text{C—OH}}}$$

There are eight amino acids that are known as essential amino acids. This means that to sustain life they must be present in the diet of human beings. All other amino acids needed in metabolism can be synthesized in the body. The eight essential amino acids are isoleucine (ī sŏ lōō′ sēn), leucine (lōō′ sēn), lysine (lī′ sēn), methionine (mĕ thī′ ŏ nēn), phenyl-alanine (fĕn ĭl ăl′ a nēn), threonine (thrē′ŏ nēn), tryptophan (trĭp′ tŏ făn), and valine (văl′ ēn).

Methionine contains sulfur and will be mentioned in the next section.

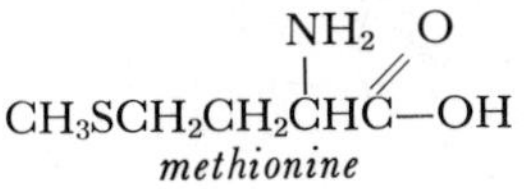

$$\underset{\text{methionine}}{CH_3SCH_2CH_2\overset{\displaystyle NH_2}{\overset{|}{CH}}\overset{\displaystyle O}{\overset{\parallel}{C}}-OH}$$

Tryptophan is 2-amino-3-(3-indolyl)propanoic acid, and is somewhat too complex for this program.

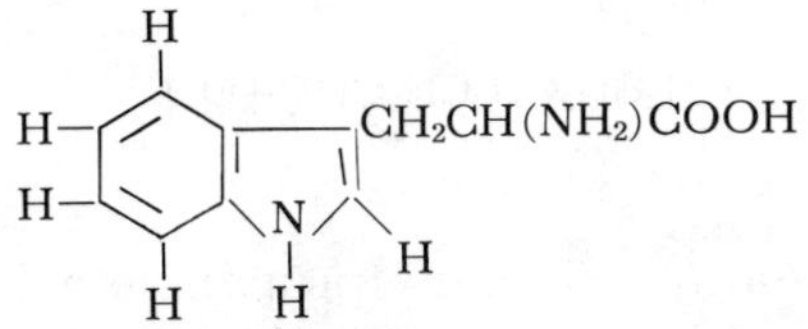

tryptophan

The systematic names for the other six essential amino acids, however, are well within your capability. They are given on the next page, followed by their structural formulas. Write the formula for each one before you uncover it.

Accent, a trade name for monosodium glutamate, is used as a condiment to enhance the flavor of foods, particularly meats. In 1955 more than 23 million pounds were produced, mostly from the hydrolysis of wheat gluten or beet sugar residues. Glutamic acid is α-aminoglutaric acid or 2-amino-1,5-pentanedioic acid.

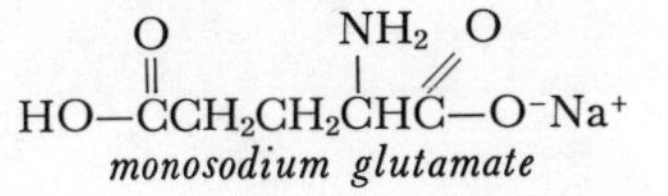

$$\underset{\text{monosodium glutamate}}{HO-\overset{\displaystyle O}{\overset{\parallel}{C}}CH_2CH_2\overset{\displaystyle NH_2}{\overset{|}{CH}}\overset{\displaystyle O}{\overset{\parallel}{C}}-O^-Na^+}$$

1. isoleucine: 2-amino-3-methylpentanoic acid

$$\underset{\text{CH}_3\text{CH}_2\overset{\displaystyle|}{\text{CH}}\overset{\displaystyle/}{\text{CH}}\overset{\displaystyle/\!/}{\text{C}}\text{—OH}}{\overset{\text{CH}_3\ \text{NH}_2\ \text{O}}{}}$$

2. leucine: 2-amino-4-methylpentanoic acid

$$\underset{\text{CH}_3\overset{\displaystyle|}{\text{CH}}\text{CH}_2\text{C}\ \overset{\displaystyle/}{\text{H}}\overset{\displaystyle/\!/}{\text{C}}\text{—OH}}{\overset{\text{CH}_3\qquad\text{NH}_2\ \text{O}}{}}$$

3. lysine: 2,6-diaminohexanoic acid

$$\underset{\overset{\displaystyle|}{\text{CH}_2}\text{CH}_2\text{CH}_2\text{CH}_2\overset{\displaystyle|}{\text{CH}}\overset{\displaystyle/\!/}{\text{C}}\text{—OH}}{\overset{\text{NH}_2\qquad\qquad\text{NH}_2\ \text{O}}{}}$$

4. phenylalanine: 2-amino-3-phenylpropanoic acid

$$\underset{\text{CH}_2\overset{\displaystyle|}{\text{CH}}\overset{\displaystyle/\!/}{\text{C}}\text{—OH}}{\overset{\text{NH}_2\ \text{O}}{}}$$

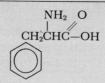

5. threonine: 2-amino-3-hydroxybutanoic acid

$$\underset{\text{CH}_3\overset{\displaystyle|}{\text{CH}}\overset{\displaystyle/}{\text{CH}}\overset{\displaystyle/\!/}{\text{C}}\text{—OH}}{\overset{\text{OH}\ \text{NH}_2\ \text{O}}{}}$$

6. valine: 2-amino-3-methylbutanoic acid

$$\underset{\text{CH}_3\overset{\displaystyle|}{\text{CH}}\overset{\displaystyle/}{\text{CH}}\overset{\displaystyle/\!/}{\text{C}}\text{—OH}}{\overset{\text{CH}_3\ \text{NH}_2\ \text{O}}{}}$$

Go on to page 219.

3.10 ORGANIC SULFUR COMPOUNDS

Many types of organic compounds contain sulfur. Since sulfur has the same number of valence electrons as oxygen, it forms several series of compounds in which it replaces oxygen wholly or in part. A few classes of sulfur-containing compounds will be discussed in this section.

Thiols are the sulfur analogs of alcohols and phenols. They are named by adding the suffix -*thiol* to the name of the parent hydrocarbon or ring system. The common names are formed by naming the alkyl or aryl group and following it with the word mercaptan. Most mercaptans have an unpleasant odor. Ethanethiol can be detected by smell when mixed with air in a ratio of 1 volume to 50,000,000,000 volumes of air.

$$CH_3CH_2SH$$
ethanethiol
(ethyl mercaptan)

The odor of skunk secretions is caused by 1-butanethiol.

$$CH_3CH_2CH_2CH_2SH$$
1-butanethiol
(n-butyl mercaptan)

The functional group, -SH, is known as the sulfhydryl or mercapto group. -SR is the alkylthio group. When it occurs along with a functional group of higher precedence such as carboxy, amino, or hydroxy, the prefix *mercapto-* denotes the -SH group. For example

$$HSCH_2CH_2OH$$
2-mercaptoethanol

If the hydrogen of the sulfhydryl group has been replaced by an alkyl radical, the name of the radical precedes the prefix thio-. For instance

$$CH_3CH_2SCH_2CH_2OH$$
2-(ethylthio)-ethanol

The groups -SH and -SR occur in many proteins, especially enzymes.

Methionine, the last of the essential amino acids (see page 217), is 2-amino-4(methylthio)butanoic acid. What is its structural formula?

A ||||||||||||||||||||||||||||||||||||||||||||||||||||||||||||||||||||||||||||||||||||||||||||||||

$$
\begin{array}{cccc}
 & \text{H} & \text{H} & \text{NH}_2 & \text{O} \\
 & | & | & | & \| \\
\text{H} - & \text{C} - & \text{C} - & \text{C} - & \text{C} - \text{OH} \\
 & | & | & | & \\
 & \text{SH} & \text{H} & \text{H} &
\end{array}
$$

B ||||||||||||||||||||||||||||||||||||||||||||||||||||||||||||||||||||||||||||||||||||||||||||||||

$$
\begin{array}{cccc}
 & \text{H} & \text{H} & \text{NH}_2 & \text{O} \\
 & | & | & | & \| \\
\text{H} - & \text{C} - & \text{C} - & \text{C} - & \text{C} - \text{OH} \\
 & | & | & | & \\
 & \text{S} & \text{H} & \text{H} & \\
 & | & & & \\
\text{H} - & \text{C} - \text{H} & & & \\
 & | & & & \\
 & \text{H} & & &
\end{array}
$$

C ||||||||||||||||||||||||||||||||||||||||||||||||||||||||||||||||||||||||||||||||||||||||||||||||

$$
\begin{array}{ccccc}
 & \text{H} & \text{H} & \text{H} & \text{NH}_2 & \text{O} \\
 & | & | & | & | & \| \\
\text{H} - & \text{C} - & \text{C} - & \text{C} - & \text{C} - & \text{C} - \text{OH} \\
 & | & | & | & | & \\
 & \text{H} & \text{SH} & \text{H} & \text{H} &
\end{array}
$$

A ||||||||||||||||||||||||||||||||||||||||||||||||||||||||||||||||||||||||||||||||||||||||||||||||||||||||||||||||||||||||||

Incorrect. This formula does not represent 2-amino-4-(methylthio)-butanoic acid.

$$
\begin{array}{cccc}
\text{H} & \text{H} & \text{NH}_2 & \text{O} \\
| & | & | & \| \\
\text{H}-\text{C}-\text{C}-\text{C}-\!\!\!\!\!-\text{C}-\text{OH} \\
| & | & | \\
\text{SH} & \text{H} & \text{H}
\end{array}
$$

Your error is one of omission rather than commission. Compare the name with the formula item by item. You will find something in the name that is not in the formula. It is a methyl group. Read page 219 again to learn where to place it in the formula.

B ||||||||||||||||||||||||||||||||||||||||||||||||||||||||||||||||||||||||||||||||||||||||||||||||||||||||||||||||||||||||||

Right. The structural formula for methionine is

$$
\begin{array}{cccc}
\text{H} & \text{H} & \text{NH}_2 & \text{O} \\
| & | & | & \| \\
\text{H}-\text{C}-\text{C}-\text{C}-\!\!\!\!\!-\text{C}-\text{OH} \\
| & | & | \\
\text{S} & \text{H} & \text{H} \\
| \\
\text{H}-\text{C}-\text{H} \\
| \\
\text{H}
\end{array}
$$

It is one of the eight essential amino acids. Go on to page 221.

C ||||||||||||||||||||||||||||||||||||||||||||||||||||||||||||||||||||||||||||||||||||||||||||||||||||||||||||||||||||||||||

You are incorrect. Methionine is 2-amino-4-(methylthio)butanoic acid. Look carefully at the formula you picked.

$$
\begin{array}{ccccc}
\text{H} & \text{H} & \text{H} & \text{NH}_2 & \text{O} \\
| & | & | & | & \| \\
\text{H}-\text{C}-\text{C}-\text{C}-\text{C}-\!\!\!\!\!-\text{C}-\text{OH} \\
| & | & | & | \\
\text{H} & \text{SH} & \text{H} & \text{H}
\end{array}
$$

Notice that it has five carbon atoms in the continuous chain. That would make it a derivative of pentanoic acid, wouldn't it? Your formula shows a mercapto- group whereas the name calls for a methylthio- group. Make both of these changes and then choose another answer.

Sulfides are the sulfur analogs of ethers and are named in a similar manner. Their general formula is R—S—R. Simple symmetrical sulfides such as methyl sulfide and phenyl sulfide have the formulas:

CH_3SCH_3

methyl sulfide

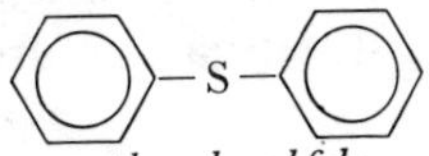

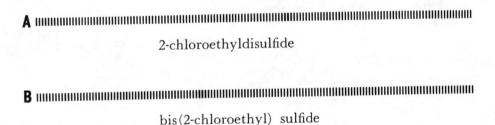

phenyl sulfide

Unsymmetrical sulfides are named by giving the names of the two radicals followed by the word sulfide. For instance

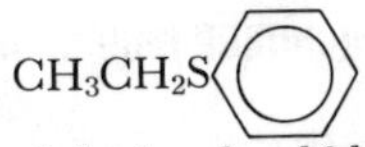

ethyl phenyl sulfide

Mustard gas, one of the powerful vesicants used in warfare, is not really a gas but an oily liquid which boils at 217° C. Its condensed structural formula is

$ClCH_2CH_2SCH_2CH_2Cl$

What is its preferred systematic name?

A ||||||||||||||||||||||||||||||||||||||||||||||||||||||||||||||||||||||||||||||||||||||||||||||||||||||||||||||||||

2-chloroethyldisulfide

B ||||||||||||||||||||||||||||||||||||||||||||||||||||||||||||||||||||||||||||||||||||||||||||||||||||||||||||||||||

bis(2-chloroethyl) sulfide

C ||||||||||||||||||||||||||||||||||||||||||||||||||||||||||||||||||||||||||||||||||||||||||||||||||||||||||||||||||

2-chloroethyl sulfide

A ||||||||||||||||||||||||||||||||||||||||||||||||||||||||||||||||||||||||||||||||||||||||||||||||||||||||||||||||||||||||||||||||||||||

Incorrect. Organic sulfides have the general formula R—S—R. The family called the disulfides has the general formula R—S—S—R. Which family does mustard gas belong to?

$$ClCH_2CH_2SCH_2CH_2Cl$$

Turn back and choose another answer.

B ||||||||||||||||||||||||||||||||||||||||||||||||||||||||||||||||||||||||||||||||||||||||||||||||||||||||||||||||||||||||||||||||||||||

Right. The multiplicative prefixes *bis-*, *tris-*, etc., are used to prevent confusion when a substituted radical appears more than once in an organic molecule. In mustard gas, the 2-chloroethyl group needs to be given the *bis-* prefix. Mustard gas is bis(2-chloroethyl) sulfide. Go on to page 223.

C ||||||||||||||||||||||||||||||||||||||||||||||||||||||||||||||||||||||||||||||||||||||||||||||||||||||||||||||||||||||||||||||||||||||

Incorrect. The preferred systematic name for mustard gas is not 2-chloroethyl sulfide. When the radical is complex, as the 2-chloroethyl radical is, the multiplicative prefixes *bis-*, *tris-*, etc., must be used. Mustard gas is properly named bis(2-chloroethyl) sulfide. Go on to page 223.

Sulfoxides and sulfones are compounds which contain both sulfur and oxygen. Their general formulas are

$$R-\underset{\underset{}{\overset{\overset{O}{\|}}{S}}}{}-R$$

sulfoxide

$$R-\underset{\underset{O}{\|}}{\overset{\overset{O}{\|}}{S}}-R$$

sulfone

Methyl sulfoxide has been used for many years as an organic solvent.

$$CH_3-\underset{}{\overset{\overset{O}{\|}}{S}}-CH_3$$

It recently came into prominence under the name dimethyl sulfoxide (DMSO).

Sulfonic acids contain the functional group —SO_3H. Although they are not prepared in this way, they may be viewed as the product obtained by replacing one hydroxy group in sulfuric acid with an aklyl or aryl group

$$HO-\underset{\underset{O}{\|}}{\overset{\overset{O}{\|}}{S}}-OH$$

sulfuric acid

$$CH_3CH_2\underset{\underset{O}{\|}}{\overset{\overset{O}{\|}}{S}}-OH$$

ethanesulfonic acid

The names are formed by adding the functional ending *sulfonic acid* to the name of the corresponding hydrocarbon. The general formula is RSO_3H.

Benzenesulfonic acid is an important intermediate in organic synthesis. What is its formula?

A |||||||||||||||||||||||||||||||||||||||||||||||||||||||||||||||||||||||||||||||||||||||||||||||||||||

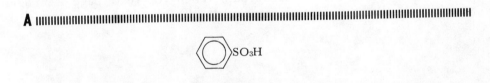

B |||||||||||||||||||||||||||||||||||||||||||||||||||||||||||||||||||||||||||||||||||||||||||||||||||||

C |||||||||||||||||||||||||||||||||||||||||||||||||||||||||||||||||||||||||||||||||||||||||||||||||||||

A ||||||||||||||||||||||||||||||||||||||||||||||||||||||||||||||||||||||||||||||||||||||||||||||||||||||||||||||||||||||||||||||||

You are correct. The formula for benzenesulfonic acid is

$$\bigcirc\!\!-\!\!SO_3H$$

Continue on to page 225.

B ||||||||||||||||||||||||||||||||||||||||||||||||||||||||||||||||||||||||||||||||||||||||||||||||||||||||||||||||||||||||||||||||

Incorrect. This formula does not have the proper functional group to be a sulfonic acid. The functional group of the sulfonic acids is —SO_3H. The formula shown here

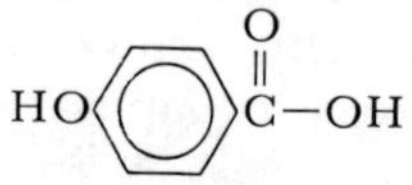

$$HO\!\!-\!\!\bigcirc\!\!-\!\!\overset{\overset{O}{\|}}{C}\!\!-\!\!OH$$

is a derivative of benzoic acid, a carboxylic acid. Turn back to page 223 and choose another answer.

C ||||||||||||||||||||||||||||||||||||||||||||||||||||||||||||||||||||||||||||||||||||||||||||||||||||||||||||||||||||||||||||||||

You are wrong. This formula does not represent a sulfonic acid. It does not have the right functional group.

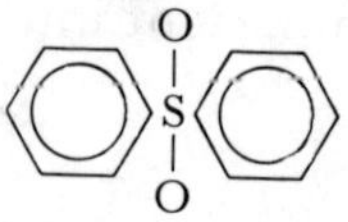

$$\bigcirc\!\!-\!\!\overset{\overset{O}{|}}{\underset{\underset{O}{|}}{S}}\!\!-\!\!\bigcirc$$

Sulfonic acids have the —SO_3H group. When you read page 223 again, you will see that this formula represents phenyl sulfone.

Sulfonic acids form both esters and amides. The amide of benzenesulfonic acid has the formula

SO₂NH₂

benzenesulfonamide

The amide can be viewed as the result of the reaction between the hydroxy group and ammonia as shown here

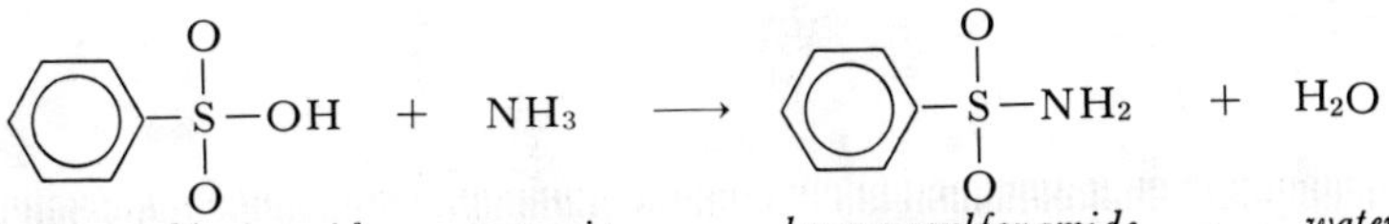

benzenesulfonic acid   *ammonia*   *benzenesulfonamide*   *water*

Sulfanilamide, one of the sulfa drugs, is the amide of another aromatic sulfonic acid.

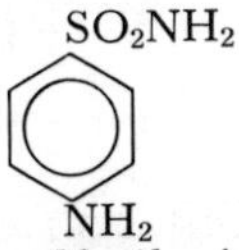

SO₂NH₂

NH₂
sulfanilamide

The acid, sulfanilic acid, is

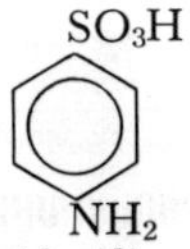

SO₃H

NH₂
sulfanilic acid

What is the systematic name of sulfanilic acid?

A |||||||||||||||||||||||||||||||||||||||||||||||||||||||||||||||||||||||||||||||||||||||||||||||||||||||

p-aminobenzenesulfonic acid

B |||||||||||||||||||||||||||||||||||||||||||||||||||||||||||||||||||||||||||||||||||||||||||||||||||||||

aminobenzenesulfonic acid

C |||||||||||||||||||||||||||||||||||||||||||||||||||||||||||||||||||||||||||||||||||||||||||||||||||||||

p-aminophenylsulfonic acid

Although the reasons may not be apparent, this compound was discovered during the course of research on fluorinated hydrocarbons.

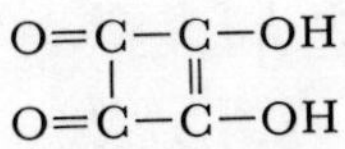

$$O=C-C-OH$$
$$O=C-C-OH$$

The name of the compound suggests that chemists are not entirely devoid of humor. Can you guess it? See answer on page 226.

A ||||||||||||||||||||||||||||||||||||||||||||||||||||||||||||||||||||||||||||||||||||||||||||||||||||||||||||||||||

Right you are. Sulfanilic acid is *p*-aminobenzenesulfonic acid.

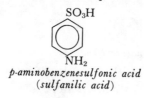

p-aminobenzenesulfonic acid
(sulfanilic acid)

Go on to page 227.

B ||||||||||||||||||||||||||||||||||||||||||||||||||||||||||||||||||||||||||||||||||||||||||||||||||||||||||||||||||

You named sulfanilic acid as aminobenzenesulfonic acid.

You are right as far as you went, but you did not go far enough. Aren't there other places where the amino group could be attached to the ring? If there are, the location must be specified. Turn back and choose another answer.

C ||||||||||||||||||||||||||||||||||||||||||||||||||||||||||||||||||||||||||||||||||||||||||||||||||||||||||||||||||

Incorrect. Sulfanilic acid is not *p*-aminophenylsulfonic acid. When a functional group such as —SO₃H or —COOH is substituted on a benzene ring, the name benzene is maintained. For example, phthalic acid is 1,2-benzenedicarboxylic acid.

Benzenesulfonic acid is

Turn back to page 225 and choose another answer.

O=C—C—OH
| ‖
O=C—C—OH
squaric acid
(No kidding.)

Alkylated benzenesulfonic acid salts are used in detergents. They are present as mixtures rather than individual pure compounds. Typical formulas for the parent acids are

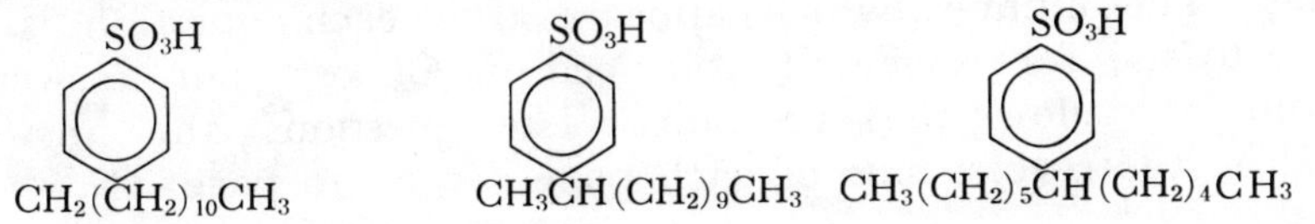

$$SO_3H \qquad\qquad SO_3H \qquad\qquad SO_3H$$

$$CH_2(CH_2)_{10}CH_3 \qquad CH_3CH(CH_2)_9CH_3 \quad CH_3(CH_2)_5CH(CH_2)_4CH_3$$

The aromatic ring may be substituted on any carbon of the 12-carbon chain. Detergents having the ring at or near the end of the chain are claimed to be most efficient.

As a final exercise for this chapter on functional groups, you need the opportunity to demonstrate your knowledge of them as well as compounds which contain them. On the following pages are 20 matching questions. The number which appears after each question is a page reference to use for review if you need it. Choose your answers from the formulas below the questions. The questions and answers are matched on the reverse side of each page. Go on to page 229.

1. Secondary aliphatic alcohol (123)
2. A diol (125)
3. An aromatic alcohol (127)
4. An aliphatic aldehyde (133)
5. Benzaldehyde (137)

6. A ketone (139)
7. A carboxylic acid (145)
8. Benzoic acid (159)
9. An anhydride (161)
10. An acyl chloride (163)

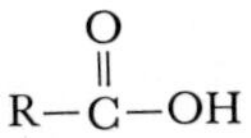

$$\begin{matrix} & O \\ & \| \\ R-&C-OH \end{matrix}$$

(a)

$$\begin{matrix} & OH \\ & | \\ R-&C-R' \\ & | \\ & R'' \end{matrix}$$

(b)

$$\begin{matrix} & O \\ & \| \\ R-&C-Cl \end{matrix}$$

(c)

CH_3O⟨benzene ring with OH⟩CH_3

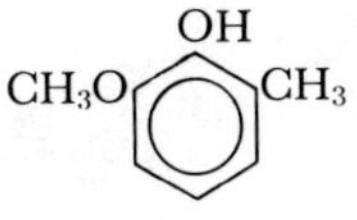

(d)

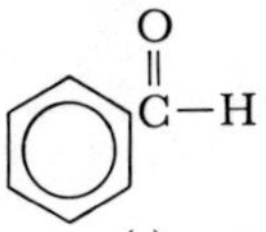

⟨benzene ring⟩$\overset{O}{\overset{\|}{C}}-H$

(e)

$$\begin{matrix} & O \\ & \| \\ R-&C-OCl \end{matrix}$$

(f)

$\overset{O}{\overset{\|}{C}}-OH$⟨benzene ring⟩

(g)

$$\begin{matrix} & O \\ & \| \\ R-&C-R' \end{matrix}$$

(h)

$$\begin{matrix} & OH \\ & | \\ R-&C-R' \\ & | \\ & H \end{matrix}$$

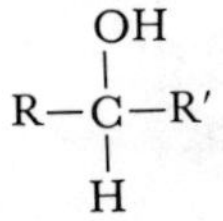

(i)

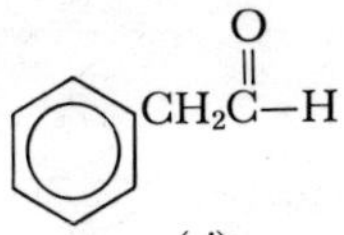

⟨benzene ring⟩$CH_2\overset{O}{\overset{\|}{C}}-H$

(j)

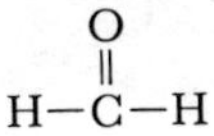

$$\begin{matrix} & O \\ & \| \\ H-&C-H \end{matrix}$$

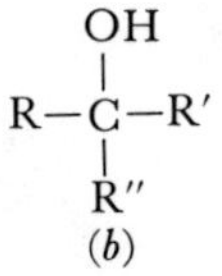

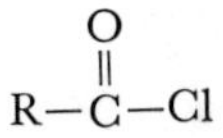

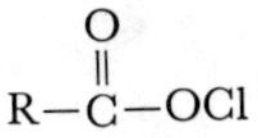

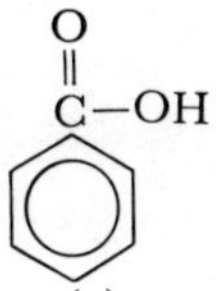

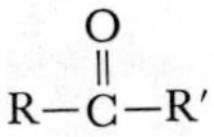

(k)

$$\begin{matrix} & O & & O \\ & \| & & \| \\ R-&C-&O-&C-R \end{matrix}$$

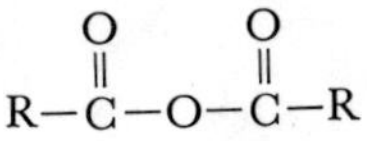

(l)

$HOCH_2CH_2OH$

(m)

1. *i*

2. *m*

3. *d*

4. *k*

5. *e*

6. *h*

7. *a* or *g*

8. *g*

9. *l*

10. *c*

Go on to page 231

11. An ester (165)
12. A mixed ether (177)
13. A mixed amine (197)
14. A primary amine (193)
15. A tertiary amine (193)

16. Aniline (199)
17. An amide (205)
18. An amino acid (213)
19. A sulfide (221)
20. A sulfonic acid (223)

$C_6H_5-NH_2$

(n)

$R-NH_2$

(o)

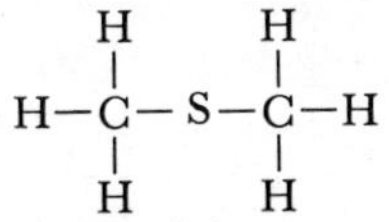

$H-\overset{\overset{\displaystyle H}{|}}{\underset{\underset{\displaystyle H}{|}}{C}}-S-\overset{\overset{\displaystyle H}{|}}{\underset{\underset{\displaystyle H}{|}}{C}}-H$

(p)

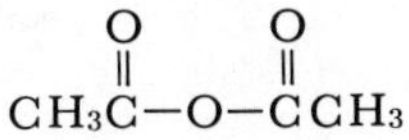

$CH_3\overset{\overset{\displaystyle O}{\|}}{C}-O-\overset{\overset{\displaystyle O}{\|}}{C}CH_3$

(q)

$CH_3CH_2OCH_3$

(r)

$H_3C-C_6H_4-SO_3H$

(s)

CH_3SSCH_3

(t)

$C_6H_5-HNCH_3$

(u)

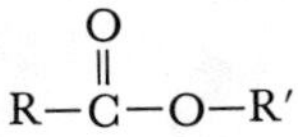

$R-\overset{\overset{\displaystyle O}{\|}}{C}-O-R'$

(v)

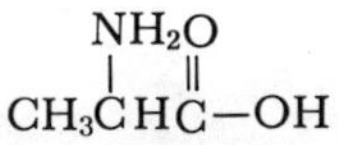

$CH_3\overset{\overset{\displaystyle NH_2}{|}}{C}H\overset{\overset{\displaystyle O}{\|}}{C}-OH$

(w)

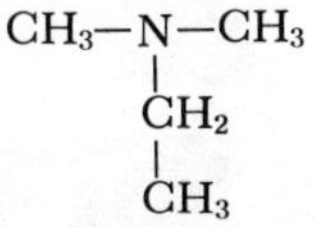

$CH_3-\overset{\overset{\displaystyle CH_3}{|}}{\underset{\underset{\displaystyle CH_2}{|}}{N}}-CH_3$
    $\overset{}{\underset{\underset{\displaystyle CH_3}{|}}{}}$

(x)

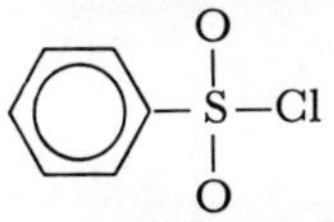

$C_6H_5-\overset{\overset{\displaystyle O}{\|}}{\underset{\underset{\displaystyle O}{\|}}{S}}-Cl$

(y)

$R-\overset{\overset{\displaystyle O}{\|}}{C}-\overset{\overset{\displaystyle H}{|}}{N}-R'$

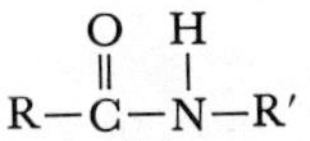

(z)

11. *v*

12. *r*

13. *u*

14. *o* or *n*

15. *x*

16. *n*

17. *z*

18. *w*

19. *p*

20. *s*

4

Natural Products

Organic compounds derived from living or once-living plant and animal organisms are called natural products. An almost infinite variety of these compounds has been isolated and identified. Their structures are usually rather complicated and, for this reason, their nomenclature leans heavily upon common names. They can be grouped into about a dozen classes on the basis of certain structural features and chemical reactions. Three classes — carbohydrates, proteins, and fats — are particularly important because they are the three main foodstuffs. Each will be discussed briefly in this chapter.

4.1 CARBOHYDRATES

Carbohydrates are compounds of carbon, hydrogen, and oxygen in which the hydrogen and oxygen are ordinarily present in the same ratio as they are in water: 2 to 1. The term carbohydrate stems from this fact. Many of them have the empirical formula $C_nH_{2n}O_n$ which formally corresponds to a "hydrate of carbon," $C_n(H_2O)_n$. Carbohydrates are synthesized more or less directly from CO_2 and H_2O in photosynthesis. Sugar, starch, and cellulose are all carbohydrates. Sugars, besides being foodstuffs, are important functional parts of all living organisms. Starch is the principal constituent of seeds and grain, while cellulose is the main constituent of wood.

Which of these formulas represents a typical carbohydrate?

A |||||||||||||||||||||||||||||||||||||||||||||||||||||||||||||||||||||||||||||||||||||||||||||||||||||||||

$C_{12}H_{22}O_{11}$

B |||||||||||||||||||||||||||||||||||||||||||||||||||||||||||||||||||||||||||||||||||||||||||||||||||||||||

$C_6H_{10}O_6$

C |||||||||||||||||||||||||||||||||||||||||||||||||||||||||||||||||||||||||||||||||||||||||||||||||||||||||

$C_{12}H_{22}O_{11}N$

A ||||||||||||||||||||||||||||||||||||||||||||||||||||||||||||||||||||||||||||||||||||||||||||||||||||||||||||||||||||||||||||||

You are right. $C_{12}H_{22}O_{11}$ is the molecular formula for common table sugar, or sucrose. Incidentally, it is the most widely available pure organic compound. Go on to page 235.

B ||||||||||||||||||||||||||||||||||||||||||||||||||||||||||||||||||||||||||||||||||||||||||||||||||||||||||||||||||||||||||||||

No. Although not all carbohydrates have hydrogen and oxygen in the ratio of 2 to 1, most of them do. For example, glucose is $C_6H_{12}O_6$; arabinose is $C_5H_{10}O_5$; erythrose is $C_4H_8O_4$. One exception is rhamnose; its formula is $C_6H_{12}O_5$. Go back and choose another answer.

C ||||||||||||||||||||||||||||||||||||||||||||||||||||||||||||||||||||||||||||||||||||||||||||||||||||||||||||||||||||||||||||||

You are wrong. Carbohydrates contain only three elements: carbon, hydrogen, and oxygen. The latter two are usually present in a ratio of 2 to 1. The formula you have chosen, $C_{12}H_{22}O_{11}N$, contains nitrogen. Turn back and choose another answer.

Structurally, the basic units of carbohydrates are hydroxylated aldehydes and ketones. Here are the formulas of two simple sugars, glucose and fructose:

```
        CHO                        CH2OH
         |                          |
     H—C—OH                     C=O
         |                          |
    HO—C—H                    HO—C—H
         |                          |
     H—C—OH                     H—C—OH
         |                          |
     H—C—OH                     H—C—OH
         |                          |
       CH2OH                      CH2OH
   glucose (aldehyde)          fructose (ketone)
```

The nature of the functional group in the molecules of sugars leads to a further degree of classification. Those with aldehyde groups are known as *aldoses* while those with ketone groups are called *ketoses*.

The number of carbon atoms in the unit is also used as a means of classification. Glucose and fructose both contain six carbon atoms and are hexoses. Pentoses contain five carbon atoms; tetroses, four; and so on. Here are some examples to illustrate these points:

```
                                                       CHO
                             CHO                        |
        CHO                   |                     HO—C—H
         |                H—C—OH                        |
     H—C—OH                   |                     H—C—OH
         |                H—C—OH                        |
       CH2OH                  |                     H—C—OH
                            CH2OH                        |
                                                       CH2OH

   glyceraldehyde         erythrose                  arabinose
   (aldotriose)          (aldotetrose)              (aldopentose)
```

How would you classify galactose?

```
        CHO
         |
     H—C—OH
         |
    HO—C—H
         |
    HO—C—H
         |
     H—C—OH
         |
       CH2OH
```

A ||||||||||||||||||||||||||||||||||||||||||||||||||||||||||||||||||||||||||||||||||||||||||||||||||||||||

aldopentose

B ||||||||||||||||||||||||||||||||||||||||||||||||||||||||||||||||||||||||||||||||||||||||||||||||||||||||

aldohexose

C ||||||||||||||||||||||||||||||||||||||||||||||||||||||||||||||||||||||||||||||||||||||||||||||||||||||||

ketohexose

A ‖‖‖

Partly right. Galactose is an aldose, but not an aldopentose. Count the carbon atoms again. What is the prefix for six?

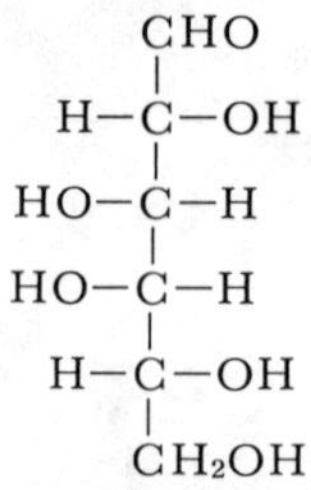

$$
\begin{array}{c}
\text{CHO} \\
| \\
\text{H}-\text{C}-\text{OH} \\
| \\
\text{HO}-\text{C}-\text{H} \\
| \\
\text{HO}-\text{C}-\text{H} \\
| \\
\text{H}-\text{C}-\text{OH} \\
| \\
\text{CH}_2\text{OH} \\
\textit{galactose}
\end{array}
$$

Turn back and choose another answer.

B ‖‖

You are right. Galactose has six carbon atoms and an aldehyde group. Therefore it is an aldohexose. Go on to page 237.

C ‖‖

Wrong. Galactose is a hexose, but not a ketohexose. Don't forget that the functional group of aldehydes is $-\overset{\displaystyle \text{O}}{\overset{\|}{\text{C}}}-\text{H}$; that of ketones is $-\overset{\displaystyle \text{O}}{\overset{\|}{\text{C}}}-$. Look at the formula again. Then choose another answer.

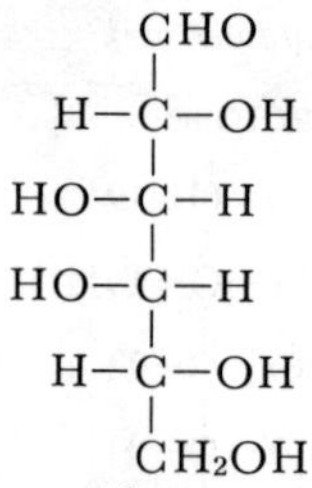

$$
\begin{array}{c}
\text{CHO} \\
| \\
\text{H}-\text{C}-\text{OH} \\
| \\
\text{HO}-\text{C}-\text{H} \\
| \\
\text{HO}-\text{C}-\text{H} \\
| \\
\text{H}-\text{C}-\text{OH} \\
| \\
\text{CH}_2\text{OH} \\
\textit{galactose}
\end{array}
$$

Glucose, fructose, and galactose are called monosaccharides because they are single sugar units and cannot easily be degraded to simpler carbohydrates. When more than one sugar unit is present in a carbohydrate molecule, it is a polysaccharide. Polysaccharides may be further designated as disaccharides, trisaccharides, etc.

Sucrose, ordinary table sugar, is a disaccharide composed of one glucose and one fructose unit.

sucrose
(α–D–*glucosido*)–β–D–*fructofuranoside*

Hydrolysis of sucrose in the presence of acids or the enzyme sucrase yields glucose and fructose.

The complete hydrolysis of starch or cellulose yields only glucose. About 200 to 1,000 glucose units are linked to form starch molecules. The molecular weight of cellulose is higher; it is made up of about 1,500 glucose units.

Carbohydrates exhibit a kind of isomerism that is new to us in this program. It is called optical isomerism. You will recall that isomers are compounds which are chemically different but have the same molecular formula. In the past we have considered only structural isomerism, in which compounds differed in the order in which the atoms were attached to one another. For instance, ethanol and methyl ether are structural isomers.

$$CH_3CH_2OH$$
ethanol C_2H_6O

$$CH_3OCH_3$$
methyl ether C_2H_6O

Glucose and galactose both have the molecular formula $C_6H_{12}O_6$. Furthermore, they can both be represented by the same structural formula. That they are two different compounds can be shown by the different rotations which their solutions give to plane-polarized light. This effect is the origin of the term optical isomerism.

The difference between glucose and galactose lies in the spatial arrangement of the atoms in the molecules. This spatial arrangement is known as *configuration*. Only a brief discussion of configuration can be included in this program.

What kind of isomerism accounts for the difference between glucose and fructose?

glucose

fructose

A ||||||||||||||||||||||||||||||||||||||||||||||||||||||||||||||||||||||||||||||||||||||||||||||||||||||||||||

Optical isomerism

B ||||||||||||||||||||||||||||||||||||||||||||||||||||||||||||||||||||||||||||||||||||||||||||||||||||||||||||

Structural isomerism

C ||||||||||||||||||||||||||||||||||||||||||||||||||||||||||||||||||||||||||||||||||||||||||||||||||||||||||||

No isomerism at all

Answers are on page 240.

"Pep pills, bennies, and goof balls" contain either Benzedrine or Dexedrine. Benzedrine, whose generic name is amphetamine, is a racemic mixture of the compound shown here; Dexedrine is the dextrorotatory isomer and its generic name is dextroamphetamine.

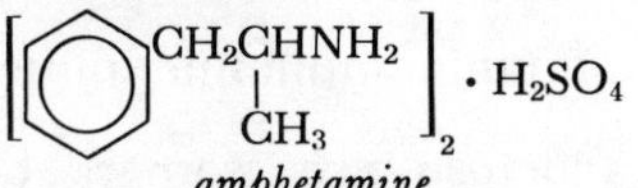

$$\left[\bigcirc\kern-0.5em\begin{array}{c} CH_2CHNH_2 \\ | \\ CH_3 \end{array} \right]_2 \cdot H_2SO_4$$

amphetamine
DL-*α-methylphenethylamine sulfate*

A ||||||||||||||||||||||||||||||||||||||||||||||||||||||||||||||||||||||||||||||||||||||||||||||||||||||||||||||||||

You are wrong. Both glucose and fructose are optically active, but the difference is more apparent. You can see that glucose is an aldohexose whereas fructose is a ketohexose. This type of isomerism is sometimes called functional isomerism, but we have given it another name. Turn back and choose another answer.

```
        CHO                      CH₂OH
         |                         |
    H—C—OH                     C=O
         |                         |
   HO—C—H                    HO—C—H
         |                         |
    H—C—OH                     H—C—OH
         |                         |
    H—C—OH                     H—C—OH
         |                         |
      CH₂OH                     CH₂OH
     glucose                    fructose
```

B ||||||||||||||||||||||||||||||||||||||||||||||||||||||||||||||||||||||||||||||||||||||||||||||||||||||||||||||||||

You are right. Glucose and fructose are structural isomers. The atoms are attached to each other in different ways. Glucose is an aldohexose while fructose is a ketohexose. This type of isomerism is sometimes termed functional isomerism, but we have called it structural isomerism. Go on to page 241.

C ||||||||||||||||||||||||||||||||||||||||||||||||||||||||||||||||||||||||||||||||||||||||||||||||||||||||||||||||||

Wrong. Glucose and fructose are isomers because they both have the molecular formula $C_6H_{12}O_6$. Examine the formulas closely when you turn back to see if you can discover any difference between the two.

Optical isomerism is characteristic of molecules which lack symmetry. The condition necessary for the existence of optical activity is that the arrangement of the atoms in a molecule be such that the molecule and its mirror image are not superposable. If a molecule has a plane or center of symmetry, it and its mirror image are superposable; they are optically inactive. Consider these two pitchers for a moment.

(a) (b)

A plane through pitcher (a) would bisect it and is called a plane of symmetry. Pitcher (b) has no such plane of symmetry. Pitcher (a) and its mirror image are superposable; pitcher (b) and its mirror image are not.

Since it is not always easy to visualize elements of symmetry in molecules, a simple system has been devised to determine whether or not a molecule is capable of optical activity. If a carbon atom has four different groups or atoms attached to it, it is called an *asymmetric carbon atom* and the molecule can have optical isomers. To prove to yourself that molecules containing asymmetric carbon atoms are not superposable, construct the tetrahedral models on pages 243 and 245. The two are nonsuperposable mirror images of each other.

Which of these compounds has an asymmetric carbon atom?

A ||||||||||||||||||||||||||||||||||||||||||||||||||||||||||||||||||||||||||||||||||||||||||||||||||||||||||||

$$\underset{\underset{Cl}{|}}{\overset{\overset{I}{|}}{Br-C-Cl}}$$

B ||||||||||||||||||||||||||||||||||||||||||||||||||||||||||||||||||||||||||||||||||||||||||||||||||||||||||||

$$\underset{\underset{OH}{|}}{\overset{\overset{CH_2Cl}{|}}{Cl_2CH-C-CH_3}}$$

C ||||||||||||||||||||||||||||||||||||||||||||||||||||||||||||||||||||||||||||||||||||||||||||||||||||||||||||

$$\overset{\overset{Br}{|}}{Cl-C=CH_2}$$

A ||||||||||||||||||||||||||||||||||||||||||||||||||||||||||||||||||||||||||||||||||||||||||||||||||||||||||

Wrong. The carbon atom in

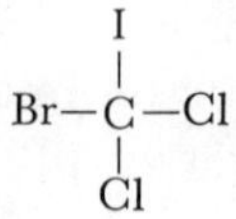

$$Br-\underset{\underset{Cl}{|}}{\overset{\overset{I}{|}}{C}}-Cl$$

is not asymmetric. The compound does not have optically active isomers. If you mark your model tetrahedrons to represent the compound, you will discover that they are always superposable. Turn back to page 241 and select another answer.

B ||||||||||||||||||||||||||||||||||||||||||||||||||||||||||||||||||||||||||||||||||||||||||||||||||||||||||

Right. The carbon atom indicated by * is asymmetric because

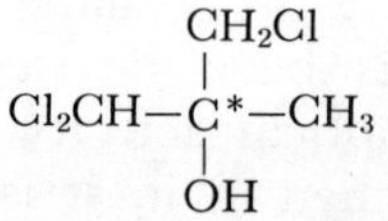

$$Cl_2CH-\underset{\underset{OH}{|}}{\overset{\overset{CH_2Cl}{|}}{C}}*-CH_3$$

it is attached to four different groups: $-CH_2Cl$, $-CHCl_2$, $-CH_3$, and $-OH$. If you mark your tetrahedrons to show mirror images of this compound, you will find that they are not superposable. The compound could have two optically active froms. Go on to page 243.

C ||||||||||||||||||||||||||||||||||||||||||||||||||||||||||||||||||||||||||||||||||||||||||||||||||||||||||

You are wrong. An asymmetric carbon atom must be attached to four different groups. Is this true of either carbon atom in this compound?

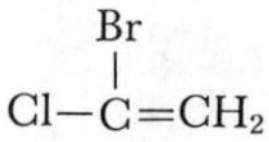

$$Cl-\underset{\underset{}{\overset{\overset{Br}{|}}{C}}}=CH_2$$

The presence of the double bond limits both carbons to three groups and neither is asymmetric. Go back and pick another answer.

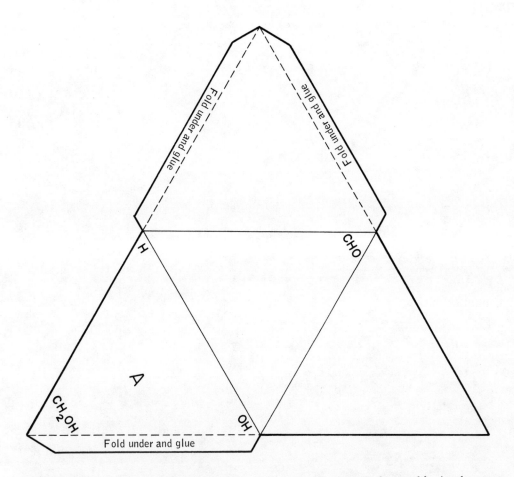

Figure 2. Tetrahedral model of L(+)glyceraldehyde. Cut out and assemble in the same way as Figure 1. See also page 249.

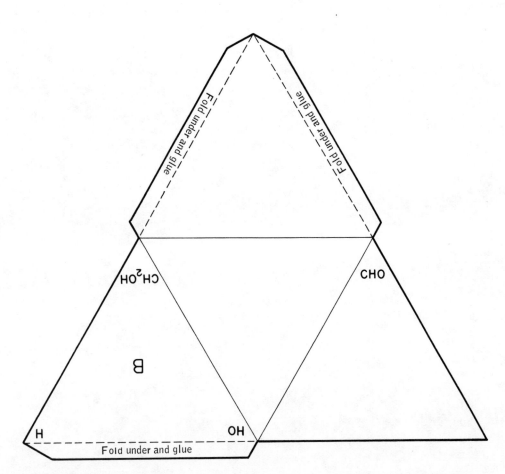

Figure 3. Tetrahedral model of D(−)glyceraldehyde. Cut out and assemble in the same way as Figure 1. See also page 249.

If a given structural formula has one asymmetric carbon atom, there may be two optical isomers which will rotate plane-polarized light equally, but in opposite directions. The two forms are called *enantiomers* (ĕn ăn' tĭ ŏ mĕrz)—a general term used to designate mirror-image forms that are not superposable. Your two models might represent enantiomers.

An equimolar mixture of enantiomers does not rotate plane-polarized light. The rotations of the two optically active isomers cancel each other. Such a 50-50 mixture is known as a *racemic* (ră sē' mĭk) *mixture*.

The maximum number of optical isomers possible in compounds with more than one asymmetric carbon atom is 2^n where n is the number of asymmetric carbon atoms in the molecule. The structural formula for glucose has four asymmetric carbon atoms. Hence 16 optical isomers are possible. All of them are known.

$$
\begin{array}{c}
CHO \\
| \\
H-C^*-OH \\
| \\
HO-C^*-H \\
| \\
H-C^*-OH \\
| \\
H-C^*-OH \\
| \\
CH_2OH
\end{array}
$$

glucose

How many optical isomers can xylose have?

$$
\begin{array}{c}
CHO \\
| \\
H-C-OH \\
| \\
HO-C-H \\
| \\
H-C-OH \\
| \\
CH_2OH
\end{array}
$$

xylose

A ||||||||||||||||||||||||||||||||||||||||||||||||||||||||||||||||||||||||||||||||||||||||||||

4

B ||||||||||||||||||||||||||||||||||||||||||||||||||||||||||||||||||||||||||||||||||||||||||||

8

C ||||||||||||||||||||||||||||||||||||||||||||||||||||||||||||||||||||||||||||||||||||||||||||

16

D ||||||||||||||||||||||||||||||||||||||||||||||||||||||||||||||||||||||||||||||||||||||||||||

Help!

A |||||||||||||||||||||||||||||||||||||||||||||||||||||||||||||||||||||||||||||||||||||||||||||||||||||||||

Wrong. Your answer is too small. Remember that the number of possible isomers is given by 2^n, where n is the number of asymmetric carbons in the molecule. An asymmetric carbon atom is one which is attached to *four* different atoms or groups. Go back and examine the formula again.

B |||||||||||||||||||||||||||||||||||||||||||||||||||||||||||||||||||||||||||||||||||||||||||||||||||||||||

Right. There are three asymmetric carbon atoms in xylose.

$$
\begin{array}{c}
\text{CHO} \\
| \\
\text{H}-\overset{}{\text{C}}{}^*-\text{OH} \\
| \\
\text{HO}-\overset{}{\text{C}}{}^*-\text{H} \\
| \\
\text{H}-\overset{}{\text{C}}{}^*-\text{OH} \\
| \\
\text{CH}_2\text{OH}
\end{array}
$$

These are indicated by *. The number of possible optical isomers is $2^3 = 8$. Continue to page 249.

C |||||||||||||||||||||||||||||||||||||||||||||||||||||||||||||||||||||||||||||||||||||||||||||||||||||||||

Wrong. Your answer is too large. Remember that an asymmetric carbon atom must be attached to four different atoms or groups. Turn back and examine the formula carefully.

D |||||||||||||||||||||||||||||||||||||||||||||||||||||||||||||||||||||||||||||||||||||||||||||||||||||||||

So you need help. OK, see if this will do it.

$$
\begin{array}{c}
\text{CHO} \\
| \\
\text{H}-\overset{}{\text{C}}-\text{OH} \\
| \\
\text{HO}-\overset{}{\text{C}}-\text{H} \\
| \\
\text{H}-\overset{}{\text{C}}-\text{OH} \\
| \\
\text{CH}_2\text{OH}
\end{array}
$$

To determine the number of possible optical isomers for a given structural formula, we must first count the asymmetric carbon atoms. Asymmetric carbon atoms are attached to *four* different groups or atoms. Neither of the terminal carbons of xylose is asymmetric. One is attached to only three groups and the other is attached to two hydrogens. Examine the other three carbons, then choose an answer.

A compound which rotates the plane of polarization to the right (as the observer faces the light source) is called *dextrorotatory*; one which rotates it to the left is *levorotatory*. Dextrorotatory compounds are indicated by (+) at the beginning of their names; levorotatory forms by (−). For example, (+)-glyceraldehyde and (−)-lactic acid.

The answer to the question "Which of two enantiomorphic models represents the (+) form of a compound and which the (−) form?" is given by its absolute configuration. Until 1951, the question had no answer. However, if the configuration of a reference compound was assigned an arbitrary configuration, the configurations of other optically active compounds could be compared to it. This configuration is known as relative configuration.

The substance used for reference is (+)-glyceraldehyde. In 1951, a special kind of x-ray analysis was used to prove that its absolute configuration is that shown by the perspective formula (*a*). Formula (*b*) is a projection of the perspective formula on the plane of the paper.

	CHO		CHO
(*a*)	H⟨⋮⟩OH	(*b*)	H—C—OH
	CH$_2$OH		CH$_2$OH

Your two models represent (+)-glyceraldehyde (Model A) and its levorotatory enantiomer, (−)-glyceraldehyde (Model B). Model A should help you to grasp the spatial relationships of (*a*) and (*b*).

There is no apparent correlation between the configuration of an asymmetric carbon atom and the direction of rotation. Active compounds are divided into two families on the basis of their configuration, since configuration is more important than direction of rotation. Compounds related to (+)-glyceraldehyde are said to belong to the D (pronounced dee) family, and those related to (−)-glyceraldehyde belong to the L (pronounced ell) family. D and L refer to configuration and not to direction of rotation.

Both the relative configuration and direction of rotation are often specified in the names of carbohydrates and other optically active compounds. For example, D(+)-glyceraldehyde indicates both the configuration and direction of rotation.

The most important carbohydrate is glucose (also called dextrose). It is dextrorotatory and has a configuration related to (+)-glyceraldehyde. How should it be designated?

A ||||||||||||||||||||||||||||||||||||||||||||||||||||||||||||||||||||||||H|||||||||||||||||||||||||

L(+)-glucose

B ||||||||||||||||||||||||||||||||||||||||||||||||||||||||||||||||||||||||||||||||||||||||||||||||||

L(−)-glucose

C ||||||||||||||||||||||||||||||||||||||||||||||||||||||||||||||||||||||||||||||||||||||||||||||||||

D(+)-glucose

D ||||||||||||||||||||||||||||||||||||||||||||||||||||||||||||||||||||||||||||||||||||||||||||||||||

D(−)-glucose

A |||||||||||||||||||||||||||||||||||||||||||||||||||||||||||||||||||||||||||||||||||||||||||||||||||||||||||||||||

Incorrect. If glucose is dextrorotatory, it should have (+) in its name. So far, so good. If its configuration is related to D(+)-glyceraldehyde, however, it is a member of the D family and is correctly designated as D(+)-glucose. Bear in mind that configuration and direction of rotation are not directly related. That is why both are specified. Go on to page 251.

B |||||||||||||||||||||||||||||||||||||||||||||||||||||||||||||||||||||||||||||||||||||||||||||||||||||||||||||||||

You are wrong. By convention, the dextrorotatory direction is indicated by (+). Since glucose is dextrorotatory, it must have (+) in its name rather than (−). Read the question again to see if it belongs to the D family or the L family. Then choose another answer.

C |||||||||||||||||||||||||||||||||||||||||||||||||||||||||||||||||||||||||||||||||||||||||||||||||||||||||||||||||

Correct. A dextrorotatory compound with a configuration related to D(+)-glyceraldehyde belongs to the D family and its rotation is in the (+) direction. D(+)-glucose is the proper name. Go on to page 251.

D |||||||||||||||||||||||||||||||||||||||||||||||||||||||||||||||||||||||||||||||||||||||||||||||||||||||||||||||||

Incorrect. Since its configuration is related to D(+)-glyceraldehyde, glucose belongs to the D family. Rotation of plane-polarized light to the right is indicated by (+). Therefore glucose is properly named D(+)-glucose. Bear in mind that both configuration and direction of rotation need to be specified because they are not directly related to each other. Go on to page 251.

An important point which needs emphasis is that the correspondence of the functional groups in a compound to the functional groups of D (+)-glyceraldehyde must be given in order to determine its relative configuration. For instance, the configuration of (+)-isoserine is the same as that of (+)-glyceraldehyde if the carboxy and aminomethyl groups of isoserine correspond respectively to the aldehyde and hydroxymethyl groups of glyceraldehyde as shown here.

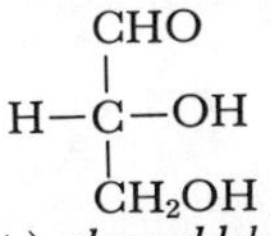

$$
\begin{array}{c}
\text{CHO} \\
| \\
\text{H—C—OH} \\
| \\
\text{CH}_2\text{OH} \\
(+)\text{-}glyceraldehyde
\end{array}
\qquad\qquad
\begin{array}{c}
\text{COOH} \\
| \\
\text{H—C—OH} \\
| \\
\text{CH}_2\text{NH}_2 \\
(+)\text{-}isoserine
\end{array}
$$

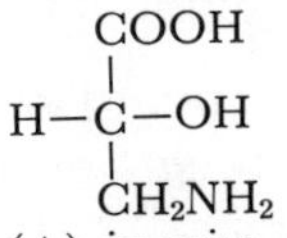

If the carboxy and aminomethyl groups of isoserine correspond to the hydroxymethyl and aldehyde groups of glyceraldehyde, then (−)-isoserine corresponds to (+)-glyceraldehyde.

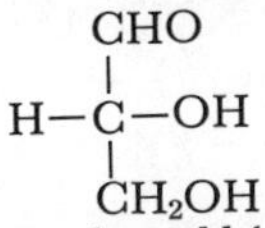

$$
\begin{array}{c}
\text{CHO} \\
| \\
\text{H—C—OH} \\
| \\
\text{CH}_2\text{OH} \\
(+)\text{-}glyceraldehyde
\end{array}
\qquad\qquad
\begin{array}{c}
\text{CH}_2\text{NH}_2 \\
| \\
\text{H—C—OH} \\
| \\
\text{COOH} \\
(−)\text{-}isoserine
\end{array}
$$

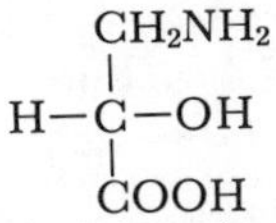

In the case of isoserine, it is understood that the first correspondence is to be used and the enantiomers are called D(+)-isoserine and L(−)-isoserine. If you continue your study of carbohydrates, you will learn a great deal more about their optical activity and configurations.

4.2 PEPTIDES AND PROTEINS

Proteins may well be the most important chemical constituents of living animal organisms. Muscle fiber, skin, nerves, and blood are largely composed of proteins. Moreover, certain hormones, enzymes, and antibodies are proteins.

In a chemical sense, proteins can be defined as high-molecular-weight polymers which can be hydrolyzed to yield amino acids. The amino acid "building blocks" are connected by this sort of linkage:

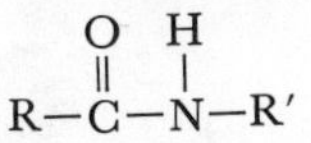

$$
\begin{array}{c}
\text{O}\quad\text{H} \\
\|\quad| \\
\text{R—C—N—R}'
\end{array}
$$

What kind of linkage is this?

A ||||||||||||||||||||||||||||||||||||||||||||||||||||||||||||||||||||||||||||||||||||||||

amide

B ||||||||||||||||||||||||||||||||||||||||||||||||||||||||||||||||||||||||||||||||||||||

ester

C ||||||||||||||||||||||||||||||||||||||||||||||||||||||||||||||||||||||||||||||||||||||||

ether

A ||||||||||||||||||||||||||||||||||||||||||||||||||||||||||||||||||||||||||||||||||||||||||||||||||||||||||||||||||

Right. Peptides and proteins are built from amino acids through amide linkages. You should recall that the textile fiber nylon has the same linkage. Continue to page 253.

B ||||||||||||||||||||||||||||||||||||||||||||||||||||||||||||||||||||||||||||||||||||||||||||||||||||||||||||||||||

You are wrong. Don't you remember that esters are formed from the reaction between an alcohol and a carboxylic acid? Neither of them has nitrogen in its functional group.

$$R{-}OH \quad + \quad HO{-}\underset{acid}{\overset{\overset{\displaystyle O}{\|}}{C}}{-}R' \quad \longrightarrow \quad R{-}O{-}\underset{ester}{\overset{\overset{\displaystyle O}{\|}}{C}}{-}R' \quad + \quad \underset{water}{H_2O}$$

$\underset{alcohol}{R{-}OH}$

Perhaps you need to go back and review Chapter 3. If this was only a careless mistake, go back to page 251 and choose another answer.

C ||||||||||||||||||||||||||||||||||||||||||||||||||||||||||||||||||||||||||||||||||||||||||||||||||||||||||||||||||

Don't you remember that the functional group of the ether family is —O—? Here is the peptide and protein linkage again.

$$R{-}\overset{\overset{\displaystyle O}{\|}}{C}{-}\overset{\overset{\displaystyle H}{|}}{N}{-}R'$$

The functional group of the linkage is

$$-\overset{\overset{\displaystyle O}{\|}}{C}{-}\overset{\overset{\displaystyle H}{|}}{N}-$$

It is formed when an amine reacts with a carboxylic acid. Does this spur your memory? If not, you should review Chapter 3. If it does, turn back and choose another answer.

The amide linkages in proteins are also known as peptide bonds or peptide linkages. Formation of a peptide linkage involves the separation of a molecule of water from the reaction between a carboxyl group and an amino group, as illustrated here.

$$R'-NH_2 \quad + \quad HO-\overset{\overset{\displaystyle O}{\|}}{C}-R \quad \longrightarrow \quad R'-\overset{\overset{\displaystyle H}{|}}{N}-\overset{\overset{\displaystyle O}{\|}}{C}-R \quad + \quad H_2O$$

amine   acid   peptide bond   water

Because amino acids have both the carboxy and amino functional groups, they can form large polymeric molecules in which the amino group of one reacts with the carboxy group of a second, while the amino group of the second reacts with the carboxy group of a third, and so forth. Polymers made up of a small number of amino acid units (up to about 100) are commonly called *peptides*, the larger ones (up to 10,000 or more) are called *proteins*.

The individual amino acids and the order of their combination determine the nature and function of the protein. Because they are less complex, the structures of peptides are better known than the structures of proteins. Glutathione, a common component of tissues, is γ-L-glutamyl-L-cysteinylglycine. Its structure is:

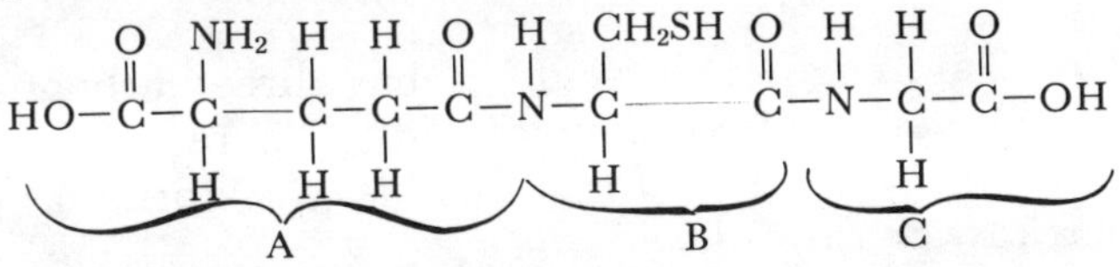

Which letter indicates the glycine portion of the peptide? (Glycine is 2-aminoethanoic acid.)

A

B

C

A |||||||||||||||||||||||||||||||||||||||||||||||||||||||||||||||||||||||||||||||||||||||||||||||||||||||||||||||||||

Incorrect. If glutathione were hydrolyzed, the amino acid in the "A" portion of the molecule would have the formula:

$$HO-\overset{\overset{O}{\|}}{C}-\overset{\overset{NH_2}{|}}{\underset{\underset{H}{|}}{C}}-\overset{\overset{H}{|}}{\underset{\underset{H}{|}}{C}}-\overset{\overset{H}{|}}{\underset{\underset{H}{|}}{C}}-\overset{\overset{O}{\|}}{C}-OH$$

It has five carbon atoms in its chain and is a derivative of pentane. Its common name is glutamic acid. Go back and choose another answer, remembering that glycine is a derivative of ethane.

B |||||||||||||||||||||||||||||||||||||||||||||||||||||||||||||||||||||||||||||||||||||||||||||||||||||||||||||||||||

Wrong. When glutathione is hydrolyzed, the amino acid. from the "B" portion of the molecule is

$$H_2N-\overset{\overset{CH_2SH}{|}}{\underset{\underset{H}{|}}{C}}-\overset{\overset{O}{\|}}{C}-OH$$

It can hardly be 2-aminoethanoic acid. It has three carbon atoms in its chain and is a derivative of propanoic acid. There is also a mercapto (—SH) group to be accounted for. This is the formula of cysteine. Choose another answer carefully.

C |||||||||||||||||||||||||||||||||||||||||||||||||||||||||||||||||||||||||||||||||||||||||||||||||||||||||||||||||||

You are right. When glutathione is hydrolyzed, the "C" portion of the molecule yields glycine.

$$H-\overset{\overset{NH_2}{|}}{\underset{\underset{H}{|}}{C}}-\overset{\overset{O}{\|}}{C}-OH$$

glycine

Go on to page 255.

During the investigation of peptides and proteins, many amino acids have been synthesized. It has been found that these synthetic amino acids are identical to their natural counterparts in all respects save one. The exception is their optical activity. Amino acids which are isolated from proteins all belong to the L family; the synthetic acids are always formed as optically inactive racemic mixtures.

The behavior of two enantiomers in living systems is often quite different. In some extreme cases, one form can be necessary for the health of the organism while the other may be a poison.

Which of these amino acids cannot have optically active forms?

A ||||||||||||||||||||||||||||||||||||||||||||||||||||||||||||||||||||||||||||||||||||||||||||||||||||||||||||||||

$$\begin{array}{c} \quad\; NH_2 \quad O \\ \quad\;\; | \qquad\; || \\ H-C\!\!-\!\!-\!\!-\!\!C-OH \\ \quad\;\; | \\ \quad\;\; H \end{array}$$

glycine

B ||||||||||||||||||||||||||||||||||||||||||||||||||||||||||||||||||||||||||||||||||||||||||||||||||||||||||||||||

$$\begin{array}{c} \;\; H \quad NH_2 \quad O \\ \;\; | \qquad | \qquad\; || \\ H-C-C\!\!-\!\!-\!\!C-OH \\ \;\; | \qquad | \\ \;\; H \quad\; H \end{array}$$

alanine

C ||||||||||||||||||||||||||||||||||||||||||||||||||||||||||||||||||||||||||||||||||||||||||||||||||||||||||||||||

$$\begin{array}{c} \quad H \qquad H \quad NH_2 \quad O \\ \quad | \qquad\;\; | \qquad | \qquad\; || \\ H-C\!\!-\!\!-\!\!C-C\!\!-\!\!-\!\!C-OH \\ \quad | \qquad\;\; | \qquad | \\ \quad H \quad H\text{-}CH \quad H \\ \qquad\qquad | \\ \qquad\qquad H \end{array}$$

valine

A |||||||||||||||||||||||||||||||||||||||||||||||||||||||||||||||||||||||||||||||||||||||||||||||||||||||||||||

You are right. Neither of the carbon atoms in glycine is

$$
\begin{array}{c}
\quad\ \ \overset{\displaystyle NH_2}{|}\ \ \overset{\displaystyle O}{\|} \\
H-C\ —\ C-OH \\
\quad\ \ \underset{\displaystyle H}{|}
\end{array}
$$

asymmetric. It does not have optically active forms. Go on to page 257.

B ||||||||||||||||||||||||||||||||||||||||||||||||||||||||||||||||||||||||||||||||||||||||||||||||||||||||||||||

Incorrect. Examine the formula of alanine again. Isn't the carbon marked by * asymmetric? If it is, alanine can have two

$$
\begin{array}{c}
\ \ \overset{\displaystyle H}{|}\ \ \overset{\displaystyle NH_2}{|}\ \ \overset{\displaystyle O}{\|} \\
H-C-\overset{*}{C}\ —\ C-OH \\
\ \ \underset{\displaystyle H}{|}\ \ \underset{\displaystyle H}{|}
\end{array}
$$

optically active forms. It does. Turn back and choose another answer.

C ||||||||||||||||||||||||||||||||||||||||||||||||||||||||||||||||||||||||||||||||||||||||||||||||||||||||||||||

Wrong. This is the formula of valine. Look at it carefully.

$$
\begin{array}{c}
\ \ \overset{\displaystyle H}{|}\qquad\ \overset{\displaystyle H}{|}\qquad\ \overset{\displaystyle NH_2}{|}\ \ \overset{\displaystyle O}{\|} \\
H-C\ —\ C\ —\ \overset{*}{C}-C-OH \\
\ \ \underset{\displaystyle H}{|}\ \ \underset{\displaystyle H-C-H}{|}\ \ \underset{\displaystyle H}{|} \\
\qquad\quad \underset{\displaystyle H}{|}
\end{array}
$$

Isn't the carbon atom marked with * asymmetric? If it is, valine can have two optically active isomers. It does. Go back and select another answer.

4.3 FATS

Fats are the third group of natural products used as foodstuffs. They are esters of the higher fatty acids and the triol, glycerol. Because they are derived from glycerol, these esters are frequently called glycerides. Liquid fats are called oils and solid fats are called tallows or butters. The dividing line between oils and tallows or butters is not clear-cut because of differences in the temperature of various environments. Palm oil may be a solid in Alaska.

Most of the fatty acids have an even number of carbon atoms because they are synthesized in biological systems from the ethanoate (acetate) ion, CH_3COO^-, which contains two carbon atoms. For this reason, carboxylic acids with odd numbers of carbon atoms are not common in natural products.

Glycerol, the alcohol portion of fat molecules, is properly named 1,2,3-propanetriol. Which of these is its structural formula?

A ||||||||||||||||||||||||||||||||||||||||||||||||||||||||||||||||||||||||||||||||||||||||||||||||||||||||||||

$$HO-CH_2-\underset{\underset{OH}{|}}{\overset{\overset{OH}{|}}{C}}-CH_3$$

B ||||||||||||||||||||||||||||||||||||||||||||||||||||||||||||||||||||||||||||||||||||||||||||||||||||||||||||

$$HOCH_2\underset{\overset{|}{OH}}{C}HCH_2OH$$

C ||||||||||||||||||||||||||||||||||||||||||||||||||||||||||||||||||||||||||||||||||||||||||||||||||||||||||||

$$HOCH_2\underset{\overset{|}{OH}}{C}HCH_2CH_2OH$$

A ||||||||||||||||||||||||||||||||||||||||||||||||||||||||||||||||||||||||||||||||||||||||||||||||||||||||||||||||||||||||||||||||||

Incorrect. The correct systematic name for glycerol is 1,2,3-propanetriol. The formula you picked is

$$\text{HOCH}_2\overset{\displaystyle \text{OH}}{\underset{\displaystyle \text{OH}}{\text{C}}}\text{CH}_3$$

If this compound existed, it would be named 1,2,2-propanetriol. In general, compounds with two hydroxy groups on the same carbon atom are unstable. Turn back and choose another formula.

B ||||||||||||||||||||||||||||||||||||||||||||||||||||||||||||||||||||||||||||||||||||||||||||||||||||||||||||||||||||||||||||||||||

Right. The structural formula for glycerol is

$$\text{HOCH}_2\overset{\displaystyle \text{OH}}{\text{CH}}\text{CH}_2\text{OH}$$

Go on to page 259.

C ||||||||||||||||||||||||||||||||||||||||||||||||||||||||||||||||||||||||||||||||||||||||||||||||||||||||||||||||||||||||||||||||||

You are wrong. You have chosen this formula to represent 1,2,3-propanetriol.

$$\text{HOCH}_2\overset{\displaystyle \text{OH}}{\text{CH}}\text{CH}_2\text{CH}_2\text{OH}$$

It is a triol, all right, but is it a derivative of propane? Aren't there four carbon atoms? It represents 1,2,4-butanetriol. Better go back and choose another formula.

Whether a fat is liquid or solid depends to some extent on the amount of unsaturation in the fatty acid segments of the molecule. In general, the more unsaturation, the lower the melting point of the glyceride. Hydrogenation or "hardening" of corn oil and cottonseed oil to make cooking fats such as Crisco and Spry is an important commercial process:

$$Unsaturated\ fat\ +\ H_2\ \xrightarrow[\text{catalyst}]{\text{Ni}}\ Saturated\ fats$$

You should recall that the hydrolysis of an ester in the presence of a strong base is called saponification. When fats are treated with sodium hydroxide or another strong base, the products are glycerol and the salts of the fatty acids.

$$
\begin{array}{l}
\overset{\displaystyle O}{\underset{\displaystyle \|}{}}\\
CH_2O{-}C{-}R\\
|\qquad\overset{\displaystyle O}{\underset{\displaystyle \|}{}}\\
CHO{-}C{-}R\ +\ 3\ Na^+OH^-\ \rightarrow\ \\
|\qquad\overset{\displaystyle O}{\underset{\displaystyle \|}{}}\\
CH_2O{-}C{-}R
\end{array}
\qquad
\begin{array}{l}
CH_2OH\\
|\\
CHOH\ +\ 3\ R{-}\overset{\displaystyle O}{\underset{\displaystyle \|}{C}}{-}C^-Na^+\\
|\\
CH_2OH
\end{array}
$$

The latter are soaps. Prior to the twentieth century, soap was usually prepared by treating animal fats with water extracts of wood ashes. These extracts contained sodium and potassium carbonates. In this process, the carbonates bring about saponification. It has been used since Babylonian times and is still practiced in primitive countries.

Which of these acids would you expect to predominate when liquid olive oil is saponified?

A ||||||||||||||||||||||||||||||||||||||||||||||||||||||||||||||||||||||||||||||||||||||||||||||||||||||||||||

  oleic acid $\qquad\qquad CH_3(CH_2)_7CH{=}CH(CH_2)_7COOH$

B ||||||||||||||||||||||||||||||||||||||||||||||||||||||||||||||||||||||||||||||||||||||||||||||||||||||||||||

  palmitic acid $\qquad CH_3(CH_2)_{14}COOH$

C ||||||||||||||||||||||||||||||||||||||||||||||||||||||||||||||||||||||||||||||||||||||||||||||||||||||||||||

  3-pentadecenoic acid $\qquad CH_3(CH_2)_{10}CH{=}CHCH_2COOH$

A |||||||||||||||||||||||||||||||||||||||||||||||||||||||||||||||||||||||||||||||||||||||||||||||||||||||||||||||||||||||||||||||||||||||

Right. The formula you have chosen represents oleic acid. Olive oil yields 69 to 84 per cent oleic acid when it is hydrolyzed. Oleic acid has an even number of carbon atoms (18) and its unsaturation contributes to the low melting point of the oil. Go on to page 261.

B |||||||||||||||||||||||||||||||||||||||||||||||||||||||||||||||||||||||||||||||||||||||||||||||||||||||||||||||||||||||||||||||||||||||

Incorrect. Although olive oil does yield 5 to 15 per cent palmitic acid when it is saponified, it is not the major constituent. Most fats, including tallow, lard, and butter, yield a higher proportion of palmitic acid. Read page 259 again and pick another answer.

C |||||||||||||||||||||||||||||||||||||||||||||||||||||||||||||||||||||||||||||||||||||||||||||||||||||||||||||||||||||||||||||||||||||||

You are wrong. 3-Pentadecenoic acid probably does not occur in any natural products since it has an odd number of carbon atoms. The vast majority of fat acids obtained from natural fats and oils have even numbers of carbon atoms. Turn back and choose another answer.

Dependence of the melting point of fats on the amount of unsaturation is illustrated by the sea anemone (*Metridium dianthus*), which contains a large amount of fat. The fats in species found along the Florida coast are mostly glycerides of saturated fatty acids, while the related species in the colder waters off New England contain fats made up of unsaturated fatty acids. An anemone from Florida would stiffen considerably if it were transplanted to the New England coast.

Two chemical features of a soap are required for its cleansing action: a long hydrocarbon chain and a polar group, the carboxylate group.

Present-day detergents usually do not have the $-\overset{\overset{\displaystyle O}{\|}}{C}-O^-$ group, but they do retain the hydrocarbon chain and a polar group. A common detergent is sodium lauryl sulfate.

$$CH_3(CH_2)_{10}CH_2O - \overset{\overset{\displaystyle O}{|}}{\underset{\underset{\displaystyle O}{|}}{S}} - O^- \; Na^+$$

Summary: Nomenclature of Natural Products

Natural products are organic compounds derived from living or once-living organisms. They are usually given common or generic names because of their complexity, but can be classified on the basis of common structural features. Carbohydrates contain carbon, hydrogen, and oxygen with the latter two present in the ratio of two to one.

Sugars, starch, and cellulose are carbohydrates. They are designated as *mono-*, *di-*, and *poly*saccharides according to the number of basic units present. The basic units are classified in two ways: the number of carbon atoms and the functional groups present. For example, D(+)-glucose is an aldohexose.

$$\begin{array}{c} CHO \\ | \\ C-OH \\ | \\ HO-C-H \\ | \\ H-C-OH \\ | \\ H-C-OH \\ | \\ CH_2OH \end{array}$$

Peptides and proteins are polymers of amino acids. They are among the most important natural products since they form most animal tissues and the biological catalysts called enzymes.

Both carbohydrates and amino acids (from the hydrolysis of proteins) can have optical isomers. That is, their solutions can rotate the plane of plane-polarized light. A simple way to determine whether or not a compound can have optical activity is to look for an asymmetric carbon atom. Asymmetric carbon atoms are those which are attached to four different atoms or groups. Glyceraldehyde (2,3-dihydroxypropanal) has two optically active forms, but 3-hydroxypropanal does not.

$$\begin{array}{ccc} CHO & CHO & CHO \\ | & | & | \\ H-C-OH & HO-C-H & H-C-H \\ | & | & | \\ CH_2OH & CH_2OH & CH_2OH \end{array}$$
$$\begin{array}{ccc} (+)\text{-}glyceraldehyde & (-)\text{-}glyceraldehyde & 3\text{-}hydroxypropanal \end{array}$$

Fats are esters of long-chain carboxylic acids and glycerol. Tallows and butters are solid or semisolid at room temperature; oils are liquid. Treatment of an oil with hydrogen in the presence of a nickel catalyst will change it into a solid since the low melting point of the oil is due to the presence of unsaturation.

When fats are treated with bases, they hydrolyze to glycerol and the salts of the fatty acids, or soaps.

The Formula Index published by *Chemical Abstracts* lists a compound with the molecular formula $C_{785}H_{1220}N_{212}O_{248}S_2$. It is a large peptide, or perhaps a small protein. To spare you the difficulty of deriving the systematic name, we offer it gratis:

Acetylseryltyrosylserylisoleucylthreonylserylprolylseryl-
glutaminylphenylalanylvalylphenylalanylleucylserylseryl-
valyltryptophylalanylaspartylprolylisoleucylglutamylleucyl-
leucylasparaginylvalylcysteinylthreonylserylserylleucyl-
glycylasparaginylglutaminylphenylalanylglutaminylthreonyl-
glutaminylglutaminylalanylarginylthreonylthreonylglutaminyl-
valylglutaminylglutaminylphenylalanylserylglutaminylvalyl-
tryptophyllysylprolylphenylalanylprolylglutaminylserylthre-
onylvalylarginylphenylalanylprolylglycylaspartylvalyltyrosyl-
lysylvalyltyrosylarginyltyrosylasparaginylalanylvalylleucyl-
aspartylprolylleucylisoleucylthreonylalanylleucylleucyl-
glycylthreonylphenylalanylaspartylthreonylarginylasparaginyl-
arginylisoleucylisoleucylglutamylvalylglutamylasparaginyl-
glutaminylglutaminylserylprolylthreonylthreonylalanylglutamyl-
threonylleucylaspartylalanylthreonylarginylarginylvalyl-
aspartylaspartylalanylthreonylvalylalanylisoleucylarginyl-
serylalanylasparaginylisoleucylasparaginylleucylvalyl-
asparaginylglutamylleucylvalylarginylglycylthreonylglycylleucyl
tyrosylasparaginylglutaminylasparaginylthreonylphenylalanylglutamyl-
serylmethionylserylglycylleucylvalyltryptophylthreonylserylalanyl-
prolylalanyl serine

5

Ring Systems

According to an advertisement in *Chemical and Engineering News*, 11,524 rings had been located in the world's chemical literature through the year 1961 by the staff of the Chemical Abstracts Service. You have already become quite familiar with a few of them: the cycloalkanes, cycloalkenes, and benzene. For a complete description of the remainder, you may refer to *The Ring Index*, published by the American Chemical Society. In this chapter we will look at some 20 examples of common rings, mostly heterocyclic, and see how the members of the rings are numbered to facilitate the specification of the location of substituent groups.

Although many of the heterocyclic compounds are classed as fully aromatic (*i.e.*, they have some of the properties characteristic of benzene), the rings are usually pictured with double bonds rather than the inner circle as in benzene.

Five-Membered Rings, One Hetero- Atom

thiophene   pyrrole   furan

carbazole or *dibenzopyrrole dibenzemopyrrole*

Six-membered Rings, One Hetero- Atom

pyridine   *piperidine*   *quinoline*

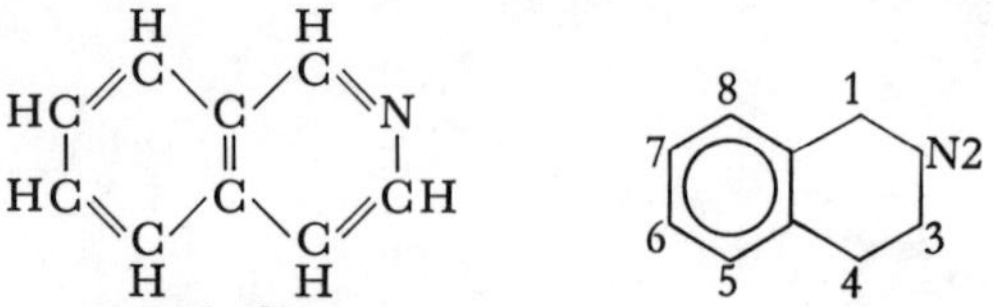

isoquinoline

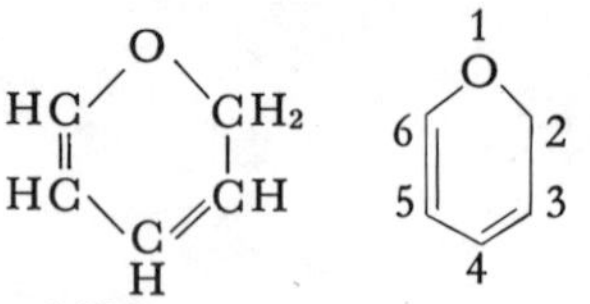

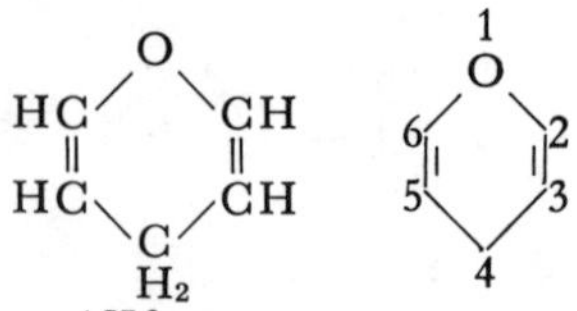

2 H-form
pyran

4H-form

The two forms of pyran cannot be distinguished from one another until the presence of a substituent group "fixes" the location of the double bonds.

Five-Membered Rings, Two Hetero- Atoms

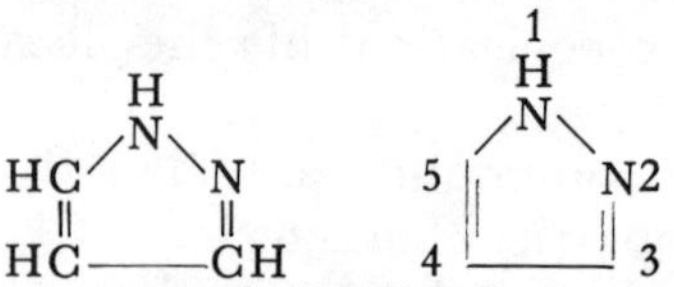

pyrazole (1,2-diazole)

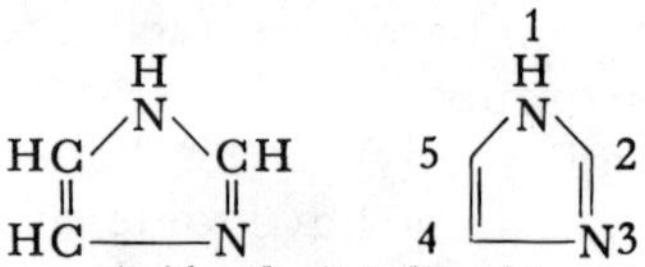

imidazole (1,3-diazole)

Six-Membered Rings, Two Hetero- Atoms

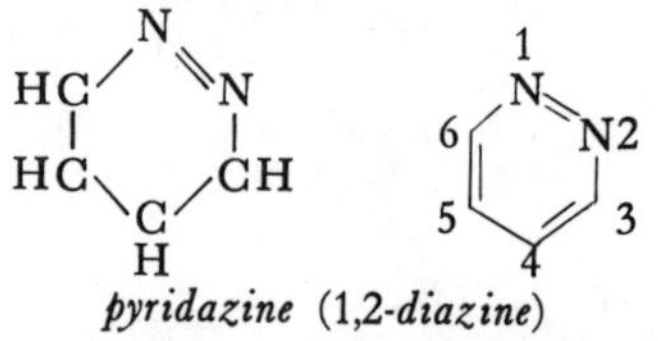

pyridazine (1,2-diazine)

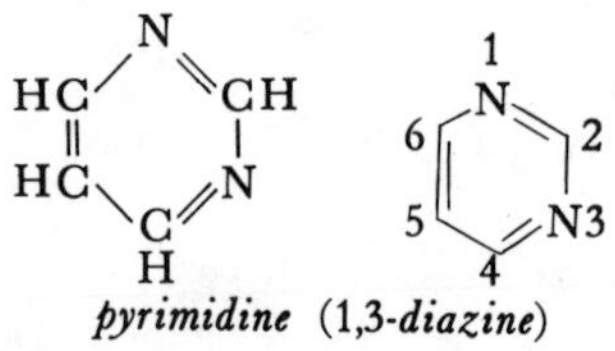

pyrimidine (1,3-diazine)

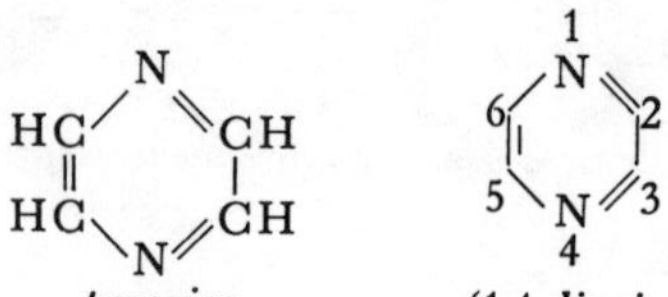

pyrazine

(1,4-diazine)

Polynuclear Hydrocarbons

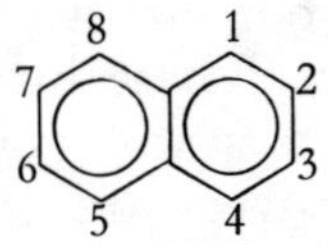

naphthalene

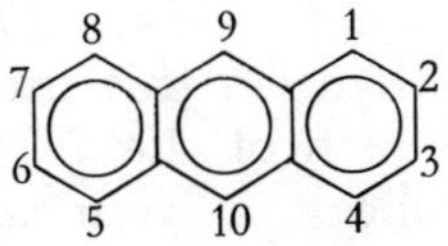

anthracene

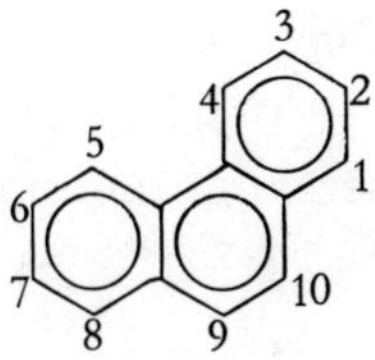

phenanthrene

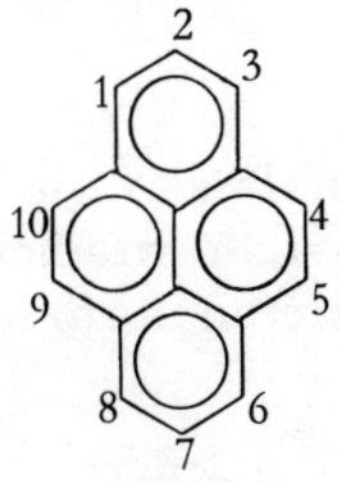

pyrene

Self-Tests

A good way to review and to test yourself is to go over the questions and problems in this program again. These brief quizzes cover the main ideas in each of the first four chapters and you may do them for an additional check on your skill. The answers are on page 269.

Chapter 1

Answer true or false.
1. 2-Pentyne and 1,3-pentadiene are isomers.
2. These two skeleton formulas represent the same compound:

$$C-C-\underset{\displaystyle \overset{\displaystyle C}{|}}{\underset{\displaystyle |}{C}}-C-C \qquad \underset{\displaystyle \overset{\displaystyle |}{C-C}}{\overset{\displaystyle C-C}{|}}C-C-\underset{\displaystyle |}{C}$$

3. Alkyl radicals have the general formula C_nH_{2n-1}.
4. Ethyne and acetylene are two suitable names for the same compound.
5. The skeleton formula for isopentane is $C-C-\underset{\displaystyle \underset{\displaystyle C}{|}}{\overset{\displaystyle \overset{\displaystyle C}{|}}{C}}$.

Give a suitable systematic name for the compound represented by each of these skeleton formulas:

6.
$$C-C-\underset{\displaystyle \underset{\displaystyle \underset{\displaystyle C}{|}}{\underset{\displaystyle C}{|}}}{\overset{\displaystyle \overset{\displaystyle C}{|}}{C}}-\overset{\displaystyle \overset{\displaystyle C}{|}}{C}-C$$

7.
$$C=C-\overset{\displaystyle \overset{\displaystyle C}{|}}{C}=C$$

8.
$$C-C-C-C-C-C$$

9.
$$C-C-\underset{\displaystyle \underset{\displaystyle C}{|}}{\overset{\displaystyle \overset{\displaystyle C}{|}}{C}}-\overset{\displaystyle \overset{\displaystyle C}{|}}{C}-C-C$$

10. $C-C\equiv C-C$

Write a skeleton formula for each of these compounds:
11. isobutane
12. 1,3,5–hexatriene
13. 4–ethyl-2-methyl-1-hexene
14. 2,2-dimethylbutane
15. 2,2-dimethyl-5-propyl-3-nonyne

Chapter 2

Match the name for each of the following compounds with one (or more) of the words at the right which describe the compound:

1. benzene	a. alicyclic
2. chlorocyclopentane	b. aliphatic
3. butane	c. aromatic
4. 1,3,5–trinitrobenzene	d. heterocyclic
5. 2,2,4–trimethylpentane	e. homocyclic

Give a suitable systematic name for the compound represented by each of these skeleton formulas.

6.

7.

Br
Br

8.

CH₃
Cl   NO₂

9.

Cl   Cl
| |
C—C=C—C

10.

C
|
C—C—C—C—NO₂

Write a skeleton formula for each of these compounds.

11. *o*-xylene
12. 1,3,5-trinitrobenzene
13. 3-chloromethylcyclopentane
14. nitromethane
15. 3-chloropropylbenzene

Chapter 3

Match each of these general formulas with one word from the column at the right:

1. R—O—R′

2. R—C(=O)—O—C(=O)—R′

3. R—C(=O)—O—R′

4. R—C(=O)—X

5. R—C(=O)—OH

6. R—SH

7. R—S(=O)(=O)—OH

8. $\begin{matrix} R \\ R' \end{matrix}$ N—H

9. R—OH

10. R—C(=O)—R′

a. acyl halide

b. alcohol

c. aldehyde

d. amine

e. anhydride

f. carboxylic acid

g. ester

h. ether

i. ketone

j. mercaptan

k. sulfide

l. sulfonic acid

Write a skeleton formula for each of these compounds:
11. ethyl phenyl ether
12. ethyl phenyl ketone
13. chloroethanal

14. 1, 3-propanediol
15. 3-aminopropanoic acid

Give a suitable systematic name for the compound represented by each of these skeleton formulas:

16.
```
C—C—N—H
    |
    C
    |
    C
    |
    C
```

17.
```
Cl      H
 \      |
  ⬡——C—OH
      |
     ⬡
      \Cl
```

18.
```
    O
    ‖
    C—OH
    |
   ⬡
```

19.
```
              O
              ‖
C—C—O—C—C—C—NH₂
```

20.
```
      O
      ‖
C—C—C—O—C
```

Chapter 4

Answer true or false:

1. This compound has optical isomers.

```
        Cl
        |
C—C—C—C
        |
       NH₂
```

2. The carbon indicated by ✳ is asymmetric.

```
       Cl
       |
C—C=C—C
    ✳
```

3. Fructose is an aldohexose.

```
    CH₂OH
    |
    C=O
    |
HO—C—H
    |
 H—C—OH
    |
 H—C—OH
    |
    CH₂OH
```

4. All members of the D family are dextrorotatory.
5. Sucrose, ordinary table sugar, is a disaccharide.
6. Fats are esters.
7. Proteins yield amino acids when hydrolyzed.
8. Natural fats yield glycerol upon saponification.
9. A racemic mixture may be either dextro- or levorotatory.
10. Animal fats bear no structural resemblance to vegetable fats.

Answers To Self-Tests

Chapter 1

1. true
2. false
3. false
4. true
5. true
6. 3-ethyl-2,3-dimethylpentane
7. 2-methyl-1,3-butadiene
8. hexane
9. 3,3,4-trimethylhexane
10. 2-butyne

11.
```
        C
        |
    C—C
        |
        C
```

12. C=C—C=C—C=C

13.
```
            C
            |
    C       C
    |       |
    C=C—C—C—C—C
```

14.
```
        C
        |
    C—C—C—C
        |
        C
```

15.
```
                    C
                    |
                    C
                    |
        C           C
        |           |
    C—C—C≡C—C—C—C—C—C
        |
        C
```

Chapter 2

1. c, e
2. a, e
3. b
4. c, e
5. b
6. methylcyclopentane
7. *m*-dibromobenzene
8. 3-chloro-5-nitrotoluene
9. 1,4-dichloro-2-butene
10. 2-methyl-1-nitrobutane

11.

12.
```
        NO₂
      /    \
  O₂N        NO₂
```

13.
```
        C
        |
    C     C—C
     \   /
   Cl—C—C
```

14. C—NO₂

15. C—C—C—Cl
(benzene ring)

269

Chapter 3

1. h
2. e
3. g
4. a
5. f

6. j
7. l
8. d
9. b
10. i

11.

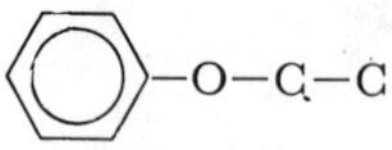

○—O—C—C

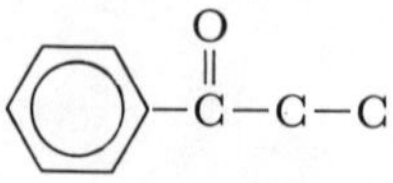

14. HO—C—C—C—OH

12.

$$\overset{O}{\overset{\|}{○—C—C—C}}$$

15.

$$\underset{H_2N—C—C—\overset{O}{\overset{\|}{C}}—OH}{}$$

13.

$$\underset{Cl—C—\overset{O}{\overset{\|}{C}}—H}{}$$

16. ethylpropylamine
17. bis(3-chlorophenyl)-methanol
18. benzoic acid
19. 3-ethoxypropanamide or 3-ethoxypropionamide
20. methyl propanoate or methyl propionate

Chapter 4

1. true
2. false
3. false
4. false
5. true

6. true
7. true
8. true
9. false
10. false

APPENDIX

Chemical Abstracts uses the following order of precedence to determine the chief function in compounds of mixed function:

"onium" compounds
peroxide
hydroperoxide
acid (carboxylic, carboximidic, carbohydroxamic, arsonic, arsonous, sulfonic, sulfinic, sulfenic, stibonic, stibonous, phosphonic, phosphonous, phosphinic, phosphinous, boronic, borinic, others)
acid halide
amide
imide
amidine
aldehyde
nitrile
isocyanide
ketone
thione
alcohol
phenol
thiol
amine
oxyamine (RONH$_2$)
imine
organometallic compounds (with carbon-metal attached radicals)
ether
sulfide
sulfoxide
sulfone

References

1. Chemical Abstracts Service, "Directions for Abstractors and Section Editors of *Chemical Abstracts* (1967)." Special Issues Sales Department, American Chemical Society, Washington, D.C., 1967.
    Concise statement of nomenclature rules, forms, and other points to observe in chemical writing.

2. Chemical Abstracts Service, "The Naming and Indexing of Chemical Compounds from *Chemical Abstracts*." Special Issues Sales Department, American Chemical Society, Washington, D.C., 1962.
    Introduction, with key and discussion, to the naming of chemical compounds for indexing in *Chemical Abstracts*. Includes a comprehensive bibliography on chemical nomenclature (Replacement manual to be published in 1967.)

3. IUPAC Commission on the Nomenclature of Organic Chemistry, *Nomenclature of Organic Chemistry*. Butterworth's, London, Sections A and B, 2nd edition, 1966; Section C, 1965.
    The complete IUPAC rules for naming organic compounds.

4. Lange, N.A., ed., *Handbook of Chemistry*. 10th edition. McGraw-Hill, New York, 1964.
    A reference volume containing physical constants of organic compounds and cross-references to common and systematic names. Also a list of organic ring systems.

5. Noller, C.R., *Chemistry of Organic Compounds*. 3rd edition. W. B. Saunders Co., Philadelphia, 1965.
    General organic chemistry textbook with sections on nomenclature as well as comprehensive listing of compounds by both common and systematic names.

6. Patterson, Capell, and Walker, *The Ring Index*. 2nd edition and 3 supplements. Special Issues Sales Department, American Chemical Society, Washington, D.C., 1960.
    Comprehensive index of ring systems compiled from the chemical literature of the world.

7. Stecher, P.G. (ed), *The Merck Index of Chemicals and Drugs*, 7th edition. Merck & Company, Inc., Rahway, New Jersey, 1960.
    Extensive list of organic and inorganic compounds used in medicine and pharmacy. Particularly good listing of trademarked names and generic names.

INDEX